THE DEVIL IN LEGEND AND LITERATURE

BY THE SAME AUTHOR

THE DEVIL IN LEGEND
AND LITERATURE

BY

MAXIMILIAN RUDWIN

THE OPEN COURT PUBLISHING COMPANY
LA SALLE, ILLINOIS 61301

OPEN COURT and the above logo are registered in the U.S. Patent and
Trademark Office.

Copyright © 1931, 1959 Open Court Publishing Company

Printed in the United States of America

Second printing 1973
Third printing 1989

ISBN: 0-87548-247-3

Library of Congress Catalog Card Number: 73-85284

TO
THE MEMORY OF
PAUL CARUS

PREFACE

THE problem of Evil is an enigma that ever seems to puzzle the human mind. The evolution of the Personality of Evil forms perhaps the most fascinating chapter in the spiritual history of man. The Devil has occupied the dreams and fancies of mankind to a greater extent than any other character, historical or mythological. From the reputed days of our first ancestors in the Garden of Eden to the present moment, Satan, or his equivalent, has always taken a deep interest in the affairs of men on this planet, and the interest has always been reciprocated.

The eternal duel between Good and Evil in the cosmic order is the very essence of all mythologies, all religions and many of the arts. "The history of mankind," said a German church historian, "would be tedious without the struggles which have sin for their background. Great periods and persons are formed by sin and suffering."

The Devil has been the object of much concern to Christianity. The New Testament is filled from cover to cover with accounts of the various snares laid by Satan for the soul. The Gospels and Epistles contain endless warnings against the Great Adversary, who, as a roaring lion, is prowling about on this earth, "seeking whom he may devour" (1 Pet. v. 8). The early monks and missionaries exerted all their efforts in fighting against the temptations of the Fiend. Public interest in the Devil kept increasing with the march of the centuries. The doings and disguises of Diabolus received their greatest elaboration at the hands of the medieval writers. Nor has the Devil diminished in interest with the beginning of the Protestant period. The Reformation, which was a movement of progress in so many respects, was no less concerned about the Great Enemy than its parent religion. The writers of the Protestant faith depicted the world as full of the demons of hell.

From the time of the Renaissance neither the revival of ancient learning nor the institution of modern science could prevail against Satan. On the contrary, the growth of the interest in the Devil and his associated personalities has been on a level with the development of the spirit of philosophical inquiry. It would seem, as a matter of fact, that, in proportion as the belief in the Devil has decreased, our interest in his moral and poetical identities has increased. Satan has never been subjected to such a substantial cross-examination as in the days when he was relegated from the citadel of asserted belief into the vaguer regions of poetic fancy. It was only after the free-thought movement of the eighteenth century and a better scientific conception of the workings of the natural laws have relieved mankind from the fear of the Fiend that the question of the reality of Evil and its personification could be freely studied in its historic and philosophic aspects.

A compilation of books on the subject of Satan would crowd several volumes. From the *Malleus maleficarum* (1489) down to Professor George Lyman Kittredge's *Witchcraft in Old and New England* (1928), and from Johannes Wierus' *De præstigiis Dæmonum* (1563) to Father Coulange's *Life of the Devil* (1930), works dealing with the Devil have poured forth in an endless succession at all times and in all tongues. The Tempter has been treated from every possible angle, dogmatical and critical, exhortatory and expository, biographical and philosophical. Such men as Roskoff in Germany, Réville in France, Graf in Italy, Conway in England, and Paul Carus in America set themselves with serious intent to trace the steps of Satan on this planet. Especially in our own days has the Devil become a subject of vital interest. He now occupies the minds of men perhaps to a greater extent than in the heyday of his glory in the Middle Ages. A symposium on the belief in his person and power ran in one of the most popular Paris papers four years ago,[1] and last year saw no less than three biographies of Beelzebub appear in this country, all of which attest the fascination that the Fiend still exerts over the fancy of man.

* * *

It is with no slight apprehension that the author presents this book to the reader. Although his method of presentation is his-

[1] Gaston Picard: "Avez-vous vu le Diable?" *L'Intransigeant,* November, 1926—January, 1927. Gaston Leroux published, in 1912, a novel with the significant title *l'Homme qui a vu le Diable.*

torical rather than philosophical, the writer is fully conscious of
the fact that even in the year of grace 1931 there still lingers some
resentment at the effort to bring under critical analysis any form
of religious belief. A book of this kind is especially apt to offer
offence to the theological or philosophical prepossessions of certain readers. In fact, every writer who deals with demonology must
run the risk of incurring public odium. The answer to conventional
critics may be found, however, in the words of the French bishop,
who wrote to Father Delaporte upon the publication of the latter's
book on the Devil: "Reverend Father, if everyone busied himself
with the Devil, as you do, the Kingdom of God would gain by it."

Let it be said that the writer has endeavored to maintain at all
times the impartiality of the scientist, who regards all phenomena
through the impersonal lens of critical judgment. In this treatise
neither the author's religious beliefs nor his prejudices are made
evident. His effort has been to interpret the diabolical concept from
a survey of myriads of beliefs and notions; to calculate the norm
with loving exactitude regardless of time, place or racial affinities.
He has stood in admiration, even adoration, before the Parthenon
frieze, which depicts the war of the Titans against the victorious
gods of the new day. He has read with delight the *Hyperion* of
Keats, in which the fall of the old deities is deplored. He has regretted with Heine the exiled gods of antiquity. But especially and
always has he been fascinated by the conflict against Evil in heaven
and on earth.

It may also be well to bear in mind that the author is no dabbler in
demonology and the black arts. He is primarily concerned with the
personality of the Devil as portrayed in the legends and literatures
of the various European peoples. He has often been forced, however, to draw upon the allied fields of magic and witchcraft, inasmuch as diabolism is so closely connected with them in its character and history that it is not an easy matter to fix definite lines of
demarcation between these three subjects.

Apart from the fear of offending moral or metaphysical sensi-
bilities, many an investigator has been frightened away from this
field of research by its elusiveness. The difficulty of dealing with
popular beliefs will be evident even to the casual reader. Heinrich
Heine, in his *Elementargeister*, has long ago pointed out the impossibility of reducing popular superstitions to a system. The German

poet compared this effort to the attempt to put the passing clouds
into frames as pictures. Or we might say that the task is just as
difficult as to weave into a cloth the mysterious cobwebs which have
collected on the ceiling of man's brain in the course of the ages. At
the most, all we can do is to bring together under certain rubrics or
headings that which is similar.

When we deal with the Devil, the matter presents still greater
difficulties. It is a toilsome, even tedious task to try to bring into
harmony the various ludicrous accounts and representations concerning this august personage, which have arisen in sundry quarters.
And yet the ill-assorted array of the demons found in the legends and
literatures of the various ages and languages fairly clamors for
classification.

To draw the demon of darkness into the bright light of critical
analysis seems almost an impossibility. How indeed can the light
of criticism be reflected on Satan, who stands for intellectual ob-
scurity and the blackest night of the soul? The Prince of Darkness naturally shuns rather than courts inquiry. Satan has often
been accused of stealing the manuscripts of books based on his activities in order to prevent their publication. Josef Görres, author of
Die christliche Mystik, a work containing rich sources for diabolism,
diabolical possession and exorcism, once fancied that the Devil, provoked by the interference of this defender of the Catholic faith
in Satanic affairs, had stolen the manuscript of his book. However,
in all justice to infernal honesty it should be added that the manuscript was found some time afterward in the author's bookcase,
and the Devil was completely exonerated. Not every writer, though,
is able to arouse the ire of his Satanic Majesty. Apparently much
that has been written about him only makes him smile. Satan seems
to squirm, however, when he is subjected to the relentless analysis
of scientific inquiry, without the element either of fear or sentimental
subjectivism.

This book is the result of research covering many years in the
legends and literatures of Semitic, Teutonic, Romanic and Slavic
peoples. But it is primarily a study based upon the literatures of
England, France and Germany. An examination of the Index will
reveal to what an extent the author has drawn upon the literatures
of these three countries.

In the treatment of so many-sided a subject, for which data

had to be gathered in different fields of investigation from the remotest times down to the present day, errors may have crept in. The writer will, therefore, be thankful for any criticisms from any sources, especially theological, which may lead to a correcter or completer interpretation of the facts.

* * *

The author wishes to express his warm thanks to Professor Allen H. Godbey, of Duke University, for many helpful suggestions in the field of Semitic philology and mythology. He is under further obligation to Professor Henry Conrad Thurnau, of the University of Kansas, and to Professor Adriaan Jacob Barnouw, of Columbia University, for bibliographical aid in the fields of German and Dutch literature respectively. The author is also under deep obligation to his friend and former colleague, Professor Roy Petran Lingle, of Drexel Institute, for many helpful criticisms in the field of English literature, and for his kindness in reading the greater part of the manuscript. He wishes further to thank Mr. Alfred A. Knopf and the publishers of *The Reflex* for their permission to reprint in this book certain matter of which they own the copyright. The author must not overlook his obligation to The Open Court Publishing Company for its co-operation in the publication of this work. To the memory of the late Paul Carus, the former editor of *The Open Court,* who was a pioneer in the critical study of religion in this country, and who always showed a sympathetic interest in the work of the author, this book is dedicated as a token of respect.

WALPURGIS NIGHT, 1931

MAXIMILIAN RUDWIN

CONTENTS

ILLUSTRATIONS

CHAPTER I

THE LEGEND OF LUCIFER[1]

THE legend of Lucifer has no biblical basis. The ancient Hebrews knew of no devil whatever. Satan in the Old Testament is no devil in the accepted meaning of the word. He was originally not an adversary but an adjutant of the Almighty. Satan was a member of the celestial court and stood high in the councils of Jehovah. He belonged to the assembly of the sons of God, but sat on the opposition bench. He was a sort of prosecuting attorney attached to the judgment seat of the Eternal.

A certain group of historians of religion maintain that the Devil is the creation of Christianity. Just as the French philosophers of the eighteenth century held that the theologians had invented the Lord, they affirm that the Devil has been expressly created by the priests for the greater glory of God. Lucifer, they claim, has been limned after the Lord as His left hand, so to speak. They call to witness the Church fathers, who baptized Beelzebub as *simia Dei*. The Christian Devil is, in their opinion, *sui generis*, without precedent. Satan is, according to this view, all by himself and has nothing to do with the evil spirits of the ethnic religions. These students of religion fail to see that no discontinuity exists in the evolution of human beliefs and institutions. In fact, the belief in a movement of rebellion within the family of gods is common to the

[1]Two mythological accounts of the origin of the demons and evil spirits may be mentioned in connection with our discussion. According to a belief current among the ancient Norsemen, the demons were produced by the ash-tree named Iggdrasil, also called the Tree of Life, the roots of which reach to the lowest depths of the underworld. A curious Jewish tradition teaches that the Devil and woman had a common origin in Adam's rib. Old Nick is believed by certain rabbins to have come out of the hole left by the removal of the rib from Adam before it was closed. According to another Jewish belief, the demons form a part of the six' days creation.

mythologies of all races. The opposition of Lucifer to the Lord has an analogy in that of Vrita to Indra in Hindu mythology, of Ahriman to Ormuzd in Persian mythology, of Set to Horus in Egyptian mythology, of Prometheus to Zeus in Greek mythology and of Loki to the gods of Asgardh in Scandinavian mythology. The conception of the imprisoned empyrean rebel may also be found in many of the ancient ethnic religions. Ahriman, who fought against Ormuzd, was bound for a thousand years; Promethus, who assailed Zeus, was chained to a rock in the Caucasus; and Loki, the calumniator of the northern gods, was strapped down with thongs of iron in Nastrond (hell), out of which he will come in the "twilight of the gods" to do battle with them and their servants in Valhalla. He will at last be slain by the son of Balder, and then there will be a new heaven and a new earth, and Allfather will reign once more.

The fact of the matter is that the Devil is as old as is man himself. He may be traced back to the animistic conception of Naure, which saw behind natural events active creative spirits. With primitive man to think of good and evil powers was to personify them. The good events were believed by him to be animated by good spirits, the bad events by evil spirits. In a later stage of the evolution of the human mind, the demons behind good acts were subordinated to a good god, and the demons behind evil acts were subordinated to an evil spirit. In this manner, the Devil entered into human thought and has remained to this day. The Fiend is thus the incarnation of human frenzy. The human mind fell a prey to its own fear.

As far as the Devil of the Christian religion is concerned, his ancestry reaches back into the history of religions. He seems to hail from India where he tempted the Buddha, and whence he migrated to Persia in the person of Ahriman. The Jews learned to know him during their Babylonian captivity, under Zoroastrian kings, blended him with their own Satan, who, as has already been stated, originally had no sulphurous odor whatever. After having thus turned Satan into a regular Devil, the Jews handed him over to the Christians, who, sad to say, show themselves no more grateful for Satan than for the Saviour, whom they likewise owe to the sons of Israel.

But Satan, as we know him, is not of pure Semitic stock. During the triumphal march of Christianity through the European countries, he assimilated many of the characteristics of the discarded gods of the old religions. All the rich wealth of ideas which the primitive European peoples associated with their ancient good and evil spirits, they ultimately distributed over the Christian Pantheon. A certain detail of dress, trait of character or trick of manner shows how Satan, in wandering over the face of the earth, has caught a trace of this or that local spirit. The Devil's identification with the uncouth Northern giants was especially momentous for the transformation of his character. It brought down the stern Satan of Judea from the height of his terrible power to the plane of pictured grotesqueness. The Devil, as he has come down to us from the Middle Ages, is a *mélange* of various elements. "He is at once," as it has been said, "of Jewish, Christian, heathen, elfish, gigantic and spectral stock."[2]

The New Testament account of a war in heaven which resulted in the defeat of Satan and his fall like a lightning from heaven (Luk. x, 18; *cf.* Rev. ix, 1) was not derived from the Old Testament which has no hint whatever of a rebellion and expulsion of angels from heaven. This belief was brought back by the Jews from their Babylonian sojourn and first finds expression in the non-canonical Hebrew writings, particularly in the Book of Enoch. It is from the Old Testament apocrypha that this idea found its way into the New Testament.

The Gospel writers also identified Beelzebub (=Baal-Zebub), the fly-god of the Phoenicians, with Satan (*cf.* Matt. xii. 24), inasmuch as the latter was modelled after the Persian Ahriman, who entered the world in the form of a fly.

The substitution of Lucifer for Satan as the rebel angel is a contribution by the Church fathers. It is the result of a wrongly interpreted biblical passage. The prophet compares the king of Babylon, on account of the worldly splendor by which he was surrounded prior to his death, to Lucifer ("light-bearer"), the Latin equivalent of the Hebrew word *hillel*, the "morning-star," *i.e.* ·the planet Venus when it appears above the Eastern horizon prior to daybreak. Just as the brilliancy of Lucifer ("day-star" A. V.) surpasses that of all other stars in the firmament, so the splendor of the king of Babylon surpasses that of all other Oriental monarchs.

[2]Cf. Jakob Grimm: *Deutsche Mythologie*. Berlin 1835. 4. Ausg. 3 Bde. 1875-7. Neudruck 1930.

WAR IN HEAVEN
Afer the Revelation of St. John
(By Albrecht Dürer)

Eusebius of Cæsarea, Tertullian, Jerome, and Gregory the Great erroneously understood the passage: "How art thou fallen from heaven, O Lucifer, son of the morning, how art thou cut down to the ground which didst weaken the nations" (Is. xiv, 12) to refer to the fall of the rebel angel. In consequence of this misinterpretation, the name of Lucifer has been used as a synonym for Satan. The two, however, were not generally identified until the time of St. Anselm, archbishop of Canterbury (1034-1093), who, in his treatise, *Dialogus de casu Diaboli,* has considerably elaborated the account of the Devil's fall from heaven.[3] In popular belief, however, Lucifer and Satan are not blended, though they are thoroughly in agreement.

*   *   *

The legend of the rebellion and expulsion of Lucifer, as formulated by Jewish and Christian writers, is as follows:

Lucifer was the chief in the hierarchy of heaven. He was pre-eminent among all created beings in beauty, power and wisdom. What better description can be given of him than the following portrait penned, according to patristic exegesis, by the prophet:

"Thou sealest up the sum, full of wisdom, and perfect in beauty. Thou has been in Eden, the garden of God; every precious stone was thy covering, the sardius, topaz, the diamond, the beryl, the onyx, and the jasper, the sapphire, the emerald, and the carbuncle, and gold: the workmanship of thy tabrets and of thy pipes was prepared in thee in the day that thou was created. Thou are the anointed cherub that covereth: and I have set thee so: thou wast the holy mountain of God: thou has walked up and down in the midst of the stones of fire. Thou wast perfect in thy ways from the day that thou wast created, till iniquity was found in thee. By the multitude of thy merchandise they have filled the midst of thee with violence, and thou has sinned; therefore I will cast thee as profane out of the mountain of God: and I will destroy thee, O covering cherub, from the midst of the stones of fire. Thine heart was lifted up because of thy beauty, thou hast corrupted thy wisdom by reason of thy brightness: I will cast thee to the ground, I will lay thee before kings, that they may behold thee" (Ez. xxviii. 12-17).

[3]Reprinted in J. P. Migne's *Patrologia latina,* vol. CLVIII, col. 325-343.

To this "anointed cherub" was apparently allotted power and dominion over the earth; and even after his fall and exclusion from his old domain, he still seems to retain a part of his power and ancient title to sovereignty (Luk. iv, 6; *cf.* also John xiv, 30; II Cor. iv, 4; Eph. ii, 2).

The downfall of the Devil is, according to Church authority, attributed to self-conceit. From the fact that "the Devil sinneth from the beginning" (I John iii, 8) and that "Pride is the beginning of all sin" (Ecclesiasticus x, 15), it was inferred that the Devil's sin was pride. Eusebius, in the third century, advanced *superbia* as the motive of the Devil's rebellion, to which Gregory of Nazianzus later added envy. This idea accounts for the familiar phrase "as proud as Lucifer." Cædmon, in his poem on the fall of Satan, sees the cause of the revolt of Satan in pride and ambition. Marlowe, following tradition, also affirms that Lucifer fell, "by aspiring pride and insolence" (*Dr. Faustus* iii. 68). We recall Coleridge's quatrain:

> "He saw a cottage with a double coach-house,
> A cottage of gentility,
> And the Devil did grin, for his darling sin
> Is pride that apes humility."

Various versions exist in the writings of the rabbis and Church fathers as to the way in which Lucifer's conceit showed itself. According to certain authorities, Lucifer's sin, which brought tribulation into the fair world, consisted in the fact that, in the haughtiness of his heart, he refused to bow before the Great White Throne. Others hold that his audacity went so far as to attempt to seat himself on it, and still others ascribe to him the bold project of seizing it and thus usurping the power of the Most High.[4]

In the medieval mysteries, Lucifer, as the governor of the heavens, is represented as seated next to the Eternal, who warns the high official of heaven: "Touch not my throne by none assent." But as soon as the Lord leaves his seat, Lucifer, swelling with pride, sits down on the throne of heaven. The archangel Michael, indignant over the audacious act of Lucifer, takes up arms against him and

---

[4]In *De partu virginis* written by Sannazaro, the "Christian Virgil," in 1526, Satan is also represented as attempting to usurp the throne of heaven.

finally succeeds in driving him out of heaven down into the dark
and dismal dwelling reserved for him from all eternity. The Mont
St. Michel on the Norman coast is the eternal monument to the
victorious leader of the hosts of heaven in the war against the
rebel angel.[5]

THE FALLEN LUCIFER (After Doré)

According to the Talmud, Satan's sin lay not in his rivalry with
God but in his envy of man. When Adam was created, so say the
rabbis, all the angels had to bow to the new king of the earth, but
Satan refused; and when threatened with the wrath of the Lord,
he replied: "If He breaks out in wrath against me, I will exalt my

[5] An interesting treatment of this legend is Maupassant's story "Légende
du Mont St. Michel" (1882).

throne above His, and I will be higher than the Most High." At once God flung Satan and his host out of heaven, down to the earth. From that moment dates the enmity between Satan and Jehovah.[6] The Koran has a similar account of the revolt of Eblis against Allah. When Allah created man, so runs the Mohammedan version of the war in heaven, he called all the angels to worship this crowning work of His hands. Eblis, in his great conceit, refused to worship Adam and was banished from heaven for failing to obey the command of Allah.[7] Irenæus is of the opinion that the angels rebelled as soon as they learned of the proposed creation of man. "When the angels were informed," says this father of the Church, "of God's intention to create man after His own image. . . , they envied man's happiness and so revolted." The orthodox teaching, however, is that man's creation followed the Devil's rebellion. Adam was created by the Lord to fill the vacancy caused in the celestial choir-stalls by the fall of the angels. This act of substitution increased still further the Devil's hatred toward the Deity, and the temptation of Eve in the Garden of Eden was a successful effort on the Devil's part to balk the will of the Lord.

There have, however, been writers who advanced other reasons for the Devil's difference with the Deity. The German mystic Jacob Bœhme, as far back as the seventeenth century, relates that when Satan was asked to explain the cause of God's enmity to him and his consequent downfall, he replied in justification of his act: "I wanted to be an author." Like the son of many a good family, he was driven out, he claims, for having had literary ambitions.[8] Anatole France suggests that Satan was banished from heaven for the reason that he wished to think for himself instead of accepting everything on authority. "Thought," says this latter day diabolist in his book, le Puits de Sainte-Claire (1895), "led Satan to revolt."

The Devil's fall from heaven according to legend, occurred on the first of August. A description of the anniversary festival of this great occasion, when all the devils appear in gala dress, is given by Heywood in his comedy The Play called the Four P. P. (1543-1547).

[6]Cf. Louis Ginzberg: The Legends of the Jews (4 vols., Philadelphia, 1909-1925), I, 64. In Vondel's Lucifer, the revolt of the angels is also caused by their jealousy of the privileges enjoyed by man.

[7]Cf. M. D. Conway, Demonology and Devil-Lore (2 vols., London, 1879), II, 143.

[8]The word "author" is used in this connection in its current meaning.

* * *

The legend of Lucifer, as solving the problem of the origin of evil and of the birth of man, and as presaging the goal of human destiny, has always been a matter of great human concern, and a subject full of fascination for the poet. Nearly all the great minds of Christendom have attempted to treat this theme. Beginning with the account of the Creation by the Spanish monk Dracontius, the Latin poem of Avitus, Bishop of Vienne, in his work *De laudibus Dei* (5th century), which carries the history of the world from Creation through the fall of man to the Flood and the Exodus, and the transcript of the biblical text of Creation by the old English poet Cædmon of the seventh century, we have had at different periods various treatments of this subject. The medieval passion plays in the end reached back to the creation and fall of the angels and the temptation of man which necessitated his salvation through Christ. In the seventeenth century, the Netherland imagination was fired with this theme. The youthful Hugo Grotius was the first to attempt it in his *Adamus exul,* a Latin drama, written in 1601, which is supposed to have given hints to Milton. Two other Dutchmen of that period, both far greater poets than Grotius, were also attracted by this subject-matter. The distinguished Jacob Cats treated it in his idyll "Gront-Houwelick" (The Fundamental Marriage of Adam and Eve),[9] and Vondel in his tragedy of *Lucifer* (1654). So many poets of so many different nations during that period chose this subject of such historical and symbolical significance. In addition to the poets just mentioned we may refer to the following: the Scotchman Andrew Ramsay, the Spaniard Azevedo, the Portuguese Camoens, the Frenchman Du Bartas and the Englishmen Phineas Fletcher and John Milton.

The Puritan poet surpassed all his predecessors in his treatment of this old subject. He overlaid the original story with a wealth of invention and imagery. It may be said without any exaggeration that he produced the greatest of all modern epics. What fascinates us primarily in his poem is the personality of the Prince of Darkness. "The finest thing in connection with this [Milton's] Paradise," says Taine, in his *Histoire de la littérature anglaise* (1863), "is Hell; and in this history of God, the chief part is taken by the

---

[9] This story is the first of a long poem, which bears the title of *Trouring* and which was published in 1637.

Devil." It is generally agreed that the hero of *Paradise Lost* (1667-1674) is none other than Satan. Daniel Defoe, in his *Political History of the Devil* (1726), remarks that "Mr. Milton has indeed made a fine poem, but it is a devil of a history." The Miltonic Satan is the greatest personification of evil in all Christian poems. In the opinion of many critics, there is no poetic character, ancient or modern, that equals Milton's Satan in grandeur. The irreconcilable and irremediable archangel is an incomparable creation,—a mighty angel fallen! The reader cannot but be affected by a sense of sorrow for this fall.

It is a curious fact, indeed, that Milton, who started out in his poem "to justify the ways of God to men" (*Par. Lost* i. 26), ended by conferring lustre upon Lucifer. The Puritan poet portrays the Devil with such a passionate concern that the reader is not at a loss where to find the author's sympathies. The fact of the matter is that Milton himself was, as William Blake has said it, "of the Devil's party without knowing it."[10]

Milton's Satan is a great spirit fallen from heaven and clothed with a certain tragic dignity. The emperean rebel in *Paradise Lost* still holds his glory and his star. The ridiculous Devil of our ancestors has become in Milton's hands a giant and a hero. He is not the stupid good-natured lout of the medieval peasant. Nor does he answer to the feathered clown of the medieval mystery plays. He is really an epic, majestic figure, a Promethean character, who vainly but valiantly opposes a power which he knows he can never conquer.

It must be admitted, though, that this conception of Satan is not wholly original with Milton. The Devil had already been drawn by Avitus as an imposing figure reminding one of the Miltonic hero. In the Eger Passion Play of 1516, we also have an approach to a higher dramatic conception of the Devil, that of a glorious, large hearted rebel Satan.

Milton's Satan is usually regarded as the mighty fallen, majesty in ruin, something to be admired and feared. We must, however, not overlook his awful grief, his wild despair. Milton knew how to render in words of surpassing beauty the impressive sorrow and the introspective pangs of the Archangel ruined. The expression of

[10]"The reason Milton wrote in fetters when he wrote of angels and God and at liberty when of devils and hell, is because he was a true poet and of the Devil's party without knowing it" (William Blake).

human emotions which Milton imparts to his Satan when this fallen angel descends into his doleful domain to summon his infernal council has aroused the admiration of readers to this day. Satan's pity for the sad plight of the spirits who fell with him, and his compassion for man, to whom he must bring destruction, are lines in *Paradise Lost* which cannot be easily forgotten.

In what beautiful terms is Satan's self-condemnation clothed by Milton! The poet follows tradition in describing Satan's punishment in hell (*Par. Lost* ii. 88). But this material pain is in Milton very insignificant as compared with the Devil's spiritual sufferings. It is the inward torments on which Milton lays chief emphasis, and this inner pain shows itself in the face of his Fiend. "Myself am Hell," Satan cries in the anguish of his soul (*ibid.,* iv. 75). What gnaws at his heart is not a serpent, but "the thought both of lost happiness and lasting pain" (*ibid.,* i. 54-55).

The pain of Milton's Satan is psychical rather than physical. His is the boundless horror and despair of one who has known "eternal joys" and is now condemned to everlasting banishment. Marlowe's Mephistopheles also complains of moral rather than material sufferings. His torment is to be hopelessly bound in the constraint of serfdom to evil. There is a suggestion of peculiar horror in the tortured protest which bursts from his lips when asked as to his condition:

"Think'st thou that I, that saw the face of God,
And tasted the eternal joys of heaven,
Am not tormented with ten thousand hells,
In being depriv'd of everlasting bliss?
O Faustus! leave these frivolous demands,
Which strike a terror to my fainting soul!" (iii. 78-83).

The idea of the repentant rebel is also not original with Milton. It is of pre-Christian origin and was also acquired by the Jews from the Persians. The writer of the Book of the Secrets of Enoch (written between 30 B. C. and 50 A. D.) already represents the apostatized angels as "weeping unceasingly." This conception is also found in the apocryphal Vision of St. Paul. In his lamentations over his expulsion from heaven in the medieval mystery plays, Satan has often given a very poetic expression to his deep yearning for the heaven which he has lost. In the Eger Passion Play, the Devil expresses his willingness to perform the most terrible penance if he can but obtain his forgiveness. A modern version of Satan's *De profundis* has been given us by Frieda Schanz:

> Der Teufel hat immer mit frechem Munde
> Den Himmel verflucht und Gott verklagt.
> Aber einmal in wunderbarer Stunde
> Hat er gesagt:
> "Und läge der Himmel noch tausendmal weiter
> Ueber dem Höllenmoor
> Und führte eine glühende Leiter
> Zu ihm empoor,
> Jede Sprosse aus eisernen Dornenzweigen,
> Jeder Schritt unausdenkbares Weh und Grau'n,
> Tausend Legionen Jahre möchte ich steigen,
> Um nur einmal Sein Angesicht zu schau'n."

It does not seem, though, that Satan is wholly satisfied with Milton's account of the events that led to his expulsion from heaven. The reader will recall Bernard Shaw's account of Satan's indignation over the Miltonic version of the celestial war. "The Englishman described me as being expelled from Heaven by cannon and gun-powder, and to this day every Briton believes that the whole of this silly story is in the Bible. What else he says, I do not know, for it is all in a long poem which neither I nor any one else ever succeeded in wading through" (*Man and Superman*, 1905).

Milton's delineation of the lesser lights of hell is not less to be admired. In *Paradise Lost* there is a distinct differentiation of demons. The personality of each devil reveals itself. Baal is not merely a devil; he is the particular devil Baal. Beelzebub, we feel, is distinct from Belial; Moloch is not Mammon, nor is Dagon, Rimmon. Milton's devils are not metaphysical abstractions. A personal devil is always a lot more interesting than an abstraction. Even his allegorical figures are living symbols. The demons in *Paradise Lost* art not ugly beasts. They have no horns, no tails. Nor are they wicked men, either. But they act in a manner which men can understand. The Devil should not be human, but he must have enough in common with human nature to play a part intelligible to human beings. In the artistic treatment of diabolical material, the chief difficulty lies in preserving the just mean between the devil-character and the imparted element of humanity.

Milton had many imitators, all of whom fell far short of their model. Klopstock tried to give to Germany what Milton had given to his country. His *Messias* (1748-1773), which treats of the Christian system of salvation, was intended to parallel the epic of the Puritan poet. But his Satan is so much below Milton's Satan that we blush to think how this Satan of Klopstock could ever sustain a conversation with the Satan of Milton or even appear in his com-

Milton's Satan (After Doré)

pany. He has neither the greatness of intellect nor the charm of personality with which Satan was clothed by Milton. The Devil of Klopstock is indeed a Miltonic Devil, "but oh how fallen! how changed!" (*Par. Lost* i. 84). It will be recalled that when somebody once called Klopstock the "German Milton," Coleridge promptly retorted that Klopstock was a very German Milton.[11]

The subject of Satan's revolt has not failed of fascination even for the writers of the modern period, which has discarded the Devil into the limbo of ancient superstitions and in which his very mention, far from causing men to cross themselves, brings a smile on

[11]Albrecht von Haller's play *Vom Ursprung des Uebels* (1734) likewise contains many reminiscences of Milton's *Paradise Lost*. A tragedy called *Lucifer* was also published, in 1717, by a Jesuit father in Silesia Manz Noel.

their faces. It cannot be denied that most of our ideas in this
realm of thought are quite different from the views that the contemporaries of Milton entertained. The tremendous belief in the
personality of the Devil that had grown up during the Middle Ages
flourished just as vigorously in the middle of the seventeenth century. Milton himself fully believed in the existence of the diabolical
beings whom he described. He was as firm, although not as fantastic, a believer in a real, personal Devil as Luther was. We never
think of doubting Milton. "As well might we doubt the reality of
those scorching fires of hell that had left their marks on the face of
Dante; or of the fearful sights and sounds that beset Christian on
his way through the Valley of the Shadow of Death." Even Christopher Marlowe, in telling the story of the bargain between Faustus
and Mephistopheles, believed that he narrated established facts.
The conception of the Devil of a Marlowe, a Milton, a Bunyan, still
represents the seriousness of the medieval fear of the Fiend. These
men lived in an age of faith in which angels and demons were not
abstract figures, but living realities. In our modern times, however,
heaven and hell have lost their "local habitation," and angels and
demons are considered as figments of the human imagination.[12]

Contrary to all expectation, however, the legend of Lucifer has
not ceased to exert a strong attraction upon the mind of man to this
day. As a matter of fact, the Devil has perhaps received his
greatest elaboration in modern times at the hands of writers who
believed in him no more than Shakespeare did in the ghost of
Hamlet's father. The treatment of this ancient legend, however,
differs radically from that given to it by the poets of former times.
It has been reserved for the last century to bring about a reversal
of poetic judgment with regard to the events which supposedly happened in the heavens in the dim beginnings of history. It must not
be forgotten that the accounts of the celestial war given by the
rabbins and Church fathers came from partisans of heaven. The
other party could perhaps furnish a different version of those events.
Samuel Butler has remarked in his *Note-Books,* published posthumously in 1912, that we have never heard the Devil's side of the
case because God has written all the books. It is apparent that he
was not familiar with the writings of a number of men in different

[12]On the conditions that tended to vivify the belief in the Devil during the
Elizabethan era, see Thomas A. Spaulding's *Elizabethan Demonology*. London,
1880.

European countries who constituted themselves, during the last century, as the spokesmen of the Devil and advocated a revision of his process. These *advocati Diaboli* endeavored to show that the Devil was after all not so black as he has always been painted.

During the period of the Romantic revolt in all European countries Satan was considered as a Prometheus of Christian mythology. He was hailed as the vindicator of reason, of freedom of thought, and of an unfettered humanity. The French Romantics saw in Satan the greatest enthusiast for the liberty and spontaneity of genius, the sublimest and supremest incarnation of the spirit of individualism, the greatest symbol of protest against tyranny, celestial or terrestial. They predicted the day when Satan would return to his former glory in heaven.

Satan received ample vindication in England from such poets as Byron, Shelley, Swinburne and James Thomson. Byron portrayed Lucifer as a rebel against celestial injustice. Shelley took his transmuted Lucifer from Milton's Satan, and deified him a little more. The imagination of the poet of *Prometheus Unbound* (1820) made of the Devil the benefactor of man and the light of the world. George Du Maurier averred that no tongue had yet uttered what might be said for the adversary of the Almighty.

In Germany, as far back as the eighteenth century, Count Stolberg, in his *Jamben* (1783), celebrated Lucifer as the Morning-Star, the Light-Bearer, to whom man is indebted for truth and enlightenment. Richard Dehmel's pantomimic drama *Lucifer* (1899) is a glorification of the Devil, whom the poet calls by such beautiful epthets as *Glanzbringer, Gluthüter, Lichtschöpfer, Mutwecker, Weltbegeistrer*.

In Scandinavia, August Strindberg, in his play, *Lucifer or God* (1877), reverses the roles between the Almighty and His adversary. Lucifer is represented in this play as a compound of Apollo, Prometheus and Christ. This divinization of the Devil has for its counterpart the diabolization of the Deity.[13]

In Italy, Carducci, in his *Inno a Satana* (1863), describes the Devil clothed with such mighty and beautiful splendor that his glory almost compels the knee to bend. This bold writer represents Satan as "the immortal enemy of autocracy and the banner-bearer of the

[13]A synopsis of this most audacious and blasphemous play, which originally appeared as an epilogue to *Master Olof*, will be found in *The International* III, 37, Febr. 1911.

great reformers and innovators of all ages." His contemporary, Rapisardi, similarly celebrates, in *Lucifero* (1877), the Devil as the bringer of light to the world.

The last to report on the revolt of the angels is Anatole France, who, in his book *la Révolte des anges* (1914), presents us with an account of a second angelic rebellion against the Ruler of the Heavens. This work contains also a new version of the first war in the skies. A number of the inhabitants of heaven, who were hurled down to earth, form a conspiracy to storm the heavens and set up Satan as ruler. After having organized their forces and equipped them with the most modern instruments of war, the leaders of the revolt seek out Satan by the waters of the Ganges and offer him the leadership. But he who first raised the flag of rebellion in heaven refuses to lead another attack against the celestial citadel. In a dream he has seen himself becoming as harsh, as intolerant and as greedy of adulation as his eternal enemy Jehovah. The successful rebel would only turn a reactionary. He will rather remain the oppressed than become an oppressor.

CHAPTER II

THE NUMBER OF THE DEVILS

THOUGH we usually speak of the Devil in the singular, it must not be forgotten that there are many devils. As a matter of fact, there are as many varieties of fiends as there are of ferns. The Devil, it has been said, is hydra-headed; he wears a thousand crowns, wields a thousand sceptres and is known by a thousand names. In all European countries, men swear by a "thousand devils." Milton, Chateaubriand, Balzac and other writers speak of demons in thousands. This number also occurs in several German expressions, such as *Sauf in tausend Teufel Namen* and *Steh in tausend Teufel Namen auf*.[1] But this sum should not be taken literally. As a matter of fact, the number of the evil spirits runs into millions.

The Old Testament knows only Satan, although, as a matter of fact, this "accuser" was in no way a devil to the ancient Hebrews. In the New Testament, the Devil already has "his angels" (Matt. xxv, 41; Rev. xii, 9), who sided with Satan in the war of the heavens and who were cast out with him into utter darkness. The Gospel writers speak even of a legion of demons. We are at least led to infer this number from the reply of the madman of Gerasa, who fancied that he was possessed by a legion (an army) of demons (Mark v, 9; Luke viii, 30).[2] The apocryphal Gospel of Nicodemus, as early as the third century, mentions already, several "legions of devils," who are under Satan's sway in hell.[3]

[1] A German writer, A. Saager, seems to be on familiar terms with three hundred thousand devils, about whom he tells anecdotes in his recently published book *Dreimal hundert tausend Teufel*. The medieval French epics, the *Chansons de geste*, speak of five hundred thousand demons.

[2] A legion is the Roman regiment of approximately 6,000 soldiers.

[3] Josephus, in his *Wars of the Jews* (VII. vi. 3) speaks also of legions of demons, but he has in mind the spirits of wicked men.

The number of the angels who participated in this movement of rebellion has never been fully ascertained. The belief current among the Catholic Schoolmen, based upon an interpretation of a biblical phrase (Rev. xii, 4), is that a third of the angels ranged themselves under Satan's standard.[4] The rebel leader's armed force seems to have comprised nearly two thousand four hundred legions (about fourteen million four hundred thousand demons), of which each demon of rank commanded a certain number. Furcas commanded twenty, Leraie thirty, Agares thirty-one, Morax thirty-six and Sabnac fifty legions in the celestial civil war. Alfred de Vigny thinks that a thousand million followed Satan in his fall (*Cinq-Mars*, 1826).

* * *

In an attempt at a reconciliation of the two contradictory passages relating to the punishment of the revolting angels (Rev. xii, 9 and xx, 3), a few Church fathers thought that not all the followers of Satan were thrown with their rebel chief into hell and cast into chains. A number of them were left on earth in order to tempt man.[5] It has been suggested that the angels who were not hurled into the bottom of hell but banished to our earth had maintained a neutral position in the rivalry between the Lord and Lucifer. It is not so generally known that during the war in heaven the angels were not wholly divided into two opposing camps. There were many spirits who, untouched by partisan passions, remained aloof from the conflict and refused to don the uniform. They demanded their right of keeping out of a war which they did not bring about and in which they had no interest whatever. When the Lord defeated His enemy and cast him and his legionaries into the abyss, He did not hurl also the neutral angels into hell, but, in order to give them another opportunity to choose between Him and His rival, cast them down to the earth, to which the scene of the battle

[4] Cf. Johannes Oswald: *Angelologie* (Paderborn, 1883), p. 95.

[5] Michael Psellus, one of the most famous Byzantine writers of the 11th century and author of *Dialogus de energia, seu operatione dæmonum*, distinguishes six kinds of demons, according to their different habitations. He names demons of fire, of the air, of the earth, of the water, of the underworld, and, lastly, demons of the night, "who shun the daylight." Coleridge, in his gloss on *The Ancient Mariner* (1798), refers his reader to Psellus on demons in illustration of the poem. The treatise by Psellus seems also to have given suggestions for *Christabel* (1816). See la *Démonologie de Michel Psellus* by K. Svoboda. Paris, 1927.

had been transferred. From these angels, who married mortal maidens, there has developed a race which has always shown a striking contrast to the human family. It has furnished humanity with its prophets and poets, with its reformers and revolutionaries. All great men at all times and in all places have belonged to this mysterious race which does not proceed from father to son, like other races, but appears here and there, at recurring intervals, in the families of mankind. The descendants of this union between the sons of God and the daughters of men have always stood in the first ranks of those who seek peace and abhor murder. They have proved valiant warriors in the eternal conflict between the Good and the Evil for the mastery of the world. No battle is fought for human freedom, but they are there; no prison where men are held for the sake of conscience, but they are there. They have long ago redeemed themselves, but they will not return to heaven until they have also redeemed all men.[6]

* * *

In addition to the angels who were hurled from heaven for their participation in the celestial civil war, other sons of God were expelled for their lust after the daughters of men (Gen. vi, 1-4).[7] Jewish tradition teaches that two hundred angels, attracted by the beauty of the daughters of Eve, descended to the summit of Mount Hermon and defiled themselves with them. No sooner had the angels left heaven and descended to earth, so say the rabbis, than they lost their transcendental qualities and were invested with sublunary bodies so that a union with the daughters of men became possible.[8]

The celestial mutineers belonged to all nine orders of angels, which Gregory the Great has named cherubim, seraphim, thrones, dominations, principalities, powers, virtues, angels, and archangels.

[6] This theory was advanced by the present writer in his essay "Dante's Devil," which appeared in the *Open Court*, vol. XXXV (1921), pp. 513-28.
[7] Higher criticism will not admit that this passage refers to a union between angels and humans. It maintains that the expression *benê-elohim*, rendered "sons of God" by the Revised Version, means in reality "spirit-folk," and that the corresponding term *nephilim* rendered "giants" means "fallen ones," i. e. descended from star-land. They are super-men, who descended from the stars to intermarry with mortals. The belief prevailed among the primitive races in many lands that their ancestors had come from the stars, and that they themselves, after a few generations, would return there. This idea is still prevalent among certain Indian tribes in our own country. The moral implication is a later exegetical addition, which is first found in the Book of Enoch.
[8] *Cf.* Louis Ginzberg: *The Legends of the Jews* (Philadelphia, 1909-1925), I, 151.

Satan was a cherub, according to certain authorities. Astaroth, Lucifer and Samael were seraphs. Among the members of the order of thrones were Acaos, Asmodeus, Beleth, Cedron, Celsus, Easa, Focalos, Gresil, Murmur, Phœnix, and Purson. Achas, Alex, Cham, and Zabulon belonged to the order of principalities. Aman and Goap were part of the powers. The order of virtues counted among its members Agares and Barbatos. Murmur belonged to the order of angels as well as to that of thrones. Satan was, according to other authorities, an archangel. He shared this honor with Belphegor.

In the seventh play of the York mysteries we are informed that of each of the nine orders the tenth part fell in Satan's revolt. Others hold that Satan, as an archangel, led only his own order to war on Jehovah. Gregory the Great conveys the idea that the order of Satan which fell was, from the very first, distinct from the other orders, which remained loyal. The rebel angels, according to this theory, belonged wholly to the order of *ophanim,* living and flaming wheels all covered with eyes.

Among the angels who forsook the celestial choir-stalls in exchange for the charms of mortal maidens, Jewish tradition mentions Asa and Asael—who later founded a great college of sorcery and astrology in the dark mountains of Egypt—Azazel, Beelzebub, Cedor, Semyaza, Shamdan and Shemhazai. The union of these sons of God and daughters of men resulted in a race of giants known for their wickedness as much as for their strength. The ghosts of these malicious giants begotten of the angels by the mortal maidens turned into demons (Book of Enoch, ch. xvi).[9] Justin Martyr expresses the belief that all demons are the offspring of the angels who yielded to the embraces of earthly women. Other Church fathers, among them Athenagoras, Clement of Alexandria, Tertullian and Cyprian, even taught that the sin of the angels which had brought about their fall consisted not in their revolt against the Lord but in their carnal relations with the daughters of men. St. Paul demands for this reason that women should veil their heads in church "because of the angels" (1 Cor. xi, 10), who might be attracted by their beautiful tresses and thus be led to sin (*cf.* also Tertullian's *De virginibus velondis*).

Byron's poem *Heaven and Earth* (1822) goes back to the days

[9] A critical edition of the Book of Enoch will be found in R. H. Charles, *The Apocrypha and Pseudo-epigrapha of the Old Testament.* 2 vols. London and New York, 1913.

when human passions "drew angels down to earth" and deals with the biblical legend of the union of the sons of heaven and the daughters of earth.

* * *

Then again all heathen gods, when driven off the earth by Christianity, went under the earth to swell the ranks of Satan. The numberless dethroned, outlawed, and fallen deities of the subjugated races and discredited religions changed, for the Christians, into demons. The ancient Hebrews already considered the gods of the nations with which they were at war as devils. What meant deity to the heathens signified devil to the Hebrews. It is wholly natural that the god of one religion or one nation should become the devil of another religion or nation, especially if these groups are enemies. Thus Baalzebub, the god of Ekron (2 Kings i, 1), was to the New Testament writers the chief of the devils (Matt. xii, 24).

In the wake of the conquering hosts of Christian mythology, the original mythical denizens of the earth were banished to hell. This was especially true in the case of the divinities which, in pagan beliefs, were already associated with the shadowy world. From St. Paul to Savonarola, the pagan gods were considered as fallen angels. The great apostle identified all ancient gods with devils (1 Cor. x, 20). The Church regarded the gods of mythology as fallen spirits who beguiled men into worshipping them in the form of idols.[10]

---

[10] "But the fundamental cause (*consummativa*) [of idolatry] must be sought in the devils, who cause men to adore them under the form of idols, therein working certain things which excited their wonder and admiration" (St. Thomas Aquinas: *Summa theologica*, II ii. 94).

Professor A. H. Godbey maintains that St. Paul does not mean the "devils" of medieval Christian fancy. In his opinion, the apostle protests against the current ancestor worship and has in mind "human spirits" speaking through a "medium (*cf.* Rev. xxii, 8-9; Acts x, 25; xvi, 8-18; xxviii, 3-6). Similarly, Professor Godbey insists that the Church fathers did not mean our horned and hoofed demons, but the spirits of the dead. Their *dæmones*, meaning "knowing spirits," refer to the patrons, friends and guardians of men. It is but necessary, he says, to read Origen's controversy with Celsus, who insisted that the worship of beneficent *dæmones* should not be abolished. This fact is also evident from the writings of Clement, Tertullian, and Arnobius. Be that as it may, it will be perfectly clear to the reader that our presentation of the subject is from the viewpoint of medieval orthodox Christianity, which denounced as evil all spirit-personalities not included in its small theological hierarchy and applied the borrowed terms "demon" and "devil" even to those powers which were not evil in the ancient world. In fact, some of the most beneficent of the ancient gods were most devilish in the eyes of the medieval Christian. On this question, consult Willibald Beyschlag's study, *Hat der Apostel Paulus die Heidengötter für Dämonen gehalten?* Halle a. S., 1894.

The pagan deities were in reality, Catholic tradition maintains, supernatural beings who exercised their powers for sinister aims and who caused themselves to be adored under different names in different countries. The Church fathers were very explicit on this point. Tertullian states unequivocally that all the old gods were disguised demons (*De spectaculis,* xix). Mohammed likewise reduced all ancient pagan deities to devils.

When the Christian religion spread over the Western Empire, the Greek and Roman gods were looked upon as allies of the Devil. The diabolization of the Greek gods is well depicted in Mrs. Browning's poem *The Dead Pan* (1844). Milton, in his *Paradise Lost* (1667-1674), also places the "Ionian Gods" in his Pandemonium (i. 508). The Puritan poet follows this tradition throughout his poem of the fall of Lucifer.

When the Teutonic nations accepted Christianity, the Devil entered upon a particularly rich inheritance. To his portion fell all the dark and gloomy powers of the original beliefs of these peoples. All the rich wealth of ideas which the primitive Germans associated with their ancient good and evil spirits, they ultimately distributed over the Christian Pantheon. Germanic mythology went primarily to enrich Christian demonology, although it also contributed a good deal to Catholic hagiography. The countless legions of earth-sprites and the army of giants that inhabited the countries of the North came under Satan's sway. Spirits such as elves, cobolds, fairies, hairy hobgoblins of the forest, waternymphs of the brookside, and dwarfs of the mountains were transformed by medieval Christianity into devils, or into hellish imps, a sort of assistant or apprentice devils. Mephistopheles in Goethe's *Faust* had this diabolization of Greek and Germanic divinities in mind when he said: "From Hartz to Hellas always cousins" (ii. 7743).

*
* *

The number of the demons keeps on increasing from day to day as a result of Death, which the Devil brought to the children of Adam. The belief was prevalent already in classical days and was expressed by Hesiod that the ghosts of the dead turn into demons. It is believed even nowadays that after death good men become angels in heaven, bad men devils in hell. As the latter outnumber on earth the former, hell must necessarily have a larger population than heaven. It cannot be gainsaid that mankind, though created to fill the places in heaven that had been occupied by the fallen angels, only replenished the cave of Tartarus. Men have, as a matter of fact, always headed downwards, and not upwards, as had been originally planned. In all probability, hell is by now filled to the point of overflowing. A French philosopher, as far back as the eighteenth century, found consolation in the thought that he would no longer find room in the infernal regions. *"Il y a longtemps,"* said he, *"que l'enfer est rempli; on n'y entre plus!"* ("Hell has been full for a long time; one can no longer enter!")

Furthermore, the population of hell increases in the same manner as that of earth. The ancient Jews believed that the demons, who are composed of both sexes, were propagated like mankind; that they were human, and ate, drank, were married and divorced. Judging from all appearances, the demons, indeed, are far from practising race-suicide. They replenish hell much faster than we increase and multiply on earth.

In addition, the demons of hell constantly receive new recruits from heaven. According to Anatole France, in *la Révolte des anges* (1914), there is a constant falling off from God—angels becoming devils. What we must not overlook, either, is the fact that the demons also multiply with synonyms and dialectical differences. Thus we find in Chateaubriand's *les Martyrs* (1809) two demons of Death named after the two French words for "death" *la Mort* and *le Trépas.*

The person and power of the Satan of the Scriptures continued to develop and multiply with the march of the centuries so that in the Catholic Middle Ages the world fairly pullulated with the demons of hell. Their number increased still further in all Protestant countries after the Reformation. Far from decreasing the power of the Devil in the world, the Reformation brought him strong reinforcements. Martin Luther firmly believed in the Devil and, in one of his hymns, affirmed that he had "seen and defied innumerable devils." In his writings, the Evil Power divided and subdivided itself into as many manifestations as there are vices in the world. Protestantism showed the rationalistic tendency of discovering the Devil in the vices of men. It reduced the Principle of Evil from a personified phantom with which no man could cope to those impersonal but all the more real moral abstractions with which every man can cope. The German reformer and his disciples thus filled Germany with devils by diabolizing all vices. The disciples, as is generally the case, outdid their master. Luther threw an inkstand at the head of the Devil, and his followers poured oceans of ink on him. The Protestant preachers of Germany began, toward the middle of the sixteenth century, to wage a bitter war with their pens against the hosts of hell. The most curious work of Protestant demonology is the *Theatrum diabolorum* (1569) by Sigmund Feyerabend, a voluminous collection of the orthodox views of Luther's followers concerning the existence, power, nature and demeanor of the devils. We find in this book all sorts of devils, such as the devil of blasphemy, the dance-devil, the servant's devil, the hunting devil, the drink devil, the wedlock devil, the devil of unchastity, the miser's devil, the devil of tyranny, the laziness-devil, the pride-devil, the pantaloon devil, the gambling devil, the courtier's devil, and so forth, and so on.

The idea of special devils, however, is not original with Luther. We find them already in medieval mystery and morality plays. We can even follow this idea further back into the history of human thought. Already in ancient times different devils presided over different moral and physical evils. The Kabbala already knows of special demons and demonesses for each sin. Among the Jews, probably as far back as the time of Christ, demons were designated according to the diseases they induced. There were demons of asthma, croup, hydrophobia, insanity and indigestion.[11] Knut Leonard Tallqvist says that, among Assyrians, demons were named after the diseases attributed to them. He further tells us that the connection was so close that names of demons and corresponding diseases came to be identical.[12]

There have, as a matter of fact, been as many devils conceived in the human mind as there have been ideas of evil. The trooping

[11]See authorities quoted by Alfred Edersheim in his *Life and Times of Jesus the Messiah* (8th ed., London, 1899), II 759.

[12]Quoted by Thomas Witton Davies: *Magic, Diviniation, and Demonology among the Hebrews and their Neighbors; including an Examination of Biblical References and of Biblical Terms* (London, 1878), p. 104.

legions of evil thoughts naturally suggested legions of devils. "Everywhere in the great world men are building little worlds of their own," observes the thoughtful Mephistopheles (*Faust* i. 4044-45) ; "and everywhere they are creating little devils of their own to inhabit them," is Miss Agnes Repplier's comment on the words of the Devil.[13]

Johannes. Wierus, a pupil of the famous Cornelius Agrippa and author of the learned treatise, *De præstigiis dæmonum* (1563), went to the considerable trouble of counting the devils and found that their number was seven and odd millions. According to this German demonologist, the hierarch of hell commands an army of 1,111 legions, each composed of 6,666 devils, which brings the total of evil spirits to 7,405,926, "without any possibility of error in calculation." A professor of theology in Basle, Martinus Barrhaus, is, as far as is known, the last man to take the census of the population of hell. According to this infernal statistician, the devils number exactly 2,665,866,746,664.

If we are to believe Richalmus, an abbot of the first part of the thirteenth century, the number of the devils exceeds all calculation, being equal to the grains of the sands of the sea. Three friars, so runs the legend which confirms the view of this monk, hid themselves one night near a Witches' Sabbath, which happened to be held in a valley in the Alps, in order that they might count the devils present at the affair. But the master of ceremonies, upon discovering the friars and divining their intention, said to them: "Reverend brothers, our army is so great that if all the Alps, their rocks and glaciers, were equally divided among us, none would have a pound's weight."

The fecund imagination of our ancestors peopled the air, the earth, and the flood with devils. Paracelsus tells us in the 16th century that the air is not so full of flies in the summer as it is at all times of invisible devils; while another philosopher maintains that the air is so full of devils that there is "not so much as an hair's breadth empty in earth or in waters above or under the earth."

Indeed, any attempt to find the sum of the evil specters that have haunted mankind would be like trying to count the shadows cast upon the earth by the rising sun.

[13]Agnes Repplier: "In Man's Image and Likeness." *Putnam's Monthly.* Vol. III (1908), pp. 549-54.

CHAPTER III

THE NAMES OF THE DEVILS

THE designations applied to the Devil are various and numerous. "I go by various names," the Devil informs Tom Walker in Washington Irving's well-known story (1824). The extent and diversity of words and phrases, synonyms and antonyms, revolving about a central notion or idea, as for example diabolism, proves how intimately connected that idea is to the human heart and interests. "A throng of thoughts and forms which else senseless and shapeless were" (Shelley) are incarnated in our speech both in prose and in "Orphic song," and rule our ideas "with dædal harmony."

The generic term "devil" (*diable* in French and *Teufel* in German) for the evil spirit is a derivation of the Latin *diabolus* (Greek διάβολος) which means an "accuser," an "assailant" and which consequently is the exact Septuagint translation of the Hebrew word *satan*.[1]

The word "demon" (from Latin *dæmonium, dæmon,* Greek δαίμων), meaning a "knowing spirit," originally had a complimentary connotation. It signified in pagan Greece a benevolent deity, but came to mean in Christian lands a malevolent being.[2] The demon of Socrates of whom Plato speaks was his good spirit.[3] The word "demon" was also generally used by the neo-Platonists of Alexandria with the meaning of a good spirit. Coleridge in his *Rime of the Ancient Mariner* (1798) and Emerson in his essay on

[1]In Louis Ménard's story "le Diable au café (1876), the Devil calls Hebrew a dead language, and, as a modern, prefers to be called by the French equivalent of his original Hebrew name.

[2]The belief in evil demons, however, is equally to be traced in Greek literature from the earliest period. As early as the fourth century B. C., Xenocrates and Chrysippus, Empedocles and Theophrastus taught that there were evil demons as well as good ones.

[3]See R. Nares: *An Essay on the Demon of Socrates.* London, n. d.

Demonology (1877) likewise use the word "dæmon" as a term for genius.

In addition to these generic and general terms "devil" and "demon," the biblical books contain several proper names for the evil spirits, such as Satan, Lucifer, Beelzebub and Belial (*alias* Beliar), although neither of the four, to speak from the historical viewpoint, originally designated a devil. It has already been shown how Satan, Lucifer and Beelzebub were raised to the honors of demonhood by rabbinic and patristic writers. As far as the word "Belial" is concerned, if it is not a variant of Bêl or Baal, this word may have been personified by the Septuagint through a mistaken rendering of the Hebrew text (2 Cor. iv. 15), which is a term for ungodliness.

But what a catalogue of demons may not be found in the rabbinic and patristic writings! The rabbins and Church fathers as well as the writers of medieval and later times have shown great ingenuity in devising names for the demons. The medieval German mysteries call sixty-two devils by name,[4] and Reginald Scot, writing in the sixteenth century, knows already the names of seventy-nine devils.[5] But this number is far from exhausting the list of the diabolical appellatives.

Many of the denominations invented for the devils bear witness to their former high estate either in the Empyrean, on the Olympus or in Asgardh. Other designations for the demons have been derived from their character, appearance, occupation, or habitation. Thus, for example, the Devil is called Old Horny or Old Hairy or the Black Bogey on account of his cornuted, capillary, or complexional characteristics. Among his many appellations denoting occupation may be mentioned "the baker," for the reason that the Devil puts the damned into the oven, or *Brendly* (meaning in German: "the stoker") for tending to the furnaces and keeping the fires of hell burning.

The infernal spirits have also been baptized after human characters. They have inherited the names of historical personages who achieved notoriety through their evil deeds, such as Nero and Napoleon. In addition, Christian devils often go by the names of

[4]*Cf.* M. J. Rudwin: *Der Teufel in den deutschen geistlichen Spielen des Mittelalters und der Reformationszeit* (Göttingen, 1915), pp. 96-98.

[5]Reginald Scot: *Discoverie of Witchcraft.* London 1584. 2nd ed., 1651. A critical edition with Explanatory Notes, Glossary and Introduction by B. Nicholson appeared, in 1886, in London.

Jews and Mohammedans, such as Ruffin and Mohammed. They even adopt many Christian household names, such as Jack, John, Richard, Robert, Roger, Thomas, Will(iam), and among women's names Mary.[6]

The following names of devils occur in the present work: Abbadona, Abiron, Aborym, Acaos, Accaron, Achas, Adonis, Adram-(m)elech, Agares, Aggareth, Alaster, Alex, Alilah, Aman, Amoyon, Andrew Malchus, Aniguel, Anizel, Antichrist, Anubis, Apollo, Apollyon, Arakiel, Ariel, Armaros, Asa, Asaël, Ashtaroth (alias Astaroth), Asmenoth, Asmodeus (alias Ashmodaï, Asmodi and Modo), Astarte, Atoti, Azazel, Aziel, Baal, Baal-Berith, Babillo, Bali, Barakel, Barbatos, Barbuel, Barfael, Barron, Beelzebub, Behemoth, Beherith, Bel, Beleh (alias Beleth), Belenus, Belial (alias Beliar), Belphegor, Belus, Belzebuth (see Beelzebub), Bellie Blind (alias Billie Blin), Berith, Bilwitz, Brahma, Brendly, Cedon, Cedor, Cedron, Celsus, Cham, Charon, Chemos, Dagon, Death, Demogorgon, Dis, Easa, Eblis (alias Iblis), Erminsul, Eros, Esau-Samaël, Eternity of Sorrows, Eurymone, Ezekeel, Federwisch, Flagel, Focalos, Furcas, Goap, Gresil, Griffael, Hecate, Hellekrugk, Hermes, Heva, Hoberdidance (alias Hobbididance and Hop-dance), Hornblas, Horus, Hutgin, Igymeth, Iris, Isaacharum, Ishtar, Isis, Jochmus, Jupiter, Kawkabel, Kobal, Kränzlein, Lästerlein, Leonard, Leraie, Leviathan, Lilith, Lucifer, Machlath, Magog, Magon, Mammon, Marbas, Marbuel, Marfael, Martinet, Mascaron, Melshom, Mephistopheles, Mercury, Minos, Misroch (alias Nisroch), Mithra, Moloch, Morax, Mullin, Murmur, Nahema (alias Nehema), Neptune, Nergal, Nicker, Nybbas, Odin, Oribel, Orphaxat, Orus, Osiris, Pan, Phœnix, Pluto, Purson, Raguhel, Rimmon, Rosenkranz, Ruffo, Rush, Sabnac, Samaël (alias Adam-Belial), Samiasa, Samsaweel, Saracen, Satan, Schönspiegel, Schorbrandt, Seriel, Shamdan, Shemhazaï, Sin, Succor-Benoth, Sydragasum, Teutates, Tham(m)uz (alias Tharung), Tobiel, Tutevillus, Uriel, Urnell, Venus, Verdelet, Vulcan, Zabulon, Zamiel, Zelinda the Fair, and Zizimar.

What a number of names and titles have been devised for his

[6]On the other hand, men have given the names of devils to animals, especially cats and dogs. Gautier gives the name Belzebuth to a cat (le Capitaine Fracasse, 1863), and Balzac names the toad used by the witch Fontaine in her divinations Astaroth. Karr gives the wasps, in les Guêpes (1839), names of devils, such as Mammone, Moloch, Astarte, Belial, etc. These wasps are so many winged messengers, who fly about Paris, enter into every council, penetrate into every chamber, buzz by every hearth, and overhear all sorts of secret gossip and scandal.

infernal Majesty! Satan is frequently called "the god of this world" (2 Cor. iv. 4), "the prince of this world" (John xii. 31, xiv. 30; xvi. 11), "the prince of the powers of the air" (Eph. ii. 2), "the prince of the devils" (Matt. ix. 34; xii. 24; Mark iii. 12), the prince of hell, the prince of darkness, "the ruler of the darkness" (Eph. xi. 12), "the angel of the bottomless pit" (Rev. ix. 11), the dark son of the night, "the lost archangel (*Par. Lost* i. 243), "the archangel ruined" (*ibid.,* i. 593), the black archangel, *the spiritus infernali,* the grim gentleman below, the genius of evil, the spirit of evil, the evil spirit, the malignant spirit, the unclean spirit, the lost spirit, the evil one, the wicked one, the bad man, the spirit that denies, the deceiver of mankind, the liar, the lying spirit, the father of lies, the father of iniquity, the tempter, the tormentor, the murderer, the arch-fiend (*Par. Lost* i. 156), the foul fiend, the enemy of mankind, "the accuser of the brethren" (Rev. xii. 10), "the spirit that worketh in the children of disobedience" (Eph. ii. 2), the beast, "the (great) worm" (Is. lxvi. 24), "the serpent" (2 Cor. ii. 3), "the old serpent" (Rev. xii. 9; xx. 2), "the infernal serpent" (*Par. Lost* i. 34), the crooked serpent, the piercing serpent, "the dragon" (Rev. xii. 7), "the great (red) dragon" (Rev. xii. 3, 9), "the roaring lion" (1 Peter v. 8), "the dog" (Phil. iii, 2; Rev. xxii, 15), the ape, the Adversary of the Almighty, the infernal rival of God, and the Other. On the other hand, the Devil is also given such flattering names as the Good Man, the Good Fellow and Gentleman Jack.

Other epithets for the Devil, for the most part mentioned in this work, are as follows: The accursed archangel, the seditious archangel, the "apostat(e)" (Milton), the rebel, the first rebel, the great rebel, the rebel angel, the rebel spirit, the rebel leader, the rebel chief, the celestial rebel, the emperean rebel, the rebel of the emperean, the champion of celestial combat, the celestial hero, the discrowned archangel, the dethroned archangel, the banished archangel, the exiled archangel, the celestial outlaw, the expatriate from Paradise, the fallen archangel, the fallen Star of the Morning, the first outlaw, the impenitent emperean, the sinner from the beginning, the arch-devil, the king-devil, the chief of the evil spirits, the chief of the infernal spirits, the lord of all the powers of darkness, the prince of demons, the leader of the rebel angels, the leader of the hosts of hell, *summum imperium infernalis,* "Emperor of the King-

dom Dolores," the monarch of hell, the infernal monarch, the arch-
regent of hell, the chief of hell, the hierarch of hell, the king of
hell, the king of the nether world, the lord of hell, the spirit of darkness, the king of darkness, the ruler of hell, the ruler of Gehenna,
the gubernator of Gehenna, the prince of the pit, the potentate
of the pit, the prisoner of the pit, the spirit beneath, the infernal being, the Very Low, the Most Low, the dark prince, Black John,
Black Jack, Hairy Jack, Horny Jack, the black man (or Blackman),
the black gentleman, the sombre gentleman, the first gentleman, the
cloven-hoofed fellow, the hell-hound, the evil being, the power of
evil, the prince of evil, the principle of evil, the author of (all) evil,
the fiend, the fiery fiend, the foul thief, the arch-felon, the cunning
spirit, the accursed spirit, the spirit of unrest, the dread spirit, the
proud spirit, the eternal malcontent, the artificer of fraud, the arch-
deceiver, the enemy, the arch-enemy, the great enemy, the old enemy,
the formidable enemy, the enemy of salvation, the grand foe, the
secret foe, the assailant, the accuser, the great accuser, the contradictor, the spirit that denies, the spirit of negation, the spirit of
destruction, the spirit of discontent, the author of mischief, the
ringleader of all mischief, the tempter of Job, the trier of men's
souls, the subtle spirit, the scorning spirit, the mocking spirit, the
mocker of mankind, the great malcontent, the contemner of the
Creator, the defier of the Deity, the Omniarch, and the Antecessor.
In Washington Irving's story, the Devil also calls himself the wild
huntsman, the black miner, and the black woodsman on account of
the various tasks he performs on earth.

Among the epithets for the demons we may mention the following: The bad angels, the disobedient angels, the rebel angels, the
rebel spirits, the revolting angels, the rebellious angels, the rebellious spirits, the celestial mutineers, the apostatized angels, the exiled
angels, the fallen angels, the fallen spirits, the evil spirits, the malignant spirits, the evil specters, the malevolent beings, the fiends of
hell, the helots of hell, the hosts of hell, the hounds of hell, the
imps of hell, the hellish imps, the monsters of hell, the (damned)
spirits of hell, the powers of hell, the infernal powers, the powers of
the pit, the demons of darkness, the denizens of darkness, the
powers of darkness, the spirits of darkness, the infernal hosts, the infernal spirits, the agents of hell, the messengers of hell, the emissaries of hell, the hellish agents, and the infernal agents.

With the flexibility of their language, the English speak of the Devil as his Majesty, his Most Christian Majesty, his Satanic Majesty, his Satanic Brilliancy, his Infernal Majesty, his Infernal Highness, and his Infernal Lowness.

The Devil owes certain of his aliases in popular speech to what is called *Volksetymologie*. The uneducated person, who does not understand certain foreign words, transforms them into analogous words familiar to his ears. Thus Bellerophon has become transmogrified in vulgar speech into Billie Ruffian. In the same way, the German domestic demon Bilwitz turns up in several old English ballads as Billie Blin or Bellie Blind. Similarly, Adram(m)elech, one of the gods to whom the Sepharvites burnt their children in fire (2 Kings xvii. 31), was transformed into Andrew Malchus. This Devil appears in several English witch-trials, and according to the testimony of William Stapleton, is one of the spirits evoked by the parson of Lessingham about the year 1527.

* * *

The Devil has perhaps a greater number of aliases in our popular speech than in the argot of any other country. The English-speaking person is afraid to call the Devil by his name. He will do his best to beat Beelzebub about the bush. The Englishman especially seems to have revised the Third Commandment to read, "Thou shalt not take the name of the Devil thy Master in vain." When the Frenchman says without hesitation, *"Que diable,"* and the German swears unblushingly, *"Was in des Teufels Namen,"* the Englishman lowers his eyes and mumbles, "What the deuce" or "What the Dickens." He does not realize that the one as the other are synonyms for Satan.

The word "deuce" is a popular corruption of the Latin *deus*. The inversion from good to bad and from bad to good in popular speech is a frequent occurrence.[7] Dickens is a derivative of Dick, which is not a nickname of Richard, but is derived from Old Hick. Lusty Dick is the name of the Devil "cast out" by the priests whose performances were exposed by Samuel Harsnett in his *Declaration of Egregious Popish Impostures* (1603). Dicken means simply "little Dick" or "Dickie," and Dickens is a variant of Dicken. Dickon is explained in Percy MacKaye's play, *The Scarecrow* (1914), as the "Yankee impersonation of the Prince of Darkness."

[7] It is interesting to note in this connection that the word "devel" is the gypsy term for God.

The English language has no equivalent for the French expression *le bon Diable*, a parallel to *le bon Dieu*, which corresponds to the German expression *der dumme Teufel* and which points to the Devil's simplicity of mind rather than to any kindness of heart. It generally expresses the half-contemptuous pity with which the giants, those huge beings with weak minds, were regarded in Northern mythology.

The English, in contrast to the other nations, have honored the Devil with the venerable prefix "old." Numerous names given him begin with this epithet. Mr. Charles P. G. Scott, in his very interesting paper, "The Devil and his Imps,"[8] lists forty-one names for the Devil with the adjective "old": Old All-ill-thing, Old Belzebub (not Old Beelzebub), Old Bendy, Old Bogie, Old Boots, Old Boy, Old Chap, Old Clootie, Old Cloots, Old Deluder, Old Devil, Old Enemy, Old Fellow, Old Fiend, Old Gentleman, Old Gooseberry, Old Hangie, Old Harry, Old Horny, Old Lad, Old Lucifer, Old Mahoun, Old Man, Old Mischanter, Old Mischief, Old Mischy, Old Nick, Old Nickie-ben, Old Nicol, Old Nicolas, Old One, Old Poker, Old Roger, Old Sam, Old Scrat, Old Scratch, Old Serpent, Old Schock, Old Shuck, Old Soss, and Old Thief. We may add the following venerable names: Old Booty, Old Cooney, Old Dragon, Old Hairy, Old Hick, Old Iniquity, Old Night, Old Noll, and Old Simmie.

It would lead us too far to explain all these designations applied to the Devil, many of which, moreover, are self-explanatory. Old Iniquity is familiar to all who are acquainted with the old medieval English morality plays. Old Scratch occurs frequently in contemporary American fiction.

In current speech the most prevalent and also the most interesting of these designations for the Devil is Old Nick. It is thus that the Devil is commonly called in this country. The origin of this name has long been a mooted question. Nick is generally believed to be an abbreviation of nicor, the old Saxon god or monster of the sea and rivers, who brings on tempests and draw men to the bottom to devour them. This ancient divinity still lives in popular belief as nix in England and Nickelmann in North Germany and Holland. In Gerhart Hauptmann's fairy-play, *Die versunkene Glocke*

---

[8]Charles P. G. Scott: "The Devil and his Imps, an Etymological Inquisition." *Transactions of the American Philological Association.* Vol XXVI (1895), pp. 79-146.

(1896), we find a water-spirit named Nickelmann.[9] Professor Ward, an authority on the old English drama, derives "Old Nick" from "Old Iniquity" of the old English morality-plays.

Nick in "Old Nick," however, seems very simply to be an abbreviation of the Christian name Nicholas. Mr. Scott, who also derives Nick from Nicholas, puts it cleverly in saying that "Nick is the Nick-name, so to speak, of Nicholas."

Samuel Butler remarked in jest that the Devil was named Nick after Niccolo Machiavelli, who has, in the world's opinion, been associated with the machinations of the Evil One. Certainly the name of the author of *The Prince*, that primer of patriotic perjury, has come down to us with certain diabolical connotations. It was especially in England that the Italian statesman was regarded as an incarnation of the Evil One himself. "Machiavelli came in vulgar speech and belief to typify the Devil," says Dr. Grosart.

Strange to say, Old Nick and St. Nicholas, the bishop of Myra, are identical in person. This kindly Christian bishop, who suffered persecution during the reign of the Roman Emperor Diocletian (284-305), and who is the giver of dowries to poor maids and of gifts to children, has, by some topsy-turvy psychological process, become in popular belief both saint and bogey. He rewards the good children with presents and sends the naughty children nothing but a bundle of switches. Inasmuch as the distribution of gifts to children, though finally transferred from St. Nicholas Day (December 6) to Christmas Day, is carried out in Anglo-Saxon countries under the name of this saint, it follows that Old Nick and Santa Claus are one and the same person. As Professor Godbey suggests, Puritanism, which denounced the Christmas festivities as pagan, tried to enroll Santa Claus among the demons of hell, but failed in this effort.

Nick as a name for the Devil occurs in Robert Burns' "Poem on Life" (1796). Nickie is a diminutive of Nick. Old Nickie-ben is the Devil on whom Robert Burns "took a thought" in his "Address to the Deil" (1785).

Names for the Devil still continue to be coined in this country. Witness the various and ingenious designatons for Diabolus devised by our American diabolist, Mr. James Branch Cabell.

Inasmuch as the idea of the Devil is both an abstraction and a striking fable or concrete metaphor, it has taken firm root not only

[9] Nicker, as a name for the Devil, appears in the Dutch language.

in the language, but also in the traditions and the consciousness of the masses. This fact proves that, though naughty, the Evil One under his many pet names is regarded as likable and even "nice." Just as a pet dog or child may be addressed in terms of affection, though mischievous in his ways, even so Old Nick continues to be abused and praised in many languages, under a variety of peculiar names.

CHAPTER IV

THE FORM OF THE FIEND

THE Devil has assumed many forms and worn many costumes. Hundreds of books, pictures and prints depict his Infernal Majesty in almost as many different disguises as there are stars in the sky. Satan is a polymorphous individual. He is the equal of Jupiter in the art of physical tergiversation, having a capacity for almost endless variations and transmutations, which he uses to the great perplexity of mortals. As successor to Hermes, he has also inherited the Greek god's ability to contract and expand at pleasure. Indeed, if we credit all the accounts of the forms in which the Fiend has shown himself on earth, he is a quick-change artist of first-rate ability.

The Devil as a fallen angel is, naturally enough, "a spirit in form and substance,"—but he has been granted the power of manifesting himself to the eyes of man in a material form as far back as the first century of the Christian era. As the adversary of corporeal saints, he necessarily and unmistakably became more material than he had been as the shadowy opponent of the spiritual angels. Although in reality incorporeal, he can, of his own inherent power, call into existence any manner of body that it pleases his fancy to inhabit, or that will be most conducive to the success of any contemplated evil.

It has been said that the Devil can manifest himself to the eyes of man in any form which exists "in the heavens above, in the earth beneath, and in the waters under the earth." He can, first of all, still manifest himself in his former rôle as an angel. St. Paul warns us that Satan can transform himself into an angel of light (2 Cor. xi. 14), and St. Thomas Aquinas, commenting on the words of the

Great Apostle, teaches that the higher natural qualities of the angels have not wholly been withdrawn from the fallen spirits.[1]

But this is not all. In order to mislead mankind, the Devil can even appear, according to Thomas Cranmer, author of *A Confutation of Unwritten Verities* (16th cent.), in the likeness of Christ. It is known that the Devil manifested himself to the Deacon Secundullus first as an angel and later as Christ himself.[2]

As a general thing, however, the Devil seeks his models among men. He has at his command, as Timon of Athens has said, "all shapes that man goes up and down in." He can appear in the form of either sex. The Fiend figured in human form when he approached the hermits of the Thebaid. The earliest known representation of the Devil in human form is found on an ivory diptych of the time of Charles the Bold (9th cent.). In Thomas Middleton's *Witch* (p. 1778), Hecate speaks of a custom that witches have of causing their familiar spirits to assume the shape of any man for whom they have a passion.[3]

But incarnation in a human body is not sufficient for Satan. The forms of the whole of the animal kingdom seem also to be at his disposal. He can adopt, in fact, the form of any animal he wishes— from a worm to an eagle. Indeed, one of the most significant elements of demonology is the persistence of the animal character in which the Devil appears. But not content with known animal forms, he even seeks further to assume incredible and impossible shapes. Popular fancy assembled, in fact, the repugnant parts of all known living beings and fashioned the Devil out of them. In order to frighten the good Christians, the Fiend had to possess a form which was particularly suited to instil terror into their hearts.

The Devil, whom our medieval ancestors detected so unerringly and feared so mortally, was a compound of all the contortions and distortions known to exist among living things on this earth. Our pious forefathers imagined him who "one day wore a crown under the eyes of God" in as horrid and hideous a form as fancy could

[1] Consult the authorities quoted on this matter by Anatole France in his novel *la Révolte des anges* (1914). A contemporary Polish novelist, Kornel Makuszynski, says in his recent story "Another Paradise Lost and Regained" (1926): "It is one of the most ancient and common of hellish tricks for a devil to take the shape of an angel."

[2] Cf. Wilhelm Fischer: *Aberglaube aller Zeiten* (Stuttgart, 1906-7), I, 55.

[3] Norman Douglas in his novel *They Went* (1921) offers an interesting variant in the person of Theophilus, the Greek merchant.

render it. Like the Greek Gorgon, the Christian Satan was meant to represent, as Anatole France has said, the sympathetic alliance between physical ugliness and moral evil. The grotesque paintings of the Devil in the medieval cathedrals were enough to scare even the Devil himself.[4] Daniel Defoe has well remarked that the Devil does not think that the people would be terrified half so much if they were to converse with him face to face. "Really," this biographer of Satan goes on to say, "it were enough to fright the Devil himself to meet himself in the dark, dressed up in the several figures which imagination has formed for him in the minds of men."

If you wish to see the Devil in his genuine form, we are told in Gogol's story "St. John's Eve" (1830), stand near a mustard seed on St. John's Eve at midnight, the only evening in the year when Satan reveals himself in his proper form to the eyes of man. Sir James Fraser suggests, in his *Golden Bough* (1911-1914), that this prince from a warmer climate may be attracted by the warmth of the mustard in the chilly air of the upper world.

The Devil, in fact, is very sensitive in regard to the unflattering portrayal of himself by the good Christians. On a number of occasions, he has expressed his bitter resentment at the ugly form given him in Christian iconography. A medieval French legend relates the discomfiture of a monk, who was forced by the indignant Devil to paint him in a less ugly fashion. Lucifer also appeared once in a dream to the Florentine painter Spinello Spinelli to ask him in what place he had beheld him under so brutish a form as he had painted him. This story is told in Giorgio Vasari's *Vite de' più eccellenti pittori, scultori ed architettori* (1550) and retold by Anatole France in his story "Lucifer" (1895).[5]

It makes us, indeed, wonder why the Devil was always represented in so repugnant a form. Rationally conceived, the Devil should be by right the most fascinating object in creation. One of his essential functions, namely temptation, is destroyed by his hideousness. To be effective in the work of temptation, a demon

[4] On the Devil in medieval art, consult Emile Mâle's three volumes: *l'Art religieux du XIIe siècle en France; l'Art religieux du XIIIe siècle en France; l'Art religieux de la fin du moyen âge en France,* and Maurice Gossart: *la Peinture des diableries à la fin du moyen-âge; Jérôme Bosch, "le faizeur de dyables," de Bois-le-Duc* (1907).

[5] In his story "les Blattes," Anatole France also expresses the fear of an Italian painter that he may have incurred the Devil's displeasure by the manner in which he presented him on the cathedral doors and church windows.

might be expected to approach his intended victim in the most fascinating form he could command.[6]

The fact is that the form given the Devil in Christian icon- ography has an historical foundation. It has been derived from the fabled gods of antiquity. The medieval monster is an amalgamation of all the heathen divinities, from whom he derived, especially of those gods or demons which, already in pagan days, were inimical to the benevolently ruling deities.

Indeed, a great number of sacred animal representations will be found in most of the religions of antiquity. The gods of India, Egypt, Assyria, Babylonia, Greece and Rome were worshipped under the form of the animals which were supposed to possess the qualities for which they were reverenced. At a later period in the history of religion, the divinity was partly humanized; and a human deity was conceived with certain animal parts to represent the form under which he had originally been worshipped. Later on, all vestiges of the ancient animal forms were discarded, and the deity emerged in full human form. This evolution accounts for the fact that the Devil has appeared to our ancestors in full animal form, in a form half animal and half human, and finally wholly human.

As a matter of fact, every animal form that was assumed by the gods in antiquity has had its body occupied by the Devil.[7] Further- more, the Devil's representation in the form of certain animals is the result of a literal interpretation of a figurative scriptural ex- pression. The medieval writers had a tendency to convert symbols and metaphors into facts. If the Devil is called in the New Testa- ment a roaring lion, a dragon, a serpent, a wolf, a dog, it was in- stantly supposed that he was in the habit of actually assuming the forms of these animals.

The elephant, which was sacred to the eyes of the Buddhist, had its body inhabited by the Devil. The bull was diabolized for the

[6] The Devil, it should be added in all truthfulness, appears on certain occasions also in an agreeabe form. Anatole France tells us that "the Devil... clothes himself in divers forms, sometimes pleasing, when he succeeds in dis- guising his natural ugliness, at other times, hideous, when he lets his true nature be seen" (la Rôtisserie de la Reine Pédauque, 1893). William Shake- speare has also remarked that "the Devil hath power to assume a pleasing shape" (Hamlet, II, ii, 628-9).

[7] The animals which were diabolized by the early Christians on account of their associations with mythological personages or ideas should not be con- fused, however, with those animals which, owing to the fact that they possess qualities inimical to man, were already feared as demons in the animistic re- ligions.

reason that he was venerated by the Egyptians. As successor to the Egyptian Seth, Satan also appeared in the form of a pig. The fox, which was sacred to certain ancient divinities, was likewise considered as the Devil's incarnation. The bear was for similar reasons one of the Devil's medieval metamorphoses.

The representation of the Devil in the shape of a goat goes back to far antiquity. Goat-formed deities and spirits of the woods existed in the religions of India, Egypt, Assyria, and Greece.[8] The Assyrian god was often associated with the goat, which was supposed to possess the qualities for which he was worshipped. This animal was also connected with the worship of Priapus, the Greek god of vegetal and animal fertility. The goat was similarly sacred to the Northern god Donar or Thor, whom, as Jacob Grimm says, the modern notions of the Devil often have in the background. Thor's chariot was drawn by goats. As the familiar of the witch, the Devil appeared in the form of a goat as well as in that of a dog. Esmeralda's goat, in Victor Hugo's novel *Notre-Dame de Paris* (1831), was believed to be her familiar demon. French witches were often thought to slip into the skin of a goat to identify themselves with their goatish god. Satan presided at the Witches' Sabbath in the form of a black buck. The goat, in the grand scene of the Last Judgment, is also the symbol of the slaves of sin.[9]

The dog has always been one of the Devil's favorite metamorphoses, especially as the familiar of the witch or wizard. The Devil had already been represented as a dog in the Bible (Phil. iii. 2; Rev. xxii. 15). He is, therefore, called hell-hound in the medieval mysteries. Mephistopheles appears to Faust in the form of an ugly dog, "a fit emblem," as Conway says, "of the scholar's relapse into the canine temper which flies at the world as at a bone he means to gnaw."[10] Cornelius Agrippa, the sceptic philosopher, who was considered a magician in the Middle Ages, was also attended by a devil in the shape of a black dog.

The Devil as guardian of hell was also equated to Cerberus and inherited the latter's triple head. Many mythologies, in fact, show

[8]On the relation of satyrs to goats, see Sir James Frazer's *Golden Bough*, vol. VIII, pp. 1 sqq.

[9] The creation of the goat has aso been ascribed to the Devil. Hans Sachs has written a farce entitled "The Devil Created Goats" (September 24, 1556). Engl. Transl. in Wm. Leighton's *Merry Tales of Hans Sachs* (London, 1920), pp. 129-131.

[10] Moncure Daniel Conway: *Demonology and Devil-Lore*. 2 vols., 3rd ed., New York, 1889.

tricephalic gods of the underworld. The Devil's trinitarian head recalls Typhon of the Egyptians, Hecate of classical mythology, Hrim-Grimmir of the Edda and Triglaf of the Slavs.[11]   The Dantean Dis has three faces: one in front, and one on each side. The middle face is red, that on the right side whitish-yellow, that on the left side black.[12]   The trinity idea of the Devil was in-

THE TRINITY	THE TRINITY OF EVIL
From a painted window of the six-teenth century in the Church of No-tre Dame at Châlons, France.	From a French MS. of the fifteenth century, preserved in the Biblio-thèque Nationale at Paris.

terpreted by the Church fathers as Satan's parody of the trinitarian God-head. The Devil is described as a three headed monster in the Gospel of Nicodemus (3rd cent.) and in the Good Friday Sermon of Eusebius of Alexandria, who addresses him as the "Three-headed Beelzebub."

The Devil inherited the form of a crow or black raven from

[11] Cf. Paul Carus: *History of the Devil and the Idea of Evil* (Chicago, 1900), p. 249.
[12] *Ibid.*

Odin, who, in Scandinavian mythology, had two ravens perched on his shoulders. Mephistopheles, in Goethe's *Faust,* is accompanied by two crows (i. 2491).

The dove, which was a sacred animal in the pagan period, was, in Christian days, gradually invested with something of the evil character of the Tempter of Job and came very nearly to represent the old fatal serpent power. This creature was sacred to all Semites, who revered it as the reincarnation of their beloved dead, and who, for this reason, avoided eating or even touching it. The Romans also held the dove in veneration and offered it as a sacrifice to Venus.

The bat, on account of its ugly form, was especially fit to offer its body for habitation by the Devil. In Anatole France's story "le Grand St. Nicolas" (1909), six devils appear in the form of bats.

The rat or mouse was also among the Devil's metamorphoses. An imp of hell jumps out of the mouth of the witch, with whom Faust dances in the Walpurgis-Night, in the form of a little red mouse (*Faust* i. 2197).[13]

The form of the fly for the Fiend was suggested by Ahriman, the Persian evil spirit, who is the ancestor of our Devil and who entered the world as a fly. The word *beelzebub* means in Hebrew "the fly-god." In Spenser's *The Faerie Queene* (1590-96), Archimago summons spirits from hell in the shape of flies.

The cat, which was considered in Egypt as a guardian genius, a friend of the family, and a slayer of evil things, has been a representation of the Devil in all Christian lands. Bast, an Egyptian goddess, was figured with the head of a cat. Inasmuch as this animal was sacred to the ancient Egyptians, it naturally enough became a devil to medieval Christians. The cat, which drew the wagon of Freya, became the Devil's pet animal, after the Scandinavian goddess had turned as Frau Holle into the Devil's grandmother. The witch was believed to transform herself into a cat.

The belief in the diabolical character of the cat has persisted to this day and has even been shared by a great number of modern poets. Gœthe, the German poet and sage, openly said that he believed black cats were of the Evil One. The French diabolists Baudelaire and Huysmans adored this animal. Verlaine, in his poem "Femme et chatte" (1866), represents the cat as the imper-

[13] On the Devil in the form of a mouse, see M. Barth's article "Dämonen in Mäusegestalt" in the *Kölnische Volkszeitung* of February 7, 1917.

sonation of the Devil, and woman as very much akin to the two. "The cat," Théophile Gautier has said in his essay on Baudelaire (1868), "has the appearance of knowing the latest sabbatical chronicle, and he will willingly rub himself against the lame leg of Mephistopheles."[14]

The dragon is a frequent diabolical figure in medieval literature. The basis of the conception of the Devil as a dragon is in the Book of Revelation (xii. 3, 7, 9). The Devil appears as a dragon in Michelet's story "Madeleine Bavent." In Bunyan's *Pilgrim's Progress* (1678), the devil Apollyon is a winged dragon covered with scales, and belching fire and smoke. The Devil appears in the form of a dragon in the pictorial representations of the combat between St. Michael and the leader of the rebel angels by Raphael in the Louvre, by Luca Giordano in the Belvedere of Vienna, by Schongauer in the Cathedral of Ulm, by Jacobello del Fiore in Berlin and by Mabuse in Munich. In the Faust-book, Faust flies in a dragon-drawn chariot through the air. In Calderon's play *el Magico prodigioso* (c. 1635), Satan appears in the end as a dragon.[15]

The basis of the conception of the Devil as a worm is in the passage "their worm shall not die" (Is. lxvi. 24; cf. Mark ix. 44, 46, 48), which has been applied to the chief of the evil spirits.

The representation of the Devil in the form of a wolf is the result of a literal interpretation of the biblical phrase "grievous wolves enter in among you" (Acts xx. 29).

Notwithstanding the biblical comparison of the Devil to the most courageous and ferocious of all wild beasts (1 Peter v. 8), representations of the Devil in the form of a lion were not popular out of respect for "the lion out of the tribe of Judah" (Rev. v. 5). The substitution of the dragon or the serpent for the lion as a general representation of the Devil was, furthermore, made necessary in certain countries by national respect as well as by Christian tradition. In the play *Pyramus and Thisbe* written by Rederijker Goosen ten Berch of Amsterdam, a lioness, appearing in a silent rôle, is, however, interpreted as the Devil.

[14] On the cat, cf. Anne Marks: *The Cat in History, Legend and Art*, London, 1909; Champfleury (pseud. of Jules Husson): *The Cat Past and Present*, translated from the French by Mrs. Hoey, London, 1885; A. M. Michelet (Mme Jules Michelet): *les Chats*, Paris, 1909. Mr. Carl Van Doren has recently published in New York two anthologies of cat stories.

[15] On the dragon, consult the following two recent books: G. Eliot Smith's *The Evolution of the Dragon* (1919) and Ernest Ingersoll's *Dragons and Dragon Lore* (1928).

The Devil's simian aspect is of patristic origin. It comes from the fact that the Church fathers called Lucifer an ape on account of his efforts to mimic the Lord. When they noticed the similarities between the observances of Christians and pagans, they explained them as diabolical counterfeits. They believed that the Devil, whose business it always is to pervert the truth, imitated the sacraments of the Church in the mysteries of the idols. The patristic appellation for the Devil as *simia Dei* was taken literally by later writers, and the Devil was represented by them under the form of a monkey.

Of all representations of Evil, that of the serpent is common to all countries, all peoples, all times and all religions. The serpent as an autumnal constellation figured among all races as an enemy of the sun-god or light-god. Moreover, the serpent, of old the "seer," was, in its Semitic adaptation, the tempter to forbidden knowledge. Satan played this part to our ancestors in the Garden of Eden. He appears in the traditional shape of the serpent in Dante's *Purgatorio* (viii. 98f.) Milton similarly mentions the infernal serpent (*Par. Lost* i. 34). A legend of the Devil in the form of a serpent will also be found in the *Dialogues* of St. Gregory the Great (593-94). Paphnutius, in Anatole France's novel *Thais* (1890), sees Lucifer as "the serpent with golden wings which twisted round the Tree of Knowledge its azure coils formed of light and love." In Gœthe's *Faust*, Mephistopheles calls the serpent his aunt (i. 2049).

The Devil may owe his office as guardian of treasures to his identification with the serpent or dragon. In Hindu mythology, homage is paid the serpent as guardian of treasures. The idea that demons are guardians of treasures is especially prevalent in the Orient. Furthermore, the Devil, who dwells in the bowels of the earth, was soon regarded as the guardian of all subterranean treasures and as the possessor of unlimited wealth. It is believed in many European countries that treasures can be found on St. John's Eve by means of the fern seed. Treasures also bloom or burn in the earth and reveal their presence by a bluish flame on Midsummer Eve.

The idea of the Devil, in the representation of the temptation of Eve, as a serpent with the head of a woman is not earlier than the Middle Ages. According to the Venerable Bede, Lucifer chose to tempt Eve through a serpent which had a female head because "like is attracted to like." Vincent of Beauvais accepts Bede's view on

the female head of the serpent in the Garden of Eden.   Pierre
Comestor, in his *Historia scholastica* (c. 1176), concludes from this
fact that, while the serpent was yet erect, it had a virgin's head. In
the temptation scene of the medieval mystery plays, Satan usually
appears as a serpent with a woman's head. The traditional serpent

THE GOOD LORD AND THE DEVIL
(In Goethe's *Faust,* by Franz Simm.)

with a woman's head coiled about a tree may also be seen on Raphael's painting of the Fall. Ruskin shows an unfamiliarity with
medieval literature and art when he states that the serpent in Paradise was for many centuries represented with the head of a man.
In Grandchamp's painting of the Temptation, however, the serpent has the head of a handsome young man.[15a]

[15a]On the symbolism of the serpent, consult M. Oldfield Howey's *The
Encircled Serpent* (London, 192-).

When the Devil was later figured in human form, he was given the head of an elephant, a camel, a pig, or a bird covered with thick locks resembling serpents, the ears of an ass, the mouth and teeth of a lion, the beard of a goat, the horns of a goat, a bull, or a stag,[16] the wings of a bat, the long tail of a dragon, the claws of a tiger, and the foot of a bull, a horse, a goat, or a cock. The Ethiopic devil's right foot is a claw, and his left foot a hoof.

The Devil inherited his bull-horns and bull-foot from Dionysus, his horse-foot from Loki and his goat-foot from Pan. He borrowed his snaky *coiffure* from the Erinyes and his batwings from the Lemures, and shares his elephant-head with Ganesa, the Hindu god of wisdom, and his dragon-tail with the Chimera.

* * *

The Devil appears in many colors, principally, however, in black. The black color presumably is intended to suggest his place of abode. Racial hatred had, however, much to do with the dark description of the Devil. There is no warrant in biblical tradition for a black devil. Satan, however, appeared as an Ethiopian or Moor as far back as the days of the Church fathers. Descriptions of the Devil as black in color will be found in the Acts of the Martyrs, the Acts of St. Bartholomew, and in the writings of Augustine and Gregory the Great. A black face was a permanent feature of the medieval representations of the Devil. "Of all human forms," Reginald Scot tells us in his *Discoverie of Witchcraft* (1584), "that of a Negro or a Moor is considered a favorite one with the demons." Satan figures as king of the Africans in John Bunyan's *Holy War* (1682). In modern literature, the Devil appears as a Black Bogey, among others, in Washington Irving's "The Devil and Tom Walker" (1824), in Robert Louis Stevenson's "Thrawn Janet" (1881) and in Anatole France's *le Livre de mon ami* (1884). It is a common belief still to-day in Scotland that the Devil is a black man. The term "Printer's Devil" is usually accounted for by the fact that Aldus Manutius, the great Venetian printer, employed in his printing shop toward the end of the fifteenth

---

[16] The Devil's horns are first mentioned in the *Vita S. Antonii* by St. Athanasius (4th cent.). Mr. R. Lowe Thompson, in his recent *History of the Devil* (1929), traces the Devil's horns to the dawn of history. He sees in the medieval demon the successor to Cernunnos, the ancient Gælic god of the dead. Adam Hamilton published anonymously a very clever essay entitled *Where Are my Horns*, in which Lucifer himself addresses the readers.

century a black slave, who was popularly thought to be an imp from hell. We now recall the popular saying that the Devil is not so black as he is painted. Even the devout George Herbert wrote:—

> "We paint the Devil black, yet he
> Hath some good in him all agree."

It should, however, be added in all truthfulness that whereas the Devil shows himself as a Negro among white men, he appears as a white man among the Negroes. Many tribes of Western Africa, as a matter of fact, represent the Devil as white.

The Devil also appears to us in flaming red colors, whether he wears tights or not. Satan is portrayed in popular imagination as a sort of eternal salamander. He was described already in the New Testament as a fiery fiend. Red was considered among all Oriental nations as a diabolical color. Agni, one of the chief gods mentioned in the Indo-Aryan sacred books, is described as red in color. Brahma of the Hindus was also represented as of a red color. Hapi, god of the Nile, is also figured red in color.

The Devil also appears in yellow and blue colors. Yellow was considered, from antiquity, the color of infamy.[17] The blue devil is a sulphurously constitutioned individual. When the Englishman suffers from melancholy, he believes himself to be possessed by the "blues," i. e. the blue devils.[18]

As a matter of fact, the Devil appears in any color that has an unpleasant look or suggestion. "As white as the Devil," say the Orientals, for whom white is the color of death and mourning. "As green as the Devil," say the Spaniards inasmuch as green was a sacred color to the Moors. "As yellow as the Devil," say the Italians, who do not like this color. The French swear-word sacré bleu, however, has no diabolical connotation. It is a euphemism for sacré Dieu. The French expression le diable vert also has no reference to the Devil's color. Gérard de Nerval has written a clever story "le Diable vert" (1849) in explanation of this expression.[19]

The Devil usually has saucer eyes all black without any white (Mérimée, Lettres à une inconnue, xxv). In Charles Nodier's story

[17] In Lenau's drama Faust (1835), the Devil is a gypsy for reasons other perhaps than the color of his skin.

[18] Luther remarked that the Devil was a mournful character and could in no way endure light, cheerful music.

[19] For the correct explanation of this expression consult Littré's dictionary.

"la Combe de l'homme mort" (1832), he has little red eyes, more sparkling than red-hot coals. In Russian iconography, the all-seeing spirit of evil is represented as covered with eyes. Edgar Allan Poe in his story "Bon-Bon" (1835) and Charles Baudelaire in his prose

The Three-Headed Serapis
(Hapi)

Aziel, the Guardian of
Hidden Treasures.

poem "les Tentations, ou Eros, Plutus et la Gloire" (1863), on the other hand, represent the Devil as an eyeless monster.

The Devil is usually figured in a lean form. His hands are long and lean. His face is generally as pale and yellow as the wax of an old candle and furrowed by wrinkled lines. The cadaverous aspect of the Devil is of old antiquity. With but one exception (the Egyptian Typhon), demons are always represented as lean. "A devil," said Cæsarius of Heisterbach of the thirteenth century," is usually so thin as to cast no shadow (*Dialogus miraculorum*, iii).

This characteristic of the Devil is a heritage of the ancient hunger-demon, who could not be felt, because his back was hollow, and, though himself a shadow, cast no shadow. The Devil was reputed, however, to cast his own shadow in Toledo, the immortal home of magic. In the course of the centuries, though, the Fiend has gained flesh.

Hairiness is a pretty generally ascribed characteristic of the Devil. He has probably inherited his hairy skin from the fauns and satyrs. Esau was also believed to have been a hairy demon.

The Devil was often represented with a long beard, but long bearded devils are more common in the representations of the Eastern church. Diabolus was formed in the image and likeness of the Greek ecclesiastic, whose crook he often carries in his hand on cathedral doors or church paintings. Satan is known to affect ecclesiastical appearance, as will be seen further in our discussion. Moreover, as the counterpart of the monarch of heaven, the monarch of hell must needs also have a long beard. Pluto has a long beard descending over his chest in Tasso's poem *Gerusalemme liberata* (iv. 53).

The Devil's beard as well as his hair is usually of a flaming red color. Satan and Judas were both represented on the medieval stage with red beards. The Devil has flaming red hair in Nodier's story already mentioned. In Egypt, red hair and red animals of all kinds were considered infernal. Typhon, the evil spirit in Egyptian mythology, has red hair. Thor or Donar, in Scandinavian mythology, also has a red beard, although this, of course, represents the lightning.[20] Red hair is down to the present day a mark of a suspicious character.

The Devil is often represented with a hump. This deformity was caused, according to the account given by Victor Hugo in his book *le Rhin* (1842), by the fact that, in escaping out of the sack in which the Devil carried them on his back to hell, the human souls left behind "their foul sins and heinous crimes, a hideous heap, which, by the force of attraction natural to the Fiend, incrusted itself between his shoulders like a monstrous wen, and remained for ever fixed." A book entitled *le Diable bossu* appeared

---

[20] On red hair as a diabolical characteristic, see E. L. Buchholz: *Deutscher Glaube und Brauch im Spiegel der heidnischen Vorzeit* (Berlin, 1867), II, 218-25.

at Nancy, in 1708, as a pendant to LeSage's novel *le Diable boiteux* published the preceding year.

The Devil often wears a suit of green cloth, as may be seen in Walter Scott's well-known ballad.[21] Shakespeare is of the opinion that the Devil wears black garments (*Hamlet* III, ii, 1223). In Poe's story "Bon-Bon" already mentioned, the Devil wears a suit of black cloth. The color of his garments has, however, also been red, bistre and golden. In Gœthe's *Faust*, Mephistopheles appears in a scarlet waist-coat and tights (i. 1536 and 2485). In Nodier's story already mentioned, the Devil is dressed in a doublet and breeches of scarlet red and wears on top of his head a woolen cap of the same color.

* * *

In our own days, the Devil has turned human, all too human for most of us. He no longer appears in the gala attire of tail, horns and cloven foot, with which he used to grace the revels on the Blocksberg. "You fancied I was different, did you not, Johannes?" Satan asks the little Dutch boy in Frederik van Eeden's novel *De kleine Johannes* (1887). "That I had horns and a tail? That idea is out of date. No one believes it now." The Devil now moves among men in their own likeness, but "the kernel of the brute is in him still." His diabolical traits appear no longer in his body, but in his face; you can see them there, although he does not mean you should.

But although the Devil can now discard his animal parts, he cannot rid himself of his limp, which is the result of his cloven hoof or broken leg. He still limps slightly, like Byron, no more and no less.[22] But notwithstanding his defect in walking, he steps firmly on this earth. The traditional explanation for the Devil's broken leg is his fall from heaven. This idea was suggested by the scriptural saying: "I beheld Satan as lightning fall from heaven" (Luke x. 18). One of the most striking indications of the fall of the demons from heaven is the wide-spread belief that they are lame. This idea has probably been derived from the crooked lightnings. Thoth, Hephaistos (=Vulcan) Loki, Wieland, each had a broken

[21]The story of this ballad is given towards the end of this chapter.

[22]Heine, in his poem "Ich rief den Teufel und er kam" (1824), is of the opinion, however, that the Devil has finally succeeded in correcting his defect in walking. Mephistopheles retains, however, his limping leg in Goethe's *Faust* (i. 2498).

or crooked leg. Asmodeus, in LeSage's novel *le Diable boiteux*
(1707), appears as a limping gentleman, who uses two sticks as
crutches.[23] He ascribes his broken leg to a fight in the air with
a brother-devil and his subsequent fall. According to rabbinical
tradition, this demon broke his leg when he hurried to meet King
Solomon. Victor Hugo, in *le Rhin,* offers another explanation for
the lameness of Asmodeus. According to this writer, a stone
crushed the demon's leg. In Maupassant's story, "la Légende du
Mont St. Michel" (1882), Satan had his leg broken when, in his
flight from St. Michael, he jumped off the roof of the castle, into
which he had been lured by the archangel.

The Devil is now clad in the costume of the period. He has on
clothes which any gentleman might wear. The Devil is very proud
of this epithet given him by Sir John Suckling ("The prince of
darkness is a gentleman" in *The Goblins*) and by William Shakespeare ("The Prince of demons is a gentleman" in *King Lear*); and
from that time on, it has been his greatest ambition to be a gentleman, in outer appearance at least; and to his credit it must be said
that he has so well succeeded in his efforts to resemble a gentleman
that it is now very difficult to tell the two apart. Satan wears with
equal ease an evening suit, a hunting coat, a scholar's gown, a professor's robe (as in the paintings of Giotto's school), or a parson's
soutane.

The Devil loves to slip into priestly robes, although it cannot
really be said that he is "one of those who take to the ministry
mostly." In the fourteenth and fifteenth centuries, Satan is frequently shown under the garb of a monk. The Devil disguised as
a monk has assumed a national character in Spain. The most characteristic treatment of the Devil in Spain is the play *el Diablo predi-
cator* attributed to Belmonte y Bermùdez, in which Lucifer is forced
to turn Franciscan monk. The conception of the Devil as a monk in
the Germanic countries after the Reformation was principally the
result of the Protestant anti-clerical sentiment. Luther declared, in
fact, that the true Satanic livery was a monk's cowl. Satan is disguised as a monk in John Bale's biblical drama *The Temptation of*

[23] The mother of the Devil is named, in the Alsfeld Passion Play of the
end of the 15th century, Hellekrugk (Höllenkrücke) for the reason that she
walks on crutches.

Jesus (1538). Mephistopheles, in the Faust-book, appears to Faust first in the guise of a monk. In Marlowe's *Dr. Faustus* (c. 1589), Mephistopheles takes the form of a Franciscan monk. In Anatole France's stories, the Fiend often borrows the apearance of a monk.[24]

According to the deeply learned Georgius Godelmannus (Georg Godelmann) in his work *Tractatus de magis, venificiis et lamiis* (1591), as quoted by Heinrich Heine, in his *Elementargeister* (1834), the Devil appeared to Martin Luther himself disguised as a monk, as noted in the following report:

> "When I was studying law in the famous University of Wittenberg, as I well recall, I heard several times there from my teachers that there came once a monk who knocked hard at Luther's door, and when the servant opening asked him what he wanted, the monk inquired if Luther was at home? When Luther heard this, he had him brought in, because it was long since he had seen a monk. And when the visitor entered, he said that he would fain speak with Luther as to certain papistical errors, and submitted to him a few syllogisms and school problems, which the latter solved easily enough. Then he brought out another much more difficult, when Luther somewhat impatiently said, 'Thou gives me much to do at a time when I have other things to attend to,' and rising showed him in the Bible the solution of his question. And while conversing, he observed that the hands of the monk were like birds' claws, and said, *'Bist du nicht Der?'* Art thou not he? Then hear the judgment which was passed on thee!' And so saying, he showed him the text in Genesis in the first book of Moses, 'The seed of the woman shall bruise the head of the serpent.' The Devil, being vanquished by this sentence, fled in a rage and growling, but first threw the ink and writing things behind, leaving a stink which smelt for many days."[25]

The Devil also often appears as a scholar, as, for example, in the painting by Lucas van Leyden of the Temptation of Jesus (1518), where the adversary is represented in scholarly costume. His university hood trails behind into a streamer, the tip of which

---

[24] On the Devil as a monk, read the interesting essay by Georg Ellinger: "Ueber den Teufel als Mönch." *Zeitschrift für vergleichende Literatur-Geschichte*. N. F. I (1887-8) S. 174-81.

[25] The Devil also appeared in the likeness of a gray friar in 1402 at Danbury, in Essex.

coils into a serpent's head.[26] According to Luther, the Devil appeared on a certain occasion in the law courts, in the character of a leading barrister, whose place he seems to have filled with the utmost propriety.[27]

The Devil has now added to the charm of his exterior, already conferred upon him by Milton, a corresponding dignity of bearing and nobility of sentiment. Marie Corelli, in her novel *The Sorrows of Satan* (1895), describes the Devil as of extraordinary physical beauty, fascination of manner, perfect health, and splendid intellectuality. In fact, he is represented by her as "a perfect impersonation of perfect manhood." The modern French writers also have a rather flattering opinion of the Devil. Georges Ohnet, in his novel *Volonté* (1889), describes his villain, Clément de Thauziat, as "resplendent in Satanic beauty." Anatole France represents the fallen angel as "black and beautiful as a young Egyptian ("l'Humaine tragédie," 1895).

The Devil manifests himself to us now as a well-bred, cultivated man of the world. In appearing among us, he generally borrows a tall handsome figure, surmounted by delicate features, dresses well, is fastidious about his rings and linen, travels post and stops at the best hotels. As he can boast of abundant means and a handsome wardrobe, it is no wonder that he should everywhere be politely received. In fact, as Voltaire has already said, he gets into very agreeable society. His brilliant powers of conversation, his adroit flattery, courteous gallantry, and elegant, though wayward, flights of imagination, soon render him the delight of the company in every *salon*. In Heine's poem already mentioned, the Devil, by grace of the prelates of the Church, is at present the most admired personage in every court and fashionable drawing-room in Christendom.

When the Devil wishes to tempt a man in the flesh, he approaches him in the form of a beautiful girl. The belief prevailed in the Middle Ages that the Devil is often manifest on earth clothed in all the natural perfections of woman, inciting men to sin until their souls are by this means snatched from their bodies and

[26]See also Ford C. Ottman's *The Devil in Cap and Gown* (New York, 1914).

[27]On the Devil in the garb of a physician, see Margaret Alice Murray: *The Witch-Cult in Western Europe* (Oxford, 1921), 36, 195.

carried off to hell. The French theologians call the Devil incorporated in a woman "the beautiful Devil." It was in this form that St. Anthony met the Tempter in the Thebaid. This may be seen in the paintings by Bosch, Altdorfer and Teniers. Temptation in the form of a woman is very common in literature as in life. There is an instance of it in Dryden's *King Arthur* (1691) and in a ballad by Walter Scott, the story of which runs as follows: Two hunters meet two beautiful ladies in green. One of the hunters goes off with one of the green ladies. The other gentleman is more prudent. After a time, he goes in quest of his companion and discovers that he has been torn to pieces by the Devil, who had assumed so fascinating a form. Beelzebub transforms himself into a beautiful girl in order to bedevil a young man in Jacques Cazotte's romance *le Diable amoureux* (1772). Théophile Gautier, in his poem *Albertus* (1832), tells how the Devil disguised himself as a woman to tempt a painter of high ideals and finally twists his neck.

The Devil has evidently in modern times changed sex as well as custom and costume. Owen Meredith has said:

> "The Devil, my friend, is a woman just now.
> 'Tis a woman that reigns in Hell."

Victor Hugo similarly believed that the Devil is now incarnated in woman, as may be seen from the following line:

> "Dieu s'est fait homme; soit. Le Diable s'est fait femme"
> (*Ruy Blas*, 1838).

Modern artists frequently represent the Devil as a woman. Felicien Rops, Max Klinger, and Franz Stuck may be cited as illustrations.

CHAPTER V

THE DEVIL'S DOMINIONS

THE habitat of the disobedient angels is Hell, where they have been cast into eternal torment after their revolt.[1] In this connection, the unsurpassed eloquence of Milton's Satan in the first book of *Paradise Lost* comes to mind. First mention of the punishment of the evil spirits is found in the Book of Enoch (x. 14; liv.; xc. 24, 25). The New Testament suggests that this punishment, "prepared for the Devil and his angels" (Matt. xxiii. 41), did not begin immediately after their banishment from heaven, but that they were hurled into hell only "to be reserved unto (the) judgment" (2 Pet. ii. 4) "of the great day" (Jude 6). In order, however, that they may not be bored by prison life while awaiting final judgment, the demons have been charged with the punishment of those wicked mortals who inhabit hell jointly with them. This task was originally assigned to good angels appointed by the Lord to that office (Enoch liii.; liv.; Rev. xx. 10), namely, to torment the souls of mortal sinners.[2] The Catholic theologians affirm explicitly that the demons of hell suffer no torments whatsoever during this era, but that they are now engaged rather in the pleasant task of torturing men and women in hell for enjoying themselves on earth.[3]

The Jewish scribes speak of seven hells, or seven lower deeps of hell, in contrast to the seven heavens. The Spaniards seem to know of seventeen hells, as may be noted from the following expression: "*Que te lleven todos los demonios de los diez-y-siete infernos*— May all the devils of the seventeen hells get you!" The Negroes in Victor Hugo's *Bug-Jargal* (1818) likewise believe in seventeen

[1] The giants in Northern mythology also received their dwellings designated by the gods.

[2] Cf. Crawford H. Toy: *Judaism and Christianity* (Boston, 1892), p. 406.

[3] Cf. Josef Bautz: *Das Fegefeuer* (Mainz, 1883), p. 149.

hells (ch. xxxiii). The orthodoxy of the Church, however, teaches that hell has only four divisions. The first two of these four consist of two regions on the border of hell called *limbos,* the limbo of the Fathers (*limbus patrum*), formerly inhabited by just pre-Christian men and now unoccupied, and the limbo of the infants (*limbus parvulorum*), a sort of nursery for unbaptized children. Then the third section is the *purgatory,* to which the souls of most mortals are sent, prior to their admission to heaven, for a greater or lesser period of purification, acording to the number and quality of the sins they have committed on earth. Lastly *hell,* properly so called, is the place of eternal torment for the wicked. Out of hell *nulla est redemptio.*

This place, inhabited jointly by the demons and the damned, is a *locus subterraneus* (Numb. xvi. 31; 1 Sam. xxviii. 13; Is. v. 14; Ez. xxvi. 20; Matt. xii. 20; Eph. iv. 9; Phil. ii. 10; Rev. v. 3; xii 9). Christianity, in setting the infernal regions apart as the joint dwelling of the demons and the dead, simply followed older Eastern religions. The localization of hell in the heart of the earth naturally followed upon the method of interment in the ground. For notwithstanding the fact that a few theological astronomers wished to place hell in the sun or moon or Mars or some other planet,[4] the good orthodox theory has persisted to the present day that hell is situated in the bowels of the earth. Earthquakes, acording to Catholic belief, are produced by the convulsions of the damned in hell, which cause the earth to roll and toss in its bed.

Access to hell is obtained through three gates, one of which is found in the inhabited land, the other in the wilderness, and the third at the bottom of the sea.[5] The shepherds in the Middle Ages sometimes saw in the depths of the caverns the infected mouths of hell. According to a recent Polish book, Witold Bunikiewicz's *Zywoty Djablow polskich—Lives of the Polish Devils* (1930), one can make one's way into hell even from Poland. In Warsaw a Dominican brother found the entrance to hell, blocked up with a huge boulder. This brother rolled away the boulder and clambered into the dark mouth, but did not progress very far, as infernal odors assailed him and took away his consciousness. Why did such a thing

---

[4] The English doctor, Tobias Swinden, in a large volume entitled *An Inquiry into the Nature and Place of Hell* (1714), endeavored to show that the damned are tortured on the fiery surface of the sun, "which is nothing more than hell, seen by the naked eye. . . ."

[5] Rodin's *Gate of Hell* will come to the reader's mind in this connection.

Hell as Conceived by a Buddhist Artist.

happen? Because this brother, self-confident and proud, had not confessed his sins first and told his Prior of his proposed journey, for which reason he was justly punished. Be that as it may, he must have seen something of the nether regions, and that is why monks and missionaries of the pitch-and-brimstone variety, in Poland as in other countries, have so much to say about hell.

* * *

It is widely believed that fire is the essential purgative and punitive element for the poor sinners in hell. This idea of burning pain rests upon many biblical passages, in both the Old and the New Testaments. In the Book of Enoch we find an abyss (x. 9) or valley (liv.) of fire prepared for the disobedient angels, and in the New Testament we read of a furnace of fire (Matt. xiii. 42, 50) or a pool or lake of fire (Rev. xix. 20; xx. 14; xxi. 8), into which the demons and their human followers will be cast (cf. also Deut. xxxii. 22; Is. ix. 18; xxx. 33; xxxiii. 11, 14; 1. 11; lxv. 5; lxvi. 24; Jer. xvii. 4; Matt. iii. 10; v. 22; viii. 30; xviii. 8; xxv. 41; Mark ix. 43-46, 48; Luke xvi. 24; 1 Cor. iii. 15; 2 Thess. i. 8; Hebr. x. 27; xii. 29; Jas. iii. 6; Jude 7; Rev. ix. 2; xviii. 8; xx. 9,10, 14; xxi. 8). In other biblical passages (Job x. 21; Matt. viii. 12: xxii. 13; xxv. 30; Eph. v. 11; 2 Pet. ii. 4, 17; Jude 6. 13), hell is described as dank darkness. Theologians, aiming at a reconciliation of these two accounts of hell, maintain that the discrepancy applies to different divisions of the infernal realm. In theological opinion, the two limbos are dark, but the other two divisions of hell consist of glaring flames.

The belief in real, material fires of hell was held by several Church fathers, among them Augustine, Cyprian, Chrysostom and Jerome. This belief has scriptural sanction, inasmuch as both the Old and the New Testaments mention pitch and brimstone for burning the damned in hell (Is. xxx. 33; xxxiv. 9; Rev. xiv. 10; xix. 20; xx. 10; xxi. 8). This tradition accounts for the belief that, when Satan disappears, an unsavory sulphuric scent remains behind. Hell was conceived by our medieval ancestors, particularly by Dante and his contemporaries, as a country of clashed kettles and cauldrons, in which the souls of sinners stew eternally.

In its conception of a flaming hell, Christianity, through its parent religion, had in mind the spot Tophet in Gehenna, the "Valley of Hinnom," consecrated to the worship of the idol Moloch with its fiery belly (2 Kings xxiii. 10; Is. xxx. 33; lxvi. 24; Neh. xl. 30; cf. Matt. v. 22; Jas iii. 6). The Jewish-Christian hell, moreover, seems to have been modeled after the Persian place of punishments. Satan is but imitating his prototype Ahriman in making impious souls burn continually.[6] We must also bear in mind that Prometheus and Loki, Satan's cousins in other religions, also had a great deal to do with the element of fire. From the fact that hell is a region of flames, Heinrich Heine, in *Die Elementargeister* (1834), concluded that Satan was a sort of salamander.

Such is the intensity of the fires of hell that, according to the belief of the Jews, the hot springs of Tiberias are due to the waters of this lake passing near the gates of Gehenna.

The idea of a hell of flames in the bowels of the earth was also confirmed by the sight of the smoking volcanoes, which have been created, according to Catholic theology, as safety valves in order that our planet should not be blown up by the infernal blasts. This theory accounts for the popular tradition that the craters of volcanoes lead directly to the pit of hell. The volcanoes of Iceland are connected with hell in some of the travels in Samuel Purchas' *Pilgrimage* (1612).[7] Mt. Etna, on the coast of Sicily, which was considered in ancient days as the habitation of the giants, is still believed to lead down to hell. According to a legend current among Neapolitan peasants, hell is situated directly under the volcano Mt. Gibel (Prosper Mérimée: "Fédérigo," 1829).

This belief in a flaming hell has been supported by many medieval theologians like Thomas Aquinas, and sincerely affirmed by many a preacher now departed. Mr. Spurgeon, the great Baptist preacher, tells us in the second series of his sermons:

"There is a real fire in hell, as truly as you now have

[6]The idea of rewards and punishments in future life was unknown to the ancient Hebrews. Sheol is a colorless abode of all the dead. Abaddon "destruction" (Job xxvi. 6; xxviii. 22; Prov. xv. 11) is simply a synonym for Sheol. The conception of a place of punishment for the wicked after death is of post-exilic origin. See Russell Scott: *An Analytical Investigation of the Scriptural Claims of the Devil; To Which is added an Explanation of the Terms Sheol, Hades and Gehenna* (London, 1822). James New's article, "The Hebrew Hell," *The Nineteenth Century*, XXVIII (1890), 269-88; is a critical study of the subject.

[7]The full title of this book runs as follows: *His Pilgrimage or Relations of the world and the religions in all Ages and Places Discovered.* This book enjoyed a great popularity in its day and was issued in four editions in the course of fourteen years. It was also used by Coleridge in his "Rime of the Ancient Mariner" (1798).

a real body — a fire exactly like that which we have
on earth, except this, that it will not consume though
it will torture you. You have seen the asbestos lying
in the fire red-hot, but when you take it out, it is un-
consumed. So your body will be prepared by God
in such a way that it will burn forever without being
consumed."

Jonathan Edwards went even further, saying:

"The damned shall be tormented in the presence
of the glorified saints. Hereby the saints will be made
more sensible how great their salvation is. The view
of the misery of the damned will double the ardor of
the love and gratitude of the saints in heaven."

When this great preacher finished his sermon, the congregation
may have opened their books, and sung Watts' hymn,

"What bliss will fill the ransomed souls,
When they in glory dwell,
To see the sinner as he rolls
In quenchless flames of hell."

Dante, Milton and other poets also shared the belief in a flaming
hell. And how can we, moreover, scorn the testimony of the contemporaries of the poet of the *Inferno,* who pointed out to each
other with holy shudders the marks which the scorching fires of
hell had left on the unhappy poet's face?

*   *   *

What is not generally known is the fact that, in addition to its
pools of fire, the infernal realm also boasts of plains covered with
ice.[8] St. Tertullian and St. Jerome affirm that Christ's own words
about the "gnashing (chattering) of teeth" (Matt. viii. 12; xiii.
50; Luke xiii. 28) suggest places of extreme cold alternating with
places of excessive heat. It is evident that the flaming and frigid
regions of hell point to two different mythical currents, which meet
in the Christian conception of hell. The idea of a cold hell can
only be the result of Northern imagination, whereas the conception
of a hot hell is the fruit of Southern speculation. This belief in
a twofold hell is cited by Scandinavian scholars as proof of the
influence of Northern ideas on Southern thought.[9] This synthesis
of Eastern belief and Western imagination is symbolized for the

[8] According to Jewish belief, hell consists of both fire and water.
[9] Cf. Paul Carus: *The History of the Devil and the Idea of Evil* (Chicago,
Ill., 1900), pp. 246-9.

Teutonic races in the very name of the Christian Underworld. It is indeed an irony of etymology that the Eastern domain of burning heat should in the West bear a name which signifies a place of cold and dreary darkness. It was Hel or Hela, the land of the dead and the name of its presiding goddess, the Proserpina of the North, that in Germanic countries gave its name to the biblical place of the sojourn of the sinners. The Scandinavian dwelling of the dead, however, originally was not at all associated with punishment.

Dante derived his description of the flaming and frigid regions of hell not from Catholic eschatology but from classical mythology. He borrowed his portrayal of the places of punishment from Virgil, who is represented as Dante's guide on his journey through hell and purgatory.[10] As a matter of fact, about all of Catholic eschatology is to be found in the sixth book of Virgil's *Æneid,* except for the fact that the Latin poet knew nothing of torments for wicked mortals.[11]

According to the Dutch fold-lorist and novelist, Dr. Frederik Willem van Eeden, Satan disclaims any connection whatever with these regions of alternating fire and ice. In the allegorical novel, *De kleine Johannes* (1887) by the Dutch author,[12] the Devil abjures ownership of the place of eternal torment which Dante visited, asserting that it belongs to the Other. He accuses the Florentine poet of unfair dealing in ascribing to him characteristics which belong to the God in whose name the Inquisition was instituted. As Little Johannes, on his spiritual pilgrimage, enters the Devil's domain, he is astonished to find it so different from the conception prevalent on earth. "What is this place, really?" asks Johannes. "Hell? Is it here that Dante was?"—"Dante?" asks the Devil. And all his retainers whisper and titter and chatter: "Dante? Dante?

[10]The present writer's lamented teacher, Anatole LeBraz, the Celtic scholar, might have considered Virgil's conception of a cold hell as another proof of his contention that the Roman poet was of Celtic origin.

[11]The authoritative interpretation of the Catholic conception of hell will be found in the two works by Josef Bautz: *Die Hölle* (1882) and *Das Fegefeuer* (1883). See also the following two Catholic treatises: Abbé Carle: *Du dogme catholique sur l'enfer* (Paris, 1842) and O. Delepierre: *l'Enfer; essai philosophique et historique sur les légendes de la vie future* (London, 1876). A critical study on the subject is Percy Dearmer's *The Legend of Hell* (London, 1929). On the popular conceptions of hell, see Markus Landau's *Hölle und Fegefeuer in Volksglaube, Dichtung und Kirchenlehre* (Heidelberg, 1909).

[12]This book has been translated into English by Clara Bell and published in London, in 1895, under the title *Little Johannes.* An English translation of this book entitled *The Quest* has also appeared in this country, in 1907.

HEL, THE GODDESS OF THE NETHER WORLD
By Johannes Gehrts

Dante?"—"Surely," resumes the King of the Nether World, "you must mean that nice place full of light which is so hot and smells so bad, where sand melts, where rivers of blood are seething, and the boiling pitch is ever bubbling, where they scream and yell and curse and lament and swear at each other."—"Yes," says Johannes. "Dante told about that."—"But, my dear little friend," replies the Devil affably, "that is not here, as you can very well see for yourself. That is not my kingdom. That is the kingdom of another, who, they say, is called Love. With me, no one suffers. I am not as cruel as that. I cause no one pain."[13]

*

* *

But although the demons after their fall were cast into hell, they appear to enjoy the liberty of leaving their prison at will to walk up and down the earth, in order to tempt and torment mankind (Job i. 7; Eph. ii. 2; v. 11; 1 Pet. v. 8; Rev. xii. 9).

When the demons have no commissions from their Chief to carry out on earth, they seek respite from their labor in deserted, chaotic or "dry places" (Matt. xii. 43; Luke xi. 24). The activity of the Northern demons was also thought to be limited to certain regions of the earth. The desert was the common home of many Semitic demons. The spirits of hell might also dwell in tombs (Matt. viii. 28). The belief in the demon that "lurks in graveyards" is prevalent among all races. Caverns were also commonly considered hiding-places for the hosts of hell.

The demons, in imitation of the dwarfs, also dwelt on mountains or among rocks. According to Victor Hugo, Jochmus, an evil spirit, who audaciously passed himself off for many centuries as St. Maclou, was believed by the Guernsey peasants to inhabit the rock called Ortach in the Norman Archipelago between Aurigny and the Caskets (*les Travailleurs de la mer,* 1866). "The Devils," we are informed in this novel, "often pass themselves off as saints. Even the Church herself is not proof against such delusions. The demons Raguhel, Oribel and Tobiel were regarded as saints un-

[13]In this connection it may be interesting to the reader to know that, after having uttered this irony, the author crawled to the Cross and embraced the Catholic religion, as he himself announced in one of his essays, which he collected and published in 1921, under the title *Het roode lampje signifische gepeinzen* and which were translated the following year into English under the title *Significant Sayings.*

til the year 745, when Pope Zachary, a connoisseur in devils, having at length discovered their identity, turned them out of the Church" (*ibid.*, I. i. 2).[14]

The demons, notwithstanding the biblical assignment to dry places, might reside in wet places as well. Anatole France affirms that "the demons inhabit brooks" (*Thaïs*, 1890), but they may also be found in larger bodies of water. It was believed that demons resided especially in the waters, the harmfulness of which is thus explained as clearly by doctrine as by science. The water must be boiled or sterilized with the sign of salvation before it can be used. For the demons dread equally the fire and the Cross. Nowadays the former means proves more efficacious in driving out the demons than the latter. Voltaire said more than a century and a half ago, "The Christians have long lost the power to expel the Devil by the sign of the Cross."

* * *

The demons do not always remain in desert places. They can also sustain themselves in the civilized spots of this earth, and indeed their presence is felt everywhere on this globe. Certain parts of this planet are evidently more favored by their presence than others, for China simply teems with demons. Indeed, there is one particular province in that country which is known as "Demonland."

As far as Christian Europe is concerned, the North is the Devil's preferred residence. The North was anciently believed to be the region of darkness and was later considered, by transferred meaning, as the realm of evil. The idea of the North as a region of darkness may first of all be traced to the ancient sun-cult. The sun, in circling around the earth, goes around south and never north of the observer on this hemisphere. This idea is emphasized by the sun-stations of certain secret societies. Some travelers may also have traveled far enough north in winter time to experience long nights, and thus arrived at the conclusion that the North was always the domain of darkness.

Evil is described as coming down upon Judah from the North in several biblical passages (Jer. i. 14; iv. 6; vi. 1). These refer-

---

[14] According to a popular belief in Iceland there are still unexorcised devils among the saints of the Catholic calendar. The soldiers in Victor Hugo's *Han d'Islande* (1823) swear by Saint Beelzebub and Saint Belphegor.

[15] On Chinese demonology, see B. N. Dennys: *The Folk-Lore of China.* London, 1867.

ences are obviously to Babylonia, but Church tradition has given a symbolical and universal meaning to them. This interpretation accords with the saying, *"Ab aquilone omne malum* — All evil comes from the North."

From ancient times the North has been associated with demons. In Cornwall, the people still believe that the North is the region of demons. In Hindu mythology, the Asuras or demons inimical to the Devas or gods also lived in the North. Ahriman, as a winter demon, had his habitation in the cold North, whence he sent down hail and snow and devastating floods upon the land. Thus Satan, in taking up his sojourn in the North, was merely following his Persian prototype.

The North is described as the dwelling of the Devil in the passage which has, erroneously enough, given rise to the legend of Lucifer as an angel fallen from heaven (Is. xiv. 13). The women are described as wailing over the dead Tammuz, who, together with all ancient gods, has been turned into a demon, at the north gate of the Lord's house (Ez. viii. 14).

The Church has always described the North as the domain of the Devil. "The Lord," says Lactantius, "so divided the world with the Devil that *occidens, septentrio, tenebræ, frigus* — the West, the North, the darkness, the cold—fell to the sphere of the Adversary" (*Institutiones divinæ*). Goethe has also said:

> "The farther northward one doth go,
> The plentier soot and witches grow."

The location of hell was believed to be somewhere in the far North (Job xxvi. 6-7). The position of hell on the medieval stage was generally in the North.[16] In the stage directions of *The Castle of Perseverance,* the oldest English morality-play, the scaffold of Belial is expressly placed in the North. Milton, in his *Paradise Lost* (v. 689), follows medieval tradition on this point.[17]

The belief in the North as the Devil's domain seems to account for the ecclesiastical rule that the northern side of a churchyard

---

[16]See D. C. Stuart: "Stage-Setting of Hell and the Iconography of the Middle Ages." *Romanic Review,* IV, July-September, 1913.

[17]Professor Ed. Ch. Baldwin, in his efforts to account for the left hand position of hell in Milton ("And on the Left Hand Hell," *Modern Language Notes,* XL [1925], 251), goes far afield in trying to find Milton's authority for this belief in the writings of the rabbis. Milton had no need to draw on the Talmud for his theology or demonology. On this point, as on so many others, the Puritan poet needed but to follow Catholic teaching and tradition.

is considered unconsecrated ground and is reserved for suicides. As the entrance to a church is at the west end, for the reason that the altar facing it must be to the east, the worshippers entering the church have the North to their left. For this reason, the left has always been the seat of, and has practically become the synonym for, the Opposition. The Devil, you must know, not unlike the traditional Hibernian, is always "agin the government" not only of heaven but of earth. This alignment will establish a kinship between the Devil and the Irishman. Indeed, the Devil is believed to feel most at home among the inhabitants of the northerly Green Isle. William Dunbar, the Scottish poet, in his famous *Dance of the Seven Sins* (sixteenth century), makes the Devil rebel against the hideous Gælic of his followers. By some demonologists Dublin was considered to be Satan's earthly capital. Strange to say, the Scandinavian form of the name for the Irish capital is Divelina. Robert Burns must have had this belief in mind when he wrote:

" . . . Is just as true's the deil's in hell
Or Dublin City."

But let not the English rejoice too soon at the expense of the Irish. England is frequented in folk-lore by demons no less than the Emerald Isle. As a matter of fact, England, partly perhaps on account of its Northern latitude and its harsh climate, once had the reputation of being the chief abode of the spirits of hell. Procopius, in his *De bello Gothico,* tells us that a demoness, leaving her loved one on the Continent, said to him, "My mother is calling me in England" (iv. 29). In an "Essay on the Devil," which appeared in the English weekly, *The New Statesman* (1919), the writer maintains that nowadays England is still considered by anti-English papers as "The Devil's Paradise." The enemies of England, on account of its political policies, claim to have good reason to declare that the very Devil is among the inhabitants of that country.[18] This is probably the reason why the English have never treated the cloven-hoofed fellow so lightly as the Germans.[19]

The English, however, maintain that they have nothing in com-

[18]There appeared in America almost a century ago a book, in two volumes, under the title *Mephistopheles in England; or Confessions of a Prime Minister,* which is a biting satire on political life in England. It is interesting to read Poe's review of this book in the *Southern Literary Messenger,* I (1835), 776-7. In this connection the reader will also be interested in George Robert Sims's satirical work: *The Devil in London* (London ,1908).

[19]Cf. M. D. Conway: "The Demons of the Shadow," *Scribner's Monthly,* V (1872), 247.

mon with the Devil, not even the language. It was long a favorite jibe with Englishmen that the fiends of hell spoke "Welsh," which means the talk of the stranger. This brings to mind Hotspur's remark, "Now I perceive the Devil understands Welsh." Victor Hugo was of the opinion that the Devil is a Latin in origin and that his language is a compound of Spanish, Italian and Latin (*le Rhin*, 1842). According to Origen, the demons have their own languages and dialects, but they also understand and speak all human languages.

Scandinavia is counted among the Devil's summer resorts. Lapland was long held to be the especial home and rendezvous of demons and witches (*Par. Lost* ii. 665). It is, however, more correct to consider Mt. Hecla, the volcano on the southwest point of Iceland, as the common place of meeting for the demons when unemployed. Some suppose that Satan holds nightly services in Troms Church, Norway, and even has a church in the village Elfdale, situated in Sweden.

Others hold the belief that the Devil dwelt preferably in Germany, and as proof point to the great number of places and edifices named after him in that country. The Poles identify the Devil and the German by using a single term — *Niemiec* or *Niemiaszek* — to describe the two.

The Devil especially frequented in the countries along the Danube. Of old this river was regarded as coming under the special guardianship of the Prince of Darkness, who made extreme efforts to check the progress of the Crusaders, voyaging down its waters on their way to rescue the Hold Land from the Saracens.

Nor is Switzerland exempt from the suspicion of enjoying Satan's sojourn. Many demonologists held the opinion that Mt. Pilatus, probably on acount of its supposedly historical connection, was the Devil's permanent place of business.

The Devil's retirement to Lombardy, which is mentioned in the medieval French drama, refers to the unsavory reputation of the Lombards in the Middle Ages as usurers and poisoners.

It is conceded by all, however, that Paris, the most worldly of worldly cities and a citadel of modern civilization, is properly the Devil's favorite field of activity. Théophile Gautier seems to have been wrong in doubting the Devil's inclination to come to the French capital. In his essay on Hoffmann (1836), this writer asks:

"...For the matter of that, what the Devil would the

Devil come to Paris for? He would come upon other people who are far more devils than he is, and he would be taken in as readily as a country bumpkin. He would have his money swindled out of him at *écarté;* he would be fooled into taking shares in some company, and if he were not provided with proper papers, he would be sent to jail."

Théophile Gautier, however, was mistaken in his belief that the Parisians would not know what to do with the Devil. Six years after this writer expressed his belief in the futility of the Fiend among Frenchmen, his contemporary, P. J. Stahl, started to publish a collection of stories in two volumes containing a general view of Paris and the Parisians, their morals and manners, their characateristics and portraits, their private and public life, and their political and artistic activities, under the title *le Diable à Paris; Paris et les Parisiens.* In his preface to this diabolical panorama of Paris, the editor set himself the task of explaining "Comment il se fit qu'un diable vint à Paris — How it happened that a devil came to Paris." In the poem, which he himself contributed to this work, and after which it is named, he represents Satan's various activities in the French capital as seducer of men and maids, as gambler, as playwright, as revolutionary and as stock broker. Edmond Texier also depicts the Devil's doings in the French capital in his story, "le Diable à Paris" (1853).

It is asserted by all moralists that Paris, the shrine of food and fashion, wine and wickedness, is the Devil's own domain.[20] In fact, the Devil calls Paris "my city" in Pierre Veber's *l'Homme qui vendit son âme au diable* (1918). Gérard de Nerval, in *Nicolas Flamel* (1830), mentions the belief current among the Parisian population of the fifteenth century that Satan reigned all night in the tower of the Church of St. Jacques-la-Boucherie. The Devil is to this day to be located in the midst of the French capital. He looks down with a malign sneer of satisfaction on the doings of the Parisians from the towers of the Cathedral of Notre-Dame, through visibly carved figures and grotesques.

Paris was often regarded, even by her inhabitants, as the dwell-

[20]Charles Selby has written, in 1840, a play entitled *Satan in Paris; or, The Mysterious Stranger.* Aimée Semple McPherson, after her return from a recent visit to Paris, declared in a statement dated September 23, 1928, that "Satan has a strong hold on the population of the French capital." Naturally, the Parisian women are counted among the Devil's chief disciples, as may be seen from Léopold Stapléaux' *les Diablesses de Paris* (Paris, 1886).

ing of the Devil. Alfred de Vigny was not certain whether he should call Paris "the hell or the Eden of the world." Auguste Barbier

A Gargolye on the West Front of Notre-Dame de Paris.
In the background to the left the tower of the
Church St. Jacques-la-Boucherie.

considered the French capital "an infernal tub." Balzac, who was the spiritual conqueror and delineator of Paris, in a letter addressed to the abbé Eglé in June, 1844, calls Paris, "the ante-chamber of hell." In his story, "la Fille aux yeux d'or," published ten years previously, the author of the *Comédie humaine* asserted emphatically that " . . . it is not only jokingly that Paris has been called a hell."

The Devil, it should be admitted in all frankness, is not unknown in this country, either. Judging by the various and numerous places named after him in these United States, the Fiend has left his footprints from the Atlantic to the Pacific.[21] In fact, many Europeans hold the opinion that this country, which they call Dollarica, is the Devil's own.[22]

It is thus evident that his Satanic Majesty's kingdom is not limited in the popular imagination to the netherworld, but that it extends to all parts of our earth. The Fiend keeps the features of his face widely scattered from pole to pole. This ubiquity is in keeping with the proverb, which says, "The Devil is nowhere in particular but everywhere in general."

The fact is that the notion of the Devil or Satanism is practically synonymous with the idea of Evil, and its train of consequences, such as pain, want, woe, jealousy, lust, malice, vindictiveness and the like. The ubiquitous nature of Evil accounts for the presence of the minions of Satan in circles high and low, in cities and in desert places, — in popular parlance, — everywhere. Not even the Society of Heaven has power to prevent his machinations. The mundane sphere, which man uses for his dwelling, is Satan's territory, from pole to pole and through all latitudes and climes, from which no power can utterly exclude him. Indeed, the Devil seems to be an integral factor in the scheme of earthly living, from which, by reason of the constitution of Nature, his exclusion is impossible.

[21]Mr. E. L. Allen, in his article, "The Devil's Property in the United States," *The Outlook*, CXXVI (1920), 246-7, has enumerated the various geographical places in this country named after the Devil, such as the Devil's Thumb, the Devil's Elbow, the Devil's Den, the Devil's Pulpit, etc.

[22]In "A Letter from the Devil" published by Francis de Miomandre in the *Nouvelles littéraires for* December 8, 1928, the ruler of the nether regions maintains that the country described by John Dos Passos and Henry K. Marks resembles his own domain in many respects.

CHAPTER VI

JOURNEYS TO HELL

AMONG the travellers' tales which delighted our wonder-loving ancestors, the greatest popularity was enjoyed by reports of journeys to the realms of the dead. Visions too numerous to tell were invented for their delectation and edification. It would, indeed, be too great a task to follow the mythical stream of a Beyond flowing out of and into the hearts and imaginations of men. It is found in Indian, Iranian, Greek, Roman, Jewish and Christian mythology, and its sources reach far back, to a time whereof "the memory of man runneth not to the contrary."

Many have been the visits of the living to the dead. Some went in the body and others out of the body. Some travelled by night and others in the light of the day. The first record of a journey to the World of the Spirits is found in Plato. The Greek philosopher recorded the testimony of Er the Arminian to the effect that he had been admitted to witness the distribution of rewards and punishments to the souls of the departed and had been permitted to return to earth and tell his story (*Rep.* x. 614ff.). Homer described the descent of Ulysses to Hades to consult Tiresias (*Odyss.* xi). From the Greek poet, the idea descended to Virgil, Seneca, Ovid, Lucian, Statius, and other Greek and Roman writers. It also entered Jewish-Christian thought, the Church fathers elaborating it into a doctrinal system. The New Testament furnished the starting-point with its visions of the Beyond. The Book of Revelation offers many glimpses of the Unseen World, and in the Epistles we learn that St. Paul was caught up to the third heaven (2 Cor. xii. 2). Details of this journey are suppressed by the biblical writer as "unspeakable words, which it is not lawful for a man to utter" (*ibid.,* 4), but are given in the apocryphal Vision of St. Paul (4th cent.). Other biblical passages (Acts ii. 31; Eph. iv. 8-10; Rom. x. 7 and especially 1 Peter iii. 19-20) were interpreted to mean that Christ after his burial descended to hell for the purpose of redeeming from infernal pain the patriarchs and prophets of the Old Dispensation. This idea was elaborated in the apocryphal Descensus Christi ad Inferos, which is the second part of the Evangelium Nicodemi (3rd cent.). It also forms part of the Apostolic formula of the Christian creed.

But while Christ visited hell after his death, others journeyed thither during their life-time. Zoroaster is said to have made midnight journeys to heaven and hell; and, according to Jewish tradition, Moses also visited the upper and lower worlds in his body.[1] The Holy Virgin and the Great Apostle likewise wandered, according to tradition, through hell and witnessed the torments inflicted upon the wicked. It would seem, in fact, that when the ancient world of spirits was divided by Christianity into two realms, an upper and a lower, the majority of travellers preferred to go in the downward direction. The idea of hell seemed to have had a great fascination for the Christian mind. What wonder that hell is writ large on the manuscripts of the medieval monks and missionaries! Many, indeed, were the visions of hell in medieval times. What we call the Dark Ages were, in fact, a perpetual spiritualistic séance with lights lowered. We need but refer to Beda Venerabilis, St. Brandan, Tundalus, Albericus, Wettin and Hildegard. Prominent among the medieval pilgrims to the Pit is Owaine the Knight. His descent into St. Patrick's Purgatory, as told by Henry of Saltrey, took place in 1153.[2] The most distinguished visitor, however, that Satan ever received at his court was Dante Alighieri, the first and greatest of the poets of Italy.

Dante, to be sure, visited all the three realms, to which the Catholic Church assigned the dead. His journey included hell, purgatory and heaven. It would seem, however, that our poet was most impressed by hell. Of his trilogy, the "Inferno" undoubtedly commends itself most to our imagination. The "Inferno" is the most powerful poem in the Divina Commedia. Next in importance is the "Purgatorio." The "Paradiso" comes last. "If Dante's great poem," says Francis Grierson, "had been a description of heaven, no one would read it. The interest centers in hell and purgatory."

[1] Cf. Louis Ginzberg: The Legends of the Jews (4 vols., Philadelphia, 1908-25), I, 309 ff.

[2] See St. Patrick's Purgatory; an Essay on the Legends of Purgatory, Hell, and Paradise, Current During the Middle Ages. London, 1844.

The great Italian poet was most successful in his description of the domain of the damned. Chateaubriand has aptly remarked that it is easier to conceive of eternal unhappiness than of endless happiness (*le Génie du Christianisme*, II. iv. 14). We can, indeed, grasp hell and even purgatory but not heaven. "Our imagination," says Anatole France, "is made up of memories." We can easily form a hell out of the material taken from earth, but we lack on our planet the stuff with which to construct a heaven. Dante had no difficulty in assembling the material for his description of moral sufferings and physical pains. "I have found," said the poet of "Inferno," "the original of my hell in the world which we inhabit." It was hell and not heaven which, according to the testimony of his contemporaries, had left the deep marks on Dante's face. It is hell and not heaven which is the most real in the consciousness of man. We all know what hell is, but when questioned in regard to heaven, we feel embarrassed to answer. The information is so scanty, as a brilliant French woman once remarked to Sainte-Beuve. "There may be heaven, there must be hell," is the conclusion reached at the end of Browning's poem, "Time's Revenges" (1845). A further illustration of this idea is the legend of the three monks of Mesopotamia, who set out one day on a journey to the dwelling of the departed and who found hell and purgatory, but not heaven.

Dante's conception of hell is not original but universal. Many of his ideas were current in his days. The "Inferno" is but a highly poetical elaboration of medieval notions. The flaming and frigid divisions of hell point to the two mythical currents, the Christian and the classical, which meet in Dante's vision of the inferno. Following the lead of all Roman writers, our poet shows, in his description of the Christian Underworld, a love of horrors and a delight in terrors for their own sakes. This predilection for bloodshed and corruption is especially typical of the art of the Etruscans.

The Devil in Dante's "Inferno" is an incarnation of ugliness, foulness and corruption. As he stands half sunk into the frozen fastness of his pit, in all his pervading brutality and cruelty, malignity and monstrosity, he is an appalling rather than an appealing sight. We cannot enter into his psychology. The action of his mind or will is closed to us. We do not even know whether it is sorrow over his departed glory or impotent fury which brings the tears flowing over his three chins. "The imagination of Dante," says Chateaubriand, in his work already mentioned, "exhausted by nine circles of torment, has made simply an atrocious monster of Satan, locked up in the center of the earth" (II. iv. 11). What wonder that the Devil in G. Bernard Shaw's *Man and Superman* (1905) is discontented with this description of himself!

* * *

Dante had many imitators who also ventured to visit the Lower World. Emmanuel Swedenborg, in the eighteenth century, is said to have journeyed to heaven and hell. Perhaps the most prominent guest that Satan welcomed in modern times was the popular French poet Jean-Pierre de Béranger (1780-1857). In his ribald song, "la Descente aux Enfers" (1812), impiously named after the Descensus Christ ad Inferos, our ballad-maker tells how he descended to the domain of the Devil on a broomstick in company with a modern witch, a young and beautiful woman. As the imps of hell by no means lack appreciation of beauty, they came in swarms to kiss the naked feet of his companion. The nether world, according to the testimony of this modern visitor to Satan, is different from the description given by the priests, who employ the fear of hell as a means of driving men into the Church. From the report of this traveller, we would say that the underworld resembles more a voluptuous Turkish harem than a vaporous Turkish bath. The court of the King-Devil cannot be surpassed in luxury by that of any earthly ruler. Our visitor to the infernal regions found no traces of kettles or cauldrons and heard there no howling or gnashing of teeth. On the contrary, he found the floor strewn with oyster shells and empty bottles. The souls who are fortunate enough to go to hell eat and drink and make merry. Nothing is less frightful than the sight of Satan. The infernal monarch is a devil of a good fellow *chez lui*. He issues his severest decrees to the clinking of glasses and the playing of reed-pipes. Satan is a very genial host and entertains his guests most royally. His Infernal Majesty is surrounded at the banquet table by a crowd of red-faced drinkers, for whom he keeps pouring bourgogne and champagne. There is not much decorum in the halls of hell. Ixion is sleeping on the shoulder of Tantalus, who is dead drunk, and Epicurus is making love to Ninon de Lenclos.

"After reading this poem, one is inclined to exclaim with St. Paul: O death, where is thy sting? O grave, where is thy victory?" (1 Cor. xv. 55). The author draws the following lesson from his description of the Devil's domain:

"Si, d'après ce qu'on rapporte,
On bâille au céleste lieu,
Que le diable nous emporte,
Et nous rendrons grâce à Dieu."

No man who descended to hell after his death is known to have returned to earth to tell others what he has seen in that dread and dismal darkness. But letters purporting to come from the inhabitants of hell appeared on several occasions during the past century.[3]

A very interesting visit to the infernal world has been paid some time ago by our own cartoonist, "Art" Young, who introduced himself to "Sate" as a newspaperman from Chicago and who reported that "Hell is now run on the broad American plan."[4] "Captain" Charon, who began his career with a little tub of a "rowboat," is now running big steamers on the Styx, "the only navigable river in hell." Judge Minos sits in court, and an Irish policeman introduces the poor wretches one by one. The lawyers are condemned to be gagged, and their objections are overruled by Satan. The inventor of the barbwire fence is seated naked on a barbwire fence; tramps are washed; policemen are clubbed until they see stars; quack doctors are cured according to their own methods; poker fiends, board of trade gamblers, and fish-story tellers are treated according to their deserts; monopolists are baked like popcorn; editors are thrown into their waste-baskets, and clergymen are condemned to listen to their own sermons, which have been faithfully recorded on phonographs.[5]

[3] Ferdinand Gregorovius: *Konrad Siebenhorns Höllenbriefe an seine lieben Freunde in Deutschland*. Hrsg. von Ferdinand Fuchsmund. Königsberg, 1843. *Letters from Hell*. Translated from the Danish by Julie Sutter. With a Preface by George MacDonald. London, 1886. 2nd ed., New York, 1911.
B. Piscator started a series of *Modern Letters from Hell* (*Moderne Höllenbriefe*) with his book *Psychologische Studien der Hölle* (*Psychological Studies of Hell*). Berlin, 1907. Rachel Hayward published a novel with the title of *Letters from Là-Bas*, named after J. K. Huysmans' novel *Là-Bas* (1891).
On letters from heaven and hell see W. Höhler's article "Zu den Himmels— und Höllenbriefen" in the *Hessische Blätter für Volkskunde*, vol. I (1902), pp. 143-9.
The *War Letters from a Living Dead Man*, written by Elsa Parker but said to have been dictated by a correspondent presumably from hell, show us his Satanic Majesty with a grim humor up to date.
[4] Art Young: *Hell Up to Date*. Chicago, 1892. Wilhelm Waiblinger has written a report of his subterranean sojourn under the title *Drei Tage in der Unterwelt* (In his *Gesammelte Werke*, IV, 115-91).
[5] We recommend to the reader who wishes to pay a visit to hell the following book: *A Sure Guide to Hell* (London, 1770) presumed to have been written by Benjamin Brown.

CHAPTER VII

THE ORGANIZATION OF PANDEMONIUM

H ELL may be a region of disorder in comparison with heaven, but it is evident that some sort of order must prevail in the lower regions. It is certainly doubtful whether the Devil will permit any disorder or discord in his domain. This solidarity and amity among the exiled angels is explained by their common lot of suffering under adversity. Milton has himself said: "Devil with devil damn'd Firm concord holds" (*Par. Lost* ii. 496-7). Indeed, the Puritan poet, following the lead of Tasso, ascribed to the demons of hell a spirit of harmony, of loyalty, and of enthusiasm which is not often found among the inhabitants of this planet. He also granted them the power of governing and combining themselves on their own basic principles and endowed them with the faculty of deliberation and concerted action.

The demons of darkness form a regular social and political organization.[1] The infernal government was patterned after the celestial government. The Kingdom of Satan, mentioned in the New Testament (Matt. xii. 26), was established to rival the Kingdom of God. The diabolarchy was formed in imitation of the hierarchy of heaven. The Church fathers Jerome, Chrysostom, Cassianus and others speak of a hierarchy of devils. Previously, biblical authority had pointed to the fact that there are divisions in rank among the hosts of hell (Matt. xii. 26, 45, xxv. 41; Luk. xi. 15, 18; Rev. xii. 7, 9; cf. also Book of Enoch liii. 3). In Hesiod, too, the demons are divided into different orders, although the Greek poet, it must be admitted, has in mind good dæmons, who dwell above the ground and are donors of wealth to mortals.

[1] Historically considered, we might say that the demonologists collected Lucifer's routed forces after their expulsion from heaven and reorganized them according to a well laid-out plan.

At the head of the hierarchy of hell stands Satan, who, in Christian theology, is the ruler of the "accursed counter-kingdom of evil" (Book of Enoch). Satan is considered as *summum imperium infernalis.* He rules his kingdom by the law of the mailed fist. The arch-devil's Draconian discipline has become proverbial. No insubordination is tolerated in his realm. In all fairness to the Fiend, however, it should be added that he probably is no greater oppressor of his subjects than most monarchs, who rule on our own planet. This Cæsar-Satan is just like any other emperor, neither better nor worse.[2]

Satan, however, is not universally recognized as the present ruler of the "infernal kingdom" (*Titus Andronicus* v. 2. 30). It is believed by many demonologists that Satan now is a dethroned monarch and belongs in a class with William II of Germany, Ferdinand of Bulgaria, and other rulers who forfeited their crowns in the Great War. Johannes Wierus, in his treatise *Pseudo-monarchia dæmonum* (16th cent.),[3] maintains that Satan was forced long ago to resign in favor of Beelzebub, who headed a revolution against the ancient leader of the rebel angels and wrested the crown and scepter from him. We offer the suggestion that the relation between Satan and Beelzebub in hell might correspond to that between Victor Emmanuel and Mussolini on earth. Satan is the nominal ruler of Gehenna, whereas Beelzebub holds in his hands the reins of the government. Satan may still wear the crown, but it is Beelzebub who is dictator of the devils.

In Milton's poem about the fall of the angels, however, Satan remains the chief of the infernal spirits, while Beelzebub is "Satan's nearest mate" (*Par. Lost* i. 192, 238). The Faust-book of 1587 reveals Beelzebub as one of the seven principal spirits introduced to Faustus by their chief (ch. xxiii.) According to Asmodeus, the hero of LeSage's novel *le Diable boiteux* (1707), Beelzebub is among the least important Helots of hell. He calls Beelzebub a "boob" and maintains that he is the demon of domestics.

[2] In Frederik van Eeden's novel *De kleine Johannes* (1887), Satan denies the fact that he is a despotic ruler and says boastfully: "I am a king of a constitutional democracy."

[3] Victor Hugo, in his novel, *les Travailleurs de la mer* (1866), calls Wier, Weier or Weyer (Latin Wierus or Piscinarius) "a *savant,* a good strygologue, and a man of much learning in demonology." For a biography of this physician of Rhenish Prussia, that man of enlightenment, who was the first to combat the persecution of witches, the reader is referred to C. Binz: *Doktor Johann Weyer, ein rheinischer Arzt, der erste Bekämpfer des Hexenwesens.* Bonn, 1885.

In popular belief, however, Lucifer is the Potentate of the Pit. The *Black Book* by Thomas Middleton (1604) dignifies the lord of all the powers of darkness with the following titles: "The high and mightie Prince of darkness, Donsell del Lucifer, King of Acheron, Stix and Phlegeton, Duke of Tartary, Marquese of Cocytus, and Lord High Regent of Lymbo."[4] The litanies of the Witches' Sabbaths always began with a laudation of Lucifer. Marlowe's *Dr. Faustus* (c. 1589) represents Lucifer as the "Arch-regent and commander of all spirits" (iii. 64) and Beelzebub as his "companion prince in hell" (*ibid.*, vi. 92).

In the medieval mystery-plays, Lucifer is lord of hell and Satan is his chief minister and bosom friend.[5] A sharp line of demarcation is drawn in the medieval German drama between the characters of these two devils. Satan's proud self-confidence stands in pleasing contrast to Lucifer's rueful self-abasement. Lucifer is a weakling, a cowardly despot, while Satan is his strong arm, his "clever rooster," as his lord calls him. The prime minister of hell never hesitates to speak his mind in the presence of Lucifer. He makes fun of his master even to his very face and upbraids him for his old womanish manners. The arch-regent of hell is nervous and timorous, sentimental and brutal, vacillating and temporizing, always whimpering and whining with regard to his past glory. Satan, on the other hand, is bold and proud, ever optimistic, never regretful. After the fall from heaven, Satan musters all his powers of oratory to cheer and comfort his crest-fallen and despairing lord and master.

The rôles of these two devils are, however, often reversed by modern writers. Immerman's *Merlin* (1832), for instance, makes Satan the sovereign, while Lucifer is the vice-regent in the government of Gehenna.

The Italian writers, loyal to the classical tradition, consider Pluto the god of the underworld. This divinity will be found as chief of hell, among other writers, in Boccaccio, Machiavelli and Tasso. In Mérimée's *Fédérigo* (1829), based on a Neapolitan legend, Pluto is

[4] In the Renaissance period, the Christian lower world was identified with the heathen lower world. Elysium, as well as Hades and Tartarus, was confounded with hell.

[5] This relation between the two chief demons of hell will also be found in Gil Vicente's Portuguese play, *Historia de Deos*, of the sixteenth century. The *Praxis cabulæ nigræ Doctoris Johannis Fausti* of 1612, one of the many books of magic ascribed to Faust, mentions Belial as viceroy. But in many books of magic of the sixteenth century, Mephistopheles is called the vice-regent of Lucifer over all other infernal spirits.

likewise named as ruler of hell. Dante, in his *Inferno*, places Dis, the Western equivalent of Pluto, at the head of hell. Pluto appears as the monarch of the nether world also in the puppet-plays of Faust.

According to Jewish tradition, Samael is the chief of the infernal spirits, always having held undisputed sway and having never been replaced by Satan, Beelzebub, Lucifer or any of the lesser lights of hell.

In Arabian mythology, Eblis, the former Azazel, is the leader of the hosts of hell, while in rabbinic mythology, Azazel is not the king of the demons, but their viceroy.

Many systems of the infernal government constructed by the cabalists of the sixteenth and seventeenth centuries placed the supremacy of hell in the hands of Belial.

If we put faith in the words of Asmodeus, the hero of LeSage's novel already mentioned, hell is ruled by a triumvirate composed of Ashtaroth, Belphegor and Leviathan.

The belief in the four infernal chiefs, held by many demonologists, is based on the description in the Revelation of St. John of the four angels who hold the four winds, and to whom is given the power to afflict the earth (vii. 1). In connection with this passage, St. Augustine taught that the word "angel" is equally applicable to good and to bad spirits. Four devils were *sine qua non* in the medieval mystery-plays. This scenic incident explains the French expression *faire le diable à quatre* (to act as four devils would act).[6] According to the teachings of demonology, four angels were set over the quarters of the world prior to the Fall, and it was the "Prince of the East" who rebelled, and to whom the other half of the universe was henceforth closed, so that he became the "prince of this (*i.e.* Eastern) world" (John xii. 31, xiv. 30, xvi. 11). In the Faust-book (ch. xiii), Lucifer likewise rules in the Orient Marlowe, therefore, calls him "Prince of the East" (v. 104), although the same term in its Latin form ("Orientis princeps") is also applied in *Dr. Faustus* to Beelzebub (iii. 17). In other magical works, Amoyon is mentioned as king of the East, and Goap is designated as "Prince of the West." Beelzebub rules "in Septentrione," according to the Faust-book (ch. xiii). *Friar Bacon and Friar Bungay* by Robert Greene (c. 1589) gives to Asmenoth the titles of "guider" and "ruler of the North" (ix. 144 and xi. 109).

[6] Cf. A. Fabre: *Etudes sur la Basoche*, p. 248. A French revolutionary paper, which was founded in 1869, bore the title *le Diable à quatre*.

Reginald Scot, in his *Discoverie of Witchcraft* (1584), however, calls Zizimar "the lordly monarch of the North."[7]

The system of the infernal hierarchy constructed by the writers on magic in the seventeenth century considers hell as ruled by six chiefs, to whom must answer seven "electors" or grand dukes. The pseudo-Faust conjuration-book previously mentioned contains a full roster of the government officials of hell, listing Lucifer as king, Belial as viceroy, Satan, Beelzebub, Astaroth and Pluto as "gubernatores" of Gehenna, and Aniguel, Anizel, Ariel, Aziel, Barfael, Marbuel and Mephistopheles as the seven "electors." The seven archdemons, whom we also find in Leconte de Lisle's pseudo-medieval fantasy *Smarh* (1839), match the seven archangels in the enemy's camp, first mentioned in the Book of Enoch. Thus seven is a mystic number, even where infernal matters are concerned.[8]

The "kingdom of perpetual night" (*Richard III* I. iv. 47) contains many other throned, crowned and sceptered spirits. The directory of the devils reads, in fact, like the pages of the *Almanach de Gotha*. We find in it kings, princes, dukes, marquises, earls, counts, viscounts, barons, knights, presidents, and other civil and military officials. Among the diabolical dignitaries the following may be pointed out: Bel and Pluto, princes of fire; Moloch, prince of the country of tears; Eurymone, prince of death; Pan, prince of the *incubi* (Jean Bodin's *la Démonomanie des sorciers*, 1580); Agares, first duke under the power of the East; Leraie and Sabnac, marquises; Morax, a great earl and president; Marbas, a great president; Jupiter, Neptune, and Antichrist, barons (Huon de Méri's *Tournoiement d'Antechrist*, 1235).

The only order of knighthood which appears to exist among the demons of hell is the Order of the Fly founded by Beelzebub. The decoration of the Grand Cross of the Order of the Fly is bestowed for signal services to Satan. Among the demons who have received this much coveted distinction are Adramelech, Baal, Eurymone, Leviathan and Moloch.

* * *

The court of the infernal monarch is in its splendor second to none held by the rulers of this earth. The king of hell, clad in a

[7] This book, from which much of the information summarized in this paper has been taken, contains a regular muster-roll or army list of the infernal government in the sixteenth century. Collin de Plancy, in his *Dictionnaire infernal* (1818), offers later data on this subject.

[8] Cf. Friedrich von Adrian: *Die Siebenzahl im Geistesleben der Völker*. Wien, 1901.

flowing red robe, is seated on a throne of diamonds and holds the scepter of hell in his right hand. His daughters, as princesses of hell, sit on lower thrones on both sides of their father, wear sparkling crowns on their heads and hold scepters of gold in their hands (Chateaubriand's *les Martyrs,* 1809). Royalty is highly respected at the court of the infernal monarch. The crowned heads of this earth are received in hell with great ceremonies.

Johannes Wierus has presented us with a partial list of the demons attached to the royal court of Gehenna. Chemos holds the post of grand chamberlain in hell, and Verdelet is grand master of ceremonies. The banker at the *baccarat* table in the infernal casino is Asmodeus, and the manager of the court theater of hell is Kobal. The great juggler and romancer is Antichrist, and the court-fool is Nybbas, whom the German demonologist calls "the great parodist." Rimmon is chief physician to his Infernal Lowness. Behemoth fulfils the function of grand cup-bearer, while the principal *valet de chambre* to his Satanic Majesty is Mullin. The grand almoner and master of the pantry is Dagon; the chief cook in the hellish kitchen is Misroch. The captain of the eunuchs, in the harem of the infernal sultan, is Succor-Benoth.

According to Wierus, the cabinet of the government of Gehenna is composed as follows: Adramelech is grand chancellor of the lower world. Baal-Berith is master of alliances (corresponding probably to a modern minister of foreign affairs) and secretary and keeper of the archives of hell. Astaroth is grand treasurer, while Melshom is assistant treasurer and disburser of the public moneys. Moloch is general-in-chief of the Satanic army, and Baal is second in command of the fighting forces of the dread domain of darkness. Leviathan is admiral of the infernal navy.[9] Lucifer is grand judiciary and minister of justice. Nergal is chief of police in the Principality of the Pit. Pluto is the superintendent of the infernal punishments, and Alaster holds the distinguished office of executioner. Marbuel is chief engineer and superintendent of all public buildings in the underworld. The supervision of the fortifications in the infernal regions is entrusted to Sabnac. Leonard is grand master of the Witches' Sabbaths and inspector-general of magic and sorcery. Demogorgon is master of the fates. Barfael holds the

[9] This statement must be erroneous inasmuch as water is an unknown element in the lower regions. In fact, the Kingdom of Nether Darkness has no more navy than Switzerland. Byron calls Leviathan "master of the oceans without shores and of the humid universe" (*Heaven and Earth,* 1822).

secret of the philosopher's stone. Asmodeus is superintendent of the gambling houses, and Nybbas has the management of dreams and visions on earth.

Although the different duties connected with the administration of hell are thus distributed among a number of demons, the holder of one portfolio will often persist in interfering with the department of another minister. The demons, in fact, constantly thrust their claws wherever they are not wanted, to the great detriment of each other's projects. But, naturally enough, this interference accrues to the benefit of man.

*　*　*

The ruler of hell holds occasional receptions for his demons, to hear their opinions on matters of state and to listen to the reports of their recent achievements on his behalf. The source for the parliament of devils is the Descensus Christi ad Inferos, which forms the second part of the Evangelium Nicodemi (3rd cent.). In the account of this apocryphal gospel, Christ's descent to hell is followed by a session of Satan's sanhedrin called for the purpose of devising ways and means for the repopulation of hell after the delivery from limbo of our first parents and the other patriarchs and prophets of the Old Testament. The Harrowing of Hell, with its subsequent infernal council, formed an important part of the medieval mystery plays. The deliberations of the infernal deputies are also recorded by Wynkyn de Worde in his metrical tract entitled *The Parlement of Devils* (1509). A council of infernal peers is likewise found in Boccaccio's *Filocopo* (1381-8) and in Jerome Vida's *Christiad* (1535). Tasso, Milton and Chateaubriand present us also with a "Pandemonium."[10]

Democratic freedom of speech and discussion prevails at the infernal council. Its members conduct themselves as gentlemen and reason as accomplished statesmen. A disturbance may sometimes occur during the session of the infernal parliament, but not oftener than in the chamber of deputies of any European government. The accounts of frequent Tartarean tumults are pieces of propaganda directed against the government of Gehenna by its enemies. If the

---

[10] Professor Olin H. Moore, in his interesting paper "The Infernal Council" (*Modern Philology*, vol. XVI, pp. 169-93), has traced the development of the infernal council from Claudian and the Gospel of Nicodemus through Robert de Boron, Boccaccio, Sannazaro, Vida, and Tasso to Milton. The parliament assembled by Henry VI at Coventry, in 1459, was called the Devil's Parliament because it passed attainders on the Duke of York and his chief supporters.

diabolical deputies cannot always control themselves in council, let us not be too harsh with them, but remember what Byron said: "Even saints sometimes forget themselves in session" (*The Vision of Judgment*, li).

Chateaubriand, in his novel·*les Martyrs* already mentioned, pictures a disturbance during a session of the infernal council and calls upon the Lord, who, in the eyes of this royalist and Romanist, permits no disorder in the lower as well as the upper regions, to restore harmony among the spirits of darkness. "A terrible conflict would have resulted," he tells us, "if God, who maintains justice and is the author of all order, even in hell, had not ended the turmoil" (*ibid.*, ch. viii).

The infernal council, with its variety of horns, forms a very respectable and cosmopolitan company. We find among its members Adonis, Astarte, Beelzebub, Belial, Chemos, Dagon, Mammon, Moloch, Rimmon and Tammuz of the Semitic races; Bali and Brahma of the Hindus; Mithra of the Persians; Anubis, Osiris, Isis and Horus of the Egyptians; Apollo and Iris of the Greeks; Vulcan and Neptune of the Romans; Erminsul and Odin of the Scandinavians; and Dis and Teutates of the Gauls. Many of the pagan gods are thus seen to be gathered in this deliberative assembly.

The Kingdom of hell has representatives in all parts of the earth. Wierus presents us with a list of the infernal embassies and the countries to which each is assigned. Belphegor is the accredited ambassador from the infernal regions in France, Hutgin in Italy, Belial in Turkey, Thamuz (or Tharung) in Spain, Martinet in Switzerland, Mammon in England and Rimmon in Russia. Wierus, as physician to the Duke William of Cleves in Westphalia, did not care to admit that any of the German states would entertain diplomatic relations with the court of hell.

Berbiguier de Terre-Neuve du Thym, author of a very curious and voluminous work *les Farfadets, ou Tous les demons ne sont pas de l'autre monde* (1795), maintains that each great devil of hell has also a human representative on earth. The mandatories of the infernal spirits among men are too numerous to mention. Among them will be found Nicolas, a physician of Avignon, who represents Moloch; Bouge, who represents Pluto; Pinel, a physician of the Salpêtrière, who represents Satan; and Moreau, magician and sorcerer of Paris, who represents Beelzebub on earth.

But to return to hell.

Each craft and class among men has a special representative among the infernal spirits. If we are to believe Asmodeus, LeSage's limping imp of hell, Lucifer is the patron of mountebanks and other kinds of scoundrels. Beelzebub, according to the testimony of this arch-bohemian, is the demon "of governesses and gentlemen-ushers or waiting-men." Uriel, Asmodeus also maintains, is the patron of "traders, tailors, butchers, and other third-rate thieves." Marbuel, in the opinion of certain demonologists, is the patron of artisans. It is this devil who assists poor architects and mechanics to carry out their contracts and often to accomplish work that is beyond ordinary human skill. Atoti, according to *Maler* Müller, is the demon of literary men, and Babillo is the patron of painters. The Devil's friendship for artists, particularly painters, is too well known to require further comment.

Martinet is the master of the magicians. Hermes is the patron of alchemists, who practise the "hermetic" arts. Kobal is the companion of the comedians. Leviathan is the demon of the diplomats. Zamiel is the patron of archers and hunters in general.

Flagel, according to LeSage's Asmodeus, is the patron of men of law. He is "the soul of the law and the life of the bar. . . . It is he who makes out the attorneys' and bailiffs' writs; he inspires the pleaders, possesses the jury and attends the judges." Griffael, this demon affrms, is the companion of the court-clerks. It is wholly in the spirit of popular belief that the lawyers should select for their patron the Devil, who is known as the father of lies. Indeed, many legends go to show that the lawyer is more unscrupulous in robbing his neighbors than the Devil himself.[11] The tavern of the lawyers at No. 2 Fleet Street, London, was called "The Devil." When the lawyers in the neighborhood left for dinner, they hung a notice on their doors: "Gone to the Devil" so that those who wanted them might know where to find them.[12]

* * *

An atmosphere of unadulterated industry prevails in hell. Industry is, in fact, the great virtue of the demons. Diligence, it has

[11] Cf. Archer Taylor: "The Devil and the Advocate" in the *Publications of the Modern Language Association of America,* vol. XXXVI (1921), pp. 35-59. Dr. O. A. Wall, in his book *Sex and Sex Worship* (1919), also has several items on the popular belief in the alliance betwen the Devil and the lawyer.

[12] A pleasant account of the Devil's Tavern in London will be found in John Timbs's *Clubs and Club Life in London* (1873).

been said, is the crowning quality with which man has invested the devil of his dreams. "If we were all as diligent and conscientious as the Devil," observed an old Scotch woman to her minister, "it wad be muckle better for us." Anatole France assures us that "the Devil never tires," and in a medieval Italian play entitled *Brighellas* Satan says: "I am so busy that I cannot find time to scratch myself." The only object of the unceasing activity among the infernal spirits is to lead men to evil.

A specialization and division of labor seems to exist in hell. The distribution of labor among the demons is carried out with great precision. Each of them is given his allotted or enforced task. The functions of the various hellish agents parallel the rôles of the angels. As the latter specialize in their virtues, so the former particularize in their vices. Each evil deed is assigned to its special representative. The various misdeeds cultivated by the hellish specialists range from prattling in church to arson and murder. Such crimes as Sabbath-breaking, making music, attending the theater, and dancing also are included.

Asmodeus is called "prince of lechery" in *Friar Rush,* a romance of the sixteenth century. Baal, in the French medieval mysteries, is the demon of idleness, and Baal-Berith the demon of disobedience. Beelzebub is termed "prince of envy" in *Friar Rush.* He also has pride among his vices. Behemoth, in the French medieval mysteries, is the demon of despair. Belial is generally considered the demon of revolt and anarchy. Belphegor is the demon of international rivalry and enmity. Chemos is the spirit of flattery. Esau-Samael is, in Jewish mythology, the source of strife. Federwisch is the German demon of vanity. Hoberdidance, Hobbididance and Hop-dance are names given by Harsnett and Shakespeare to the dancing demon. Kränzlein is the German demon of obscenity and immorality. Lästerlein is the German demon of theft and robbery. Lucifer is called "prince of gluttony" in *Friar Rush.* Mammon is the demon of wealth and greed (Matt. vi. 24). Nahema is the demoness of debauchery and abortion. Nisroch is the demon of hatred and fatality. Rosenkranz is a *confrère* of Kränzlein. Ruffo is also a demon of robbery. Schönspiegel shares with Federwisch the vice of vanity. Schorbrandt is the German demon of discord and conflict. Succor-Benoth is the demon of jealousy. Sydragasum is the demon "who makes the girls dance all naked" (Victor Hugo: *Notre-Dame de Paris,* X, iii). Tutevillus is the demon of church gossip. Urnell, in the German medieval mysteries, is the demon of drunkenness.[13]

Tutevillus is among the most tenacious and ubiquitous demons of hell. It is his duty to attend all church services in order to listen to the gossips and to write down their speeches, with which these women are later entertained in hell. It is related that one fine Sunday morning this demon was sitting in a church on a beam, on which he held himself fast by his feet and his tail, right over two village gossips, who chattered so much during the Blessed Mass that he soon filled every corner of his parchment on both sides. Poor Tutevillus worked so hard that the sweat ran in great drops down his black brow, and he was ready to sink with exhaustion. But the gossips ceased not to sin with their tongues, and he had no fair parchment left whereon to record further their foul words. So having considered for a little while, he grasped one end of the roll with his teeth and seized the other end with his claws and pulled hard in order to stretch the parchment. He tugged and tugged with all his strength, jerking back his head mightily at each tug, and at last giving such a fierce jerk that he suddenly lost his balance and fell head over heels from the beam to the floor of the church.[14]

This legend runs counter to the popular belief that the demons avoid holy edifices and have a mortal fear of the sound of the church bells, the ringing of which, according to Sir James Frazer, originally had for its aim to drive away devils and witches. In Edgar Allan Poe's story, "The Devil in the Belfry" (1839), an imp of hell was not afraid of invading the church tower. The Devil, in Alphonse Daudet's story, "les Trois messes basses" (1869), not only enters the church, but even performs the duties of a clerk at the foot of the altar in order to tempt the priest, during the reading of the masses, with thoughts of food and drink. Thus it is seen that man can find no safety even in sacred edifices against Satan's snares.

[13] For a full list of the vices over which the demons presided in medieval German belief, the reader is referred to the present writer's monograph *Der Teufel in den deutschen geistlichen Spielen des Mittelalters und der Reformationszeit* (Göttingen, 1915), pp. 98-103.

[14] This legend has been incorporated by Mr. Francis Oscar Mann in his story "The Vision of Saint Simon of Blewberry," which will be found in his work, *The Devil in a Nunnery and Other Medieval Tales* (1914).

CHAPTER VIII

ASMODEUS, DANDY AMONG DEMONS

OF all the demons of distinction, Asmodeus has had the greatest fall in power and prestige. This Asmodeus, who has now become a laughing-stock, was in his day, on the authority of Anatole France, our great contemporary diabolist, "an important demon, more powerful than Ashtaroth, Cedon, Uriel, Beelzebub, Aborym, Azazel, Dagon, Magog, Magon, Isaacharum, Accaron, Orphaxat, or Beherith, who are nevertheless devils not to be despised."[1] Asmodeus, according to the demonologists, originally was a shining angel in heaven, and, after his fall, was counted among the most eminent personages in hell. In fact he was linked with Lucifer and the other luminaries of limbo. Medieval writers called him "Prince of Demons." In the opinion of Pope Gregory IX, Asmodi was the name under which the Devil was worshipped by the Stedingers of Friesland in the thirteenth century.

But if the demon Asmodeus is now treated by the Christians with derision, he is still in favor with the Jews, among whom he has enjoyed great popularity to this day. The sons of Israel speak of Satan with respect, but for Asmodeus they evince a warm affection. The mention of the Tempter of Job fills them with fear and trembling, but Asmodeus is their darling devil. King Ashmodaï, as this demon is popularly known among the Jewish masses, plays a prominent part in Jewish mythology. Many legends have been woven by the rabbis around this "king of the shedhim," the demons who are the offspring of fallen angels and human mothers.[2]

[1] Anatole France: "M. Maurice Bouchor et l'Histoire de Tobie," le Temps, December 8, 1899. Reprinted in la Vie littéraire, 3me série (1891), pp. 218-28. Quotations in this paper are taken from the English translation, On Life and Letters, 3rd series (1924), pp. 214-27.

[2] The shedhim, according to Talmudic tradition, are the demons who came from the union of the sons of heaven and the daughters of the earth, whereas the satanim are the fallen angels themselves. Samaël is regarded by the Talmud as the head of the latter group of demons.

Asmodeus himself, according to one Jewish tradition, is a *shed,* being the child of Shamdon, a fallen angel, and of Naamah, the sister of Tubal-Cain.[3] According to another Jewish tradition, however, he is the son of Samaël and Lilith.

The Jews claim Asmodeus as their own. The truth of the matter is that they borrowed him from the Persians during their captivity under Zoroastrian kings. Asmodeus is no other than Aêshma daêva who, in the Persian religion, is the personification of violent wrath and carnal lust. In *Friar Rush,* a romance of the sixteenth century, this demon is called "Prince of Lechery." In popular belief, he is the prince of pleasures, the patron of passions, and the lord of luxury and lust. LeSage, in his novel, *le Diable boiteux* (1707), has Asmodeus say himself, "I am the demon of lewdness, or to put it more splendidly, the god Cupid." This devil is sensuality in person.[4] In this capacity, he is the counterpart of Lilith, the demoness with the long golden hair. Just as Lilith is dangerous to men, so is Asmodeus dangerous to women. This danger to women from Asmodeus is due to the fact that he is the greatest dandy among the devils. For the Devil is most fascinating to fastidious women when he patronizes a good tailor.

Asmodeus, in addition to the qualities already mentioned, is also the father of new fads and fashions in dress, namely, the demon of frills and finery.[5] He is so fashionable that Calmet, the French demonologist of the eighteenth century, believed that the name Asmodeus signified fine dress.[6] This demon's beautiful clothes and fine manners represent the "pride of life" in Christian symbolism.

In this connection, the story told by Henry Stubbes, in his *Anatomie of Abuses* (1583), as a warning against the fashionable folly of starched ruffs, which prevailed in his day, will be of interest. According to this tale, there lived in Antwerp in 1582 a lady with a passion for dresses, the ruffs of which her washerwomen

[3] Cf. Louis Ginzberg: *The Legends of the Jews* (4 vols., Philadelphia, 1909-25), I, 150-51.

[4] This is the reason why Marcel Barrière named his highly sensual novel, *le Sang d'Asmodée* (1924).

[5] In Jewish mythology it is Azazel who has devised the cosmetics and jewelry, with which women attract men; cf. Louis Ginzberg, *op. cit.,* I, 125.

[6] Dom Augustin Calmet: *Dissertations sur les apparitions des anges, des démons et des esprits, sur les revenants et les vampires de Hongrie, de Bohème, de Moravie et de Silésie, Paris,* 1746. English translation (*The Phantom World; or, the History and Philosophy of Spirits and Apparitions*), 2 vols., London and Philadelphia, 1850.

could never succeed in starching to her satisfaction. One day in a rage she flung the starched ruffs to the ground, swearing that the Devil might take her if she wore such things again. Straightway in came the Devil himself in the guise of an elegant young man, holding out to her a beautiful ruff which he offered to adjust for her. Having done this to the great satisfaction of the lady, he wrung her neck.[7]

* * *

Asmodeus is primarily a ladies' demon. He tempts and torments especially the members of the fair sex. When he tries to bring men to fall, he employs women as his accomplices. "It is in this," says Anatole France, in the essay on Bouchor already quoted, "that his power lies in this world, especially among the white peoples." Asmodeus is the Don Juan among the devils. The story of his love-affairs would fill volumes. To attempt only to give the names of the ladies with whom he had a *liaison* would be beyond the powers even of the Recording Angel. This demon is often called the genius of matrimonial unhappiness. He is very cosmopolitan in his love-affairs, and disregards all tribal and ecclesiastical distinctions.

Tradition has it that Asmodeus plied Noah and Solomon with wine and seduced their wives. It is further recorded in the Book of Tobit (vi. 14) that this demon loved to distraction the beautiful Sarah, daughter of Raguel, and, out of jealousy, successively slew seven men to whom she was married as soon as each had entered the nuptial chamber. Asmodeus, you must know, is a fastidious devil and will not allow the object of his passions to be exposed to the embrace of any other person, terrestrial or infernal. His menace to newlyweds is, moreover, due to the fact that he maintains for himself a kind of *jus primæ noctis*. He claims this right probably as a reward for his successful efforts in obtaining from the Church the

---

[7] This story may have formed the subject of the play, *Friar Rush and the Proud Woman of Antwerp*, written by Haughton and Day and mentioned by Henslowe on July 1, 1601; cf. Robert Dodsley: *A Select Collection of Old Plays* (12 vols., 2nd ed., London, 1744-80), I, 192. Professor Schelling, in "Some Features of the Supernatural as Represented in Plays of the Reigns of Elizabeth and James," *Modern Philology*, I (1903-4), 31-47, has put erroneously Amsterdam for Antwerp. Of interest in this connection is an old Breton legend, representing the Devil as a tailor. This legend was dramatized, in 1894, by Louis Ciercelin and published with the title *le Diable couturier*.

sacramental inclusion of marriage.[8]   Raphael finally smoked him
out of Sarah's chamber by the smell of fish-liver so that the angel's
friend Tobias, who also loved Sarah, could marry her.   Asmodeus,
it should be mentioned, has delicate nostrils and cannot stand bad
odors.   The demon fled from the "fishy fume" to Upper Egypt with
Raphael hot on his heels, and was finally bound by the angel in a
cavern on the Nile, where the unfortunate demon long remained
(Tob. viii. 3).[9]

> "For he was still there in 1707 [says Anatole France in
> the essay on Bouchor already quoted], when a Rouen gold-
> smith called Paul Lucas, going up the Nile to Fayoum,
> saw and spoke to him, as he assures us in the story of his
> voyage, which was published in 1719, and forms three vol-
> umes in 12mo with maps and drawings.   Few facts are
> better attested.   None the less, this fact is embarrassing.
> For it is certain, on the other hand, that he was in Loudun
> on the 29th day of May, 1624; as he wrote on that day, in
> the register of the Church of Sainte-Croix, a declaration
> by which he engaged himself to torment Mme de Belciel,
> whom, in fact, he did torment.   The document is preserved
> in the Bibliothèque Nationale, in the department of manu-
> scripts, where anyone may use it.   It is equally certain that
> in 1635, in the same town of Loudun, he possessed Sister
> Agnes, who was seized with convulsions in the presence of
> the Duke of Orleans.   She refused to kiss the pyx, and
> twisted herself so that she formed a perfect circle, her
> hands touching her feet.   Meanwhile she uttered horrible
> blasphemies.[10]   At this period Asmodeus appeared before
> the Bishop of Poitiers; and as Paul Lucas found him in
> Egypt, it must be supposed that the devil left his cavern
> whenever he pleased, and that the angel Gabriel (sic) did
> not tie him up well. . . .
> "After Colbert's edict forbidding devils to torment
> ladies, Asmodeus appeared in France only in the excellent
> company of LeSage, the author of Gil Blas.   Asmodeus

[8] Mephistopheles in Marlowe's Dr. Faustus (ii.1), on the other hand, is
opposed to marriage.

[9] Maurice Bouchor, who, in 1889, has dramatized this story, has not taken
the jealous Asmodeus very seriously.

[10] Anatole France has reference to the famous episode of the Devils of
Loudun, in which the priest Urbain Grandier was accused of having handed
over the Ursuline nuns to the demons.   This very interesting case of diabolical
possession in modern times was treated by Alfred de Vigny in his romance,
Cinq-Mars (1826).   See also [Aubin:] Histoire des diables de Loudun, ou de
la Possession des religieuses Ursulines et de la condemnation et du supplice
d'Urbain Grandier, curé de la même ville (Amsterdam, 1716).   A popular essay
on "The Devils of Loudun" appeared in the National Review, XI (1860), 70-93

lost his theology here, but he became a man of wit. He
was then playing a rather low game, but it was at least a
cheerful one."

The work to which Anatole France refers in this passage is
LeSage's already quoted book, *le Diable boiteux*. In this novel, a
young Spanish student from Alcala, named Don Cleophas Leandro
Zambullo, for whom, on a certain evening, an ambush was laid by
his perfidious mistress, escapes by jumping from roof to roof until
he lands in a neighboring garret, which happens to be the laboratory
of a magician. Upon entering this garret, he is besought by a voice
out of a phial to deliver the speaker from durance by breaking the
glass-bottle. The request is complied with, and the imprisoned sprite
turns out to be Asmodeus. In gratitude, the demon bestows upon
his rescuer the power to sail through the air, and brings him upon
the tower of the Church of San Salvador in Madrid. From this
vantage-point, by lifting the roofs of all the houses of the Spanish
capital with a sign from his right hand, he shows the student the
secret sights of a big city at midnight. With a cynical amusement
the demon then explains to his friend the sufferings, transports and
agitations thus revealed. The new confederates also journey to the
different parts of Spain. The good-natured and grateful Asmodeus
assists the student Cleophas in his various pranks and carries him
triumphantly through a series of amusing adventures. He even
takes the shape of his human companion in rescuing a young lady
of high birth and thereby procures for his liberator a prosperous
marriage. In the end, Asmodeus is recaptured and put back into
the phial by the powerful conjurer with the help of envious demons.

In this novel, Asmodeus shows himself an excellent critic of
men and morals, and a splendid satirist of the follies and foibles of
the human family. As a result of this feat, he became very popular
in France and even in other countries. His friends imposed upon
him and had him lift the roof of every house for them so that they
might see the life that went on within. He was called upon so
often to perform the job of roofer, or still better, of unroofer, that,
as it was said, "he was not even given the time to get dressed."

Through this novel, Asmodeus won a respectable position in
French literature, and his resulting renown did much to bring
about in France the friendly feeling for the Fiend which has long
been a marked characteristic of the literature of that country. A
great number of books, periodicals and newspapers have gained

popularity through this demon's name for half a century following the publication of LeSage's novel.[11]

*

* *

Asmodeus has many other accomplishments and achievements to his credit. He is also a scholar, the most learned master of arts and the most prominent professor at his alma mater, the astrological college founded by the fallen angels Asa and Asael. Asmodeus is versed in the black arts and well known for his occult wisdom. In this quality, he is the successor to Thoth, the god of wisdom and learning in Thermopolis, who was identified by the Egyptians with Sirius, the god of occult and infernal arts.

Asmodeus is also a great philosopher, deriving his ideas from the various schools of thought. "Asmodeus is the very philosophy of all ages summed up in a caricature," says Jules Janin, the French dramatic critic.

Asmodeus also has a reputation for slyness and subtlety. In fact he is the most cunning spirit of hell (Goethe's *Faust* ii. 6961). This demon cheated Aladdin out of his ring in order to secure the magic lamp, and he also tricked Solomon out of his signet ring in order to obtain possession of the latter's harem. The Jewish monarch had great need of Asmodeus when he built the temple at Jerusalem. He wished to learn from this versatile demon the whereabouts of the worm *Shamir*, which splits and shapes stones noiselessly.[12] During their negotiations, the wisest of men and the wisest

[11] Among the books named after Asmodeus, mention may be made of S. Foote's farce *The Devil on Two Sticks* (1768); *Asmodeus; or, The Devil in London* (3 vols., London, 1808); William Combe: *The Devil Upon Two Sticks in England* (6 vols., London, 1817); and *Asmodeus in New York, or, Society and Manners in Gotham* (New York, 1868). Among the periodicals which bore his name, may be mentioned the following: *le Diable boiteux; journal critique et littéraire* (1810-1826); *le Diable boiteux; recueil politique et littéraire* (1818); *Asmodée*, a satirical periodical founded by the poet Louis Berthaud in Lyons in 1833; *le Diable boiteux; journal politique, véridique, charivarique*, a review started in 1848; *le diable boiteux à l'assemblée nationale*, a journal founded likewise in 1848 by Ch. Tondeur to report the deliberations of the French deputies; *le Diable boiteux*, which ran as a "feuilleton littéraire" in the *Journal des spectacles, des mœurs, des arts et des modes* from 1823 to 1825; *Asmodée à New York; revue critique des institutions politiques et civiles de l'Amérique; vie publique et privée, mœurs, coutumes, anecdotes romanesques*, etc. (Paris, 1868).

[12] Cf. Louis Ginzberg, *op. cit.*, IV. 166 ff.

of demons fought many a duel of wits. Asmodeus propounded difficult questions which Solomon was able to answer only with the help of his ring. The demon then tempted the king to lay aside the ring. He taunted Solomon with the challenge that all his wisdom lay in his ring and that he would be but an ordinary mortal without it. Solomon, being piqued into a denial and proudly thinking that he could answer the demon's questions by his unaided intelligence, rashly removed the ring. But the demon seized it, and, having by its might metamorphosed the monarch beyond recognition and transported him four hundred miles away, he himself assumed the appearance of Solomon, and for three years resided in the royal seraglio. According to this tradition, Asmodeus was the real author of the offences which history ascribes to the Jewish king. Solomon, after a long vagrancy, became the cook of the king of Amon. One day, as he was dressing a fish for dinner, he found in it the ring which Asmodeus had thrown into the sea, and with its aid he recovered from the demon his throne and his harem. As a punishment Solomon imprisoned Asmodeus together with many other demons in a bottle of black glass, which he cast into a deep well near Babylon. But the Babylonians, hoping to find a treasure in this well, descended into it, broke the bottle, and thus liberated the demons.[13]

Asmodeus is, moreover, the diabolic patron of letters and arts and even has literary aspirations himself. In his modesty, he refuses to publish anything under his own name, but he has helped many another writer. Among the great authors who owe their inspiration to this demon, we will mention Boccaccio, who is said to have composed his *Decameron* from the dictation of this demon, who thus wished to take his revenge on the monks, who maligned him.

But Asmodeus with all his learning has remained a play-boy. He is, in fact, an arch-Bohemian, a charlatan, a juggler and a mountebank. Asmodeus played a prominent part in the deviltry of the Middle Ages and charmed our ancestors with his tricks and antics.

Asmodeus is also addicted to gaming and card-playing. According to Johannes Wierus, the famous German demonologist, he is the banker at the *baccarat* table in the casino of hell and the superintendent of gambling houses on earth.

[13] Cf. Moncure Daniel Conway: *Solomon and Solomonic Literature.* Chicago, 1899.

In brief, Asmodeus is the most energetic of all demons. He is, as he himself claims in the already quoted LeSage's novel, "the liveliest and the most laborious devil in hell." Asmodeus explains his profession in this book as follows: "I arrange ridiculous marriages; I unite gray-beards with minors, masters with servants, and ill-dowered girls with tender lovers who have no fortune. I am he that introduced into society extravagance, debauchery, games of chance, and chemistry. I am the inventor of tournaments, dances, music, comedy, and the new French fashions. . . ." But the foregoing list by no means exhausts the multitudinous and various tasks of our demon, who has all the world for his province.

Asmodeus is also the most sympathetic of all the demons of hell. He is the most engaging of friends, ready to lend a hand when man is at the end of his natural resources. Shakespeare was very fond of him, and called him Modo for short.

Asmodeus has a very pleasing personality and is as beautiful as Apollo. But he has one physical defect. He limps slightly with one foot. The demonologists say that he may be recognized by the fact that one of his limbs is like a cock's leg. The other is normal, but provided with claws. In LeSage's novel, Asmodeus appears walking with the aid of two sticks, which support will account for the English title of the book, *The Devil on Two Sticks*. His portrait, drawn by Collin de Plancy, was approved by the Archbishop of Paris. But Anatole France, in the essay on Bouchor already mentioned several times, with good reason, doubts whether it is a faithful likeness. Whatever his proper shape may be, it is known that, in order to appear among men, he adopts various forms, all of which are engaging. His manners are always refined, and his conduct is that of a perfect gentleman. It may well be said that, through Asmodeus, the Devil has become perilously associated with wit and wisdom, gaiety and gallantry, *finesse* and **finery**.

CHAPTER IX

THE LEGEND OF LILITH

THE legend of Lilith is an intriguing revelation of old Semitic superstitions and persists to this very day in various forms. The personality of the Hebrew Lilith has been generally derived from the Babylonian-Assyrian Lilit, Lîlu or Lilitu, an evil spirit. As we shall see later, this personification was a sort of fusion of the Roman Lamia, the Greek *hetæra,* and the Turkish vampire. Belief in this demoness, growing up among the Jews during their Babylonian captivity, developed into a cult which lasted among the Jews of Mesopotamia down to the seventh century of our era. The Lilith legend is found only in the uncanonical works, although the word Lilith was already mentioned in pseudo-Isaiah. The earliest extant account of this legend is in the Alphabet of Ben Sira, but it was elaborated in the Talmud, the Targums and the Cabala.[1]

Biblical mention of Lilith occurs when depicting the scene of desolation among Edom's ruined fortresses, where "the wild beasts of the desert shall meet with the wolves, and the satyr shall cry to his fellow; *lilith* shall also settle there and find for herself a place of rest." (Is. xxxiv. 14.) This biblical reference is not to an animal, as might be supposed from the context. The translation of *lilith* in the Septuagint as "a tailless ape" and in the King James Version as "a screech owl" has been bitterly and justly assailed. Symmachus in his Greek translation and St. Jerome in his Latin translation of the Old Testament understood better the Hebrew meaning of the

[1] As for critical literature on the legend of Lilith, we will mention, in addition to the items listed later, the following: Bacher, "Lilith, Königin von Smaraged," *Monatsschrift für die Wissenschaft des Judentums,* XII 1870), 187-9; Adolf Waldauer, "Lilith," *Populär-wissenschaftliche Monatsblätter,* VI (1886), 248-50; Israel Lévi, "Lilith et Lilin," *Revue des études juives,* LXVIII (1914), 5-21. The reader will also find a chapter on Lilith in Karl Knortz's interesting book, *Hexen, Teufel und Blocksbergspuk in Geschichte, Sage und Literatur* (Annaberg, Sachsen, 1914), pp. 120-49.

word by rendering *lilith* as "night-monster." (Cf. "terror by night" in Psalms xci. 5.)

The fact is that the Hebrew word *lilith* is a feminine derivative of the Hebrew *lay'la* (Assyrian *leila*), which is the regular noun for "night." Thus Lilith was originally not a proper name but a general noun which signified "a daughter of the night" and designated any kind of monster in the form of woman who exercised her power for evil during darkness.[2] The mass of legends that gradually centered around a nocturnal monster in feminine form seems to have transformed her into a personality.

In Talmudic tradition Lilith is primarily a demoness who selects small children as her special victims. She is said to steal infants in the night and carry them off to the desert. The rabbinical writings depict this demoness as a terror to women at childbirth, whom she wishes to rob of their offspring. This specter, dressed in her finest raiment, is supposed to stand at the foot of the beds of lying-in women in order to snatch new-born babies from mothers' arms. However, this fiend in the form of woman can be fought with certain amulets, according to the Talmud. This accounts for the custom, prevailing to the present day among many orthodox Jews, of hanging an amulet, inscribed with the names of the angels Senoï, Sansenoï and Sanmangeloph around the child's neck at birth or of nailing "childbirth tablets," on walls or door-posts of the lying-in room in order to ward off Lilith's pernicious power over new-born children. Other Jews place in the chamber occupied by the new mother four coins with labels on which are inscribed the names of Adam and Eve accompanied by the words *"Avaunt thee, Lilith!"*

The hatred of Lilith for the children of men is, according to an old Jewish belief, the result of her jealousy of the mother of mankind, who replaced her in the affections of Adam and thus robbed her of the joys of motherhood. As is well depicted in poetry and painting, Lilith is represented in Jewish mythology as the first wife of Adam, whom she later abandoned and joined the demons. Another Jewish tradition has it that Lilith did not desert her human husband until after she had borne to him a host of demons, spirits and *lilin* (plural of *lilith*).[3] The Koran contains the screed that Lilith

[2] Alfred Kubin's *Dämonen und Nachtgesichte* (Dresden, 1926) contains a series of 128 fantastic illustrations of nocturnal visions, unapproached in modern art.

[3] The Hebrew word *lilin* is not a true plural of *lilith*. We would expect *lilitim* or *lilitos* as a plural. The word is in reality the masculine counterpart of *lilith* and denotes a male night-monster.

presented our common ancestor with a daughter named Zelinda the Fair, and that it was this half-sister whom Cain married. Anatole France, in "la Fille de Lilith" (1889), tells the story of another deathless daughter of Lilith, who envies her half-sisters, the daughters of Eve, and prays for the experience of death that she also may enjoy life, and for remorse that she too may know pleasure. The French author has the immortal but fatal maiden come up to earth and attach herself to a young Parisian, wherefore it requires the exorcisms of the curé Safrac to purify this modern Tannhäuser from his voluptuous relations.

Talmudic tradition has it that Lilith was created simultaneously with Adam, both being joined together at the back, for it is written "male and female created He them, and called their name Adam." (Gen. i. 27.) In this condition they constantly quarreled and tore at each other. Then the Lord repented that he had fashioned them in this way and separated them into two independent bodies; but even thus they would not live in peace. A mismated pair from the very start, their incompatability of temperament was too great for peace. Their views differed considerably on the all-important question of the headship of the family. Lilith was the first woman to challenge masculine supremacy. This *Mater malorum* is said to have started the fight for equal rights for women by contesting her husband's claim to be the head of the family. Adam began the first conversation with his bride by asserting that he was to be her master. Lilith replied that she had equal right to be the chief of the family. When she realized how hopelessly stubborn Adam was, she reached a decision similar to that of the end-of-the-nineteenth-century Nora in Ibsen's *Doll's House* (1879). She pronounced the *Shem hamephorash* (the Ineffable Name), the result of which was that she obtained wings with which she flew out of Eden and out of sight.

Adam, heart-broken over his loss of Lilith, cried in distress: "Master of the world, the woman whom Thou gavest me has flown away." The Creator then sent the three angels previously mentioned to find Lilith and persuade her to return to her husband and her hearth. She would not yield even after the angels had been sent again by the Lord to convey to her the doom that she would bear many children and that they should all die in infancy. Lilith considered the penalty so awful that she was about to put an end to her life by throwing herself into the sea. The three angels, moved by her anguish, agreed that she should have by way of compensation full power over all new-born boys during eight days after birth and over girls during twenty days after birth. In addition, she was given special power over all children born out of wedlock.

When Lilith refused to return to Adam, the second Eve (*i.e.* Mother) was now formed to compensate him for his first marital fiasco.[4] This time, however, the Lord created the woman out of man's rib in order that there might no longer be any question of her independence, and that the embarrassing problem of women's rights might never be raised again among men.[5] Evidently Jehovah with all his omniscience could not foresee the widespread suffragist movement of the present day.[6]

Samaël, chief of the fallen angels, one day found beautiful Lilith lamenting her errors in loneliness, and fell in love with her. As Lilith found Samaël radical on the question of the equality of sexes which she had raised in Eden, she accepted him, and the two settled in the Valley of Jehannum (Gehenna). As successor to Adam in the affections of Lilith, Samaël is also called in the Talmud Adam-Belial in distinction to Adam-Kadmon, our first ancestor.

Samaël found in his consort a willing conspirator against the Lord in the latter's plans for man and womankind. Lilith was jealous of Eve, who replaced her in the affections of her first husband, just as Samaël was jealous of Adam, who was destined to be his successor in the celestial choir-stalls. While the demonic pair were witnessing the pleasures of our common ancestors in Eden, they burned with envy and decided to bring man and woman to a downfall so that they would be driven out of the Garden of Eden. According to the Revelation of St. John, it was Samaël or Satan, who, disguised as a serpent, tempted Eve to disobey the Lord by eating of the forbidden fruit and thus brought upon herself and her husband the wrath of their Creator. A certain Christian tradition identifies the serpent of the Garden of Eden not with Samaël or

---

[4] The Jewish belief in the two wives of Adam is mentioned, among post-medieval Christian writers, by Robert Burton in his *Anatomy of Melancholy* (1621) and by Johann Albert Fabricius, who, in his *Codex Pseudoepigraphus Veteris Testamenti* (1713), states that two wives were created for Adam "quarum una ex luto extra paradisum, altera in paradiso ex costa condita faerit." The first is Lilith, the second is Eve.

[5] See M. D. Conway: *Demonology and Devil-Lore* (2 vols., London, 1879; 3rd ed., New York, 1889) II, 92 ff.

[6] By a curious coincidence, this chapter originally appeared in 1930, the tenth anniversary of the national law, constituting the Nineteenth Amendment, granting women equal political rights with men.

Satan but with Lilith, who thus was the main instigator in the fall
of our common ancestors. Dante Gabriel Rossetti, in his famous
poem "Eden Bower," follows this later tradition in ascribing the
temptation in Eden to this serpent-woman Lilith.

*   *

The idea of a "Devil's Dam" belongs wholly to Jewish tradition.
It is foreign to Christian thought. Church doctrine has it that the
Devil can have no wife, inasmuch as he is excluded from the sacrament of marriage. In compensation, Christianity has conferred
upon the Devil a mother or a grandmother. In the German secular
play of Pope Joan, written in 1480, Lilith appears, therefore, as the
Devil's grandmother. Victor Hugo, in *la Fin de Satan* (not published till 1886), identifies the Babylonian-Assyrian Lilith with the
Egyptian Isis and represents her not as Satan's wife or mother but
as Satan's daughter.

In addition to Lilith, who is his legal and lawful consort, Satan
has had many connubial connections. The four concubines given
the Devil by the Cabala are Nehema, Aggareth, Igymeth and
Machlath. Satan also had incestuous relations with his daughter
Sin, who, according to Milton, sprang full-blown from Satan's head,
even as Minerva sprang full-panoplied from Jupiter's head (*Par.
Lost* ii. 758). The fruit of this forbidden union is Death (*ibid.*, ii.
728 and 787.).

*   *

Samaël presented Lilith on their wedding-day with a splendid
kingdom where she was attended by four hundred and eighty troops.
But all the wealth and honors heaped upon her by her second husband failed to compensate her for her lack of children. She has
remained to this day the Lady of Sorrows. It is believed that her
voice of grief can be heard in the air at night, like that of Rachel
weeping over her children.

The grief of Lilith over the loss of her children from her first
marriage is more pronounced, since she was cursed by the Lord, who
decreed that her children by her second husband must all die in
infancy because she deserted her first husband.

According to another Jewish tradition, the Lord cursed Lilith,
for her refusal to return to Adam, to beget demons, and, during her
second marriage, she mothered a host of monsters. Asmodeus,
Leviathan, and indeed most devils of distinction, sprang from this

union. Lilith is represented by certain rabbis as giving birth to a brood of *zebub* or flies.[7] A second flock of children attributed to her by the Talmudists are the *succubi* or devils who normally retain the female form.

This parentage explains Lilith's hostility to new-born infants, for whom she lies in wait to snatch them into the desert. But Lilith may after all not be so black as she is painted. Her intention in visiting the lying-in rooms of mortal women is perhaps not to harm but to hug the babies. This fatal immortal, who has been denied the joys of motherhood, seeks to press to her heart the babies of the happier members of her sex. This supposition is supported by a certain Jewish belief to the effect that Lilith loves babies and plays with them in their sleep on the night of the Sabbath. It is written in the Talmud that, if a child smiles during the night of the Sabbath or the New Moon, it is a sign that Lilith is playing with it.

*
* *

The Legend of Lilith has had much charm for modern writers, both in poem and play, in song and story.[8]

Alfred de Vigny, in his fragment "Lilith" (1859), offers us an original interpretation in that Lilith, the first incarnation of woman-kind, is an impersonation of sensuality and sterility. When Adam wearied of her and received Eve in her place, Lilith cursed the off-spring of the woman who replaced her in the affections of Adam and started on her journey across the ages to found the religion of murderers. Through her influence, the first-born child of her rival became assassin of his own brother.

Among modern dramatizations of this ancient legend, Remy de Gourmont's *Lilith* (1891-2) merits special mention. This play is the biblical story of the creation and fall of man retold in dramatic form with great skill by a sensual sceptic. The author fabricated the revolting scenes of his play from the legends recorded in the mystical writings of the Jews. In this play, Lilith, though created

---

[7] See R. P. Dow: "The Vengeful Brood of Lilith and Samaël," *Bulletin of the Brooklyn Entomological Society*, XII (1917), 1-9.

[8] The "Bibliography of Lilith," published by A. S. Freidus in the *Bulletin of the Brooklyn Entomological Society*, XII (1917), 9-12, contains a caption "Lilith in Modern Literature," to which the reader is referred. We will add the following titles unknown to this compiler: Edmund W. Putnam, *Lilith, Epos*, 1907; G. S. Viereck, "Queen Lilith" (in his *The Candle and the Flame*), 1912; Carl Macleod Boyle, *Where Lilith Dances*, 1920; Wilhelm Jensen, "Lilith" (in his *Gedichte*), 1869; Marcellus Emants, *Lilith*, 1879 (translated into German in 1895 by Anna Crons); Willem Kloos, *Lilith Trimphatrix* (translated into German by L. Hauser).

THE EXPULSION FROM PARADISE.
(By Doré)

by the Lord as Adam's helpmeet, never shared the bed and board of our common ancestor. She displeased her Creator by sensuality, which she asserted from the very moment of her birth, and for this reason she was handed over to Satan. As soon as this woman opened her eyes, she immediately asked to be led to man in order to satisfy her appetites. When the Lord announced to her that as a punishment she would never know man, she defiantly declared that woman always gained what she wished. Being banished to hell to keep company with the fallen angel, Lilith, not satisfied with the unfruitful caresses of her infernal husband, succeeded in seducing Adam at the moment when Satan soiled the mother of men in the form of a serpent.

This interpretation of the fall in Eden is based on an ancient Jewish tradition, which interprets the sin of our ancestors as sensuality. The Slavonic version of the Book of Enoch already states that Satan committed adultery with Eve. The Cabala, which also interprets the biblical story of the gastronomical temptation as an allegory, goes a step further and represents the sin of Adam and Eve as a twofold debauchery. The Zohar expressly states that Adam and Eve led a *ménage à quatre* with Samaël and Lilith. At the moment when the demon debauched the mother of mankind, the demoness offered her beauty to the founder of the human race. In another Cabalistic work, the demon is named Leviathan, and his consort is called Heva. Other mystical writings represent Leviathan as a sort of androgyny, of whom Samaël was the male incarnation and Lilith or Heva the female. From the illicit union of Adam and Lilith issued legions of larves, *succubi* and elemental spirits, who filled the earth in order to corrupt the human race but who will be annihilated at the end of time.

The story of Adam's domestic troubles has also been treated by Robert Browning in *Adam, Lilith and Eve* (1883), by George Bernard Shaw in *Back to Methusaleh* (1921), by André Spire in *Samaël* (1921), by John Erskine in *Adam and Eve* (1927), and by Murray Sheehan in *Eden* (1927).

*
* *

The fatal power of Lilith is not limited to new-born infants. She offers a greater danger to men, particularly in their youth. In Eastern tradition, Lilith, as princess of the *succubi,* is primarily a seductress of men. "Lilith," says Langdon, "is the Semitic name

" SATAN EXULTING OVER EVE."
A Blake in the Possesion of W. Bateson.

for the beautiful and licentious unmarried harlot who seduces men in streets and fields."[9]

Lilith was so beautiful, so overpowering in physical charms and intellectual gifts, that she was known everywhere in the Orient and came to be worshipped. It may be remarked in passing that a kind of Lilith-worship also existed in southern Europe during the seventh century, just as demon-worship has sporadically broken out in almost every European country and still exists today among the Yezidis of Asia Minor and among primitive tribes in other parts of the world.[10]

Eastern tradition declares that Lilith, the Queen of Hell, disguised as the Queen of Sheba, tempted Solomon with her beauty and wit.[11] If the wisest of men fell a victim to her charms, how can poor mortals resist? It is said in fact that no man ever escaped the siren seductions of this deviless. Her beauty has attracted countless poets and painters who vied with one another to draw her portrait.

Many indeed are the inspired poetical and pictorial representations of her infernal Majesty. Dante Gabriel Rossetti has, by both his arts, celebrated the beauty of this diabo-lady.[12] J. V. Widmann, in his poem, *Der Heilige und die Tiere* (1906), speaks in enthusiastic terms of the beauty of Lilith. The Spanish novelist, Emilio Carrere, has written a novel about her eyes (*los Ojos de la Diablesa*, 1913). But the remarkable thing about her person was her hair. Ben Sira states that Lilith was beautiful with long black hair. When Lilith arrived among the Nordics, she realized that gentlemen prefer blondes and so apparently dyed her hair. Rossetti, in his sonnet, "Lilith," describes her with golden locks. But in the meshes of her hair lurk a multitude of evil spirits. This demoness cannot be proud of her feet. But, as Anatole France has well remarked, she is clever enough to "hide her cloven hoof under a trailing skirt embroidered with pearls" (*le Jardin d'Epicure*, 1894).

[9] Cf. Stephen H. Langdon: *Tammuz and Ishtar* (Oxford, 1914), p. 74. Lilith originally was not a harlot, although the temple harlot often passed herself off in the darkness as a *lilitu*, a "night-lady." See Josephus: *Jewish Antiquities* (XVIII, iii. 4) for such tricks and for the popular credulity with regard to the cohabitation of gods with mortals.

[10] See the chapter "The Synagogue of Satan," p. 150.

[11] The kernel of the legend of the Queen of Sheba is in 1 Kings x. 1 ff. On this legend, consult J. Halévy: *la Légende de la Reine de Saba. (Annuaire de l'Ecole des Hautes Etudes. Section des Sciences historiques et philosophiques.)* Paris, 1905.

[12] On Rossetti's portrayal of Lilith, read Lafcadio Hearn's *Appreciations of Poetry* (New York, 1916), pp. 97-8.

Lilith has evidently not lost allurement through the centuries. Her fascinations still operate on all who behold her. Daniel Defoe had this devil-damsel in mind when he said, "A lady-devil is about as dangerous a creature as one could meet." Like all beautiful women, this "accursed damozel" has a heart of ice. She uses her golden hair to captivate the young men; and the youth who loves her always dies, and after his death a single hair is found twisted around his heart, as described in Rossetti's sonnet.

When Faust beheld Lilith in the Walpurgis Night, Mephistopheles warned him against her charms in the following words:

"Beware the lure within her lovely tresses,
The splendid sole adornment of her hair!
When she succeeds therewith a youth to snare,
Not soon again she frees him from her jesses."
(*Faust* i. 4120-23.)

According to certain demonologists, Lady Lilith has not been exempt from the law to which all flesh is subject. She, too, could not withstand the ravages of time. Although in her younger days a woman of great beauty, she has now become a regular hell-hag. No demon of hell is a match for her in ugliness and wickedness. This Lilith forms the subject of the poem entitled *The Diabo-Lady, or a Match in Hell,* which was written in England in 1777 and "dedicated to the Worst Woman in her Majesty's Dominions." Richard Garnett, in *Madam Lucifer* (1888), paints a very unflattering portrait of the King-Devil's better or bitter half, of whom, as he says, he is "a thousand times more afraid . . . than of all the saints in the calendar." Kornel Makuszynski, in *Another Paradise Lost and Regained* (1926), represents Satan's spouse as a regular shrew, a monument of ancient art, as her husband humorously calls her.

* * *

In every legend there is some bit of eternal verity. What is there symbolic in this Lilith legend; how is it to be appraised and interpreted? Evidently Lilith as the first wife of Adam is the symbol of "first love remembered." It is a well-known fact that a man rarely marries the first woman he has loved whether in reality or in reverie. Lilith represents the ideal woman of man's dreams. She is every man's dream-wife, in a word, perfection in petticoats. Each of us has in his heart, as Flaubert has said, a chamber for a queen, which is almost always left uninhabited. The woman we marry does not seem to occupy it. But often in our dreams this "nocturnal specter" enters into this chamber bringing with her a breath of air from a supernatural world.

CHAPTER X

THE BELIEF IN THE DEVIL

THE belief in the Devil has now been abandoned by most "enlightened" men. Lucifer has been relegated by the "advanced" thinkers of today to the limbo of medieval legends. Satan nowadays gets only a sniff or a sneer. Beelzebub is used in our times as a butt at which men shoot their arrows of wit. The mention of the Devil in this period of progress, far from causing men to cross themselves, only brings a smile to their faces. At the very thought of Old Nick men burst into laughter. "I could not think of the Devil without laughing," the poet Southey confessed even a century ago.

These "enlightened" men consider themselves too far advanced with their scientific knowledge to retain even a modicum of faith in the "bogies," with which they were frightened in their childhood. They leave the belief in the Devil to what they call the backward, blind masses. They forget, however, that it is they who are blind. These scoffers at Satan should remember that not so long ago it was authoritatively declared in the ecclesiastical courts that "a denial of the Devil's personal existence constituted a man a notorious evil-liver and a depraver of the Book of Common Prayer."

The fact of the matter is that the denial of the Devil is the most successful snare Satan ever laid for our souls. Father Ravignan was indeed right when he declared that the modern disbelief in the Devil was one of the most cunning devices of the Enemy himself. "La plus grande force du diable," said this Jesuit priest, "c'est d'être parvenu à se faire nier." The Devil admitted to Charles Baudelaire that he had been very much afraid, with regard to his proper power, when he heard this prominent preacher cry from his pulpit in Paris: "My dear brethren, do not forget, when you hear the progress of lights praised that the loveliest trick of the Devil is

to persuade you that he does not exist" ("le Joueur généreux,"
1864). Baudelaire's disciple, Joris-Karl Huysmans, in his novel
Là-Bas (1891), similarly says that "the greatest power of Satan lies
in the fact that he gets men to deny him." Satan expresses his
satisfaction over his success in this regard in Frederick Beecher
Perkins's story, *Devil-Puzzlers* (1871). In Pierre Veber's novel,
l'Homme qui vendit son âme au diable (1918), on the other hand,
the Devil mocks at this theological dictum.

*

* *

The belief in the Devil forms an integral part of every religion.
"God and the Devil make up the whole of religion," said the German
rationalist, Christoph Friedrich Nicolai. It will not do for a believer in the Deity to scoff at the idea of the Devil. Disbelief in
the Devil cannot be reconciled with faith in God. A man cannot be
a believer in the Almighty and a sceptic about the Adversary.
"Dæmon est Deus inversus," says the Cabbala.[1] The Devil is nothing
but the reverse of the coin called God. George Sand has said that
"the Spirit of Evil and the Spirit of Good are but one single Spirit:
God" (*Lélia,* iii). The German mystic, Jacob Bœhme, in the seventeenth century, affirmed that God can be known only through Evil,
which means, through the Devil. To deny the Devil is to discount
the Deity. Lucifer is as necessary to the Lord, as the Lord is to
Lucifer. "God without the Devil is dead, being alone," affirms
Samuel Butler. Though they oppose each other, they also complete
each other. They are a part and parcel of the great cosmic system.
John Wesley, the founder of Methodism, well realized the need of
the belief in the Devil and issued to his followers the famous cry:
"No Devil, no God!"

This position in regard to the belief in the Devil cannot be
assailed. The assertion that the Devil is as essential to religion as
the Deity cannot be gainsaid. The Catholic never has discarded the
belief in the Devil. For the Roman religionist, the belief in the
Devil, as any other belief, has been fixed *ne varietur* by the Church.
It follows, therefore, that faith in the Fiend must form a part of the
religion of every good Catholic. But it is difficult to understand

[1] Walt Whitman, in his poem "Chanting the Square Deific," represents the
Devil as a part of a quadruple divinity.

how any Protestant can discard the Devil from his dogma. The belief in Beelzebub forms an essential part of the Christian religion. Indeed, it is the pivotal point of the body of Christian dogmatics. Voltaire proved himself as good a theologian as a philosopher when he said that the Fiend was the fount and foundation of the Christian faith. "Cette doctrine [du diable]," the old man of Ferney said, "devient depuis le fondement de la religion chrétienne" (*Essai sur les mœurs et l'esprit des nations*, iii). In fact, from the old orthodox point of view, Christianity cannot be conceived without Satan. To employ a hackneyed simile, Christianity without Satan would be to the old orthodox believer very much like the play of *Hamlet* with Hamlet left out. The fact is that the whole Christian scheme of salvation is based on the belief in the Devil. What need, pray, would there be for salvation through Christ if there were no Satan constantly plotting against man?

*

*   *

The Devil appears in the sacred books under his various aliases in his various forms and with his various functions. He is found at the very beginning of the Holy Writ. If he plays a minor part in the Old Testament, the New Testament is full of his devices and doings. The Gospels and Epistles speak of his powers of opposing truth and assisting error, of accomplishing signs and wonders, of plotting and scheming, of influencing and controlling thought, of rearing children and having a residence, a royal throne and a church of his own. They portray Satan as a roaring lion, prowling about and seeking whom he may devour (1 Pet. v. 8). The Saviour himself was not safe from Satan's snares, although he escaped them.

The Devil is encountered at the very dawn of human history, appearing to our first ancestors in the Garden of Eden; and from that day on, he has been inextricably wound up with the affairs of men. Although he played a rather minor part in the days of the patriarchs and prophets, he gradually developed in power with the march of the centuries so that in the Middle Ages he was the Prince of this world. The medieval period may well be considered the heyday of the Devil's reign over the minds and wills of men. There certainly was tremendous diabolical activity in those Catholic times. The Devil was the object of the greatest concern among our medieval ancestors, who feared him so mortally and who fought him so courageously. Our forefathers were encircled by the fiends of hell, from whom they could not flee. Any uncanny or untoward experience was ascribed to the Devil. If a person disappeared, it was supposed that the Devil had carried him off.[2] The Reformation perhaps increased the Devil's power in this world still more by withdrawing from the Church the power of beating Beelzebub with book and bell. In the eighteenth century, in this *sœculum rationalisticum,* the belief in evil as well as in good disappeared, and in the following century Diabolus was relegated to the domain of old traditions and ancient superstitions.

But just when we thought that we had discarded the Devil and lulled ourselves in the fond conviction that all was for the best in this best of all possible worlds, we awakened at the beginning of this century to a new and sudden realization of a power of evil which is still at work in the midst of men. The world-war brought us a new and appalling conviction that all the attributes which used to form the personality of the Prince of Darkness were more rampant in the world than we in our former blindness ever dreamed. It was the lesson that the French Revolution and its attendant Reign of Terror taught many of the sceptics of the eighteenth century, and it was again the lesson that the devil-doubters of our day learned from the recent war and its tragic aftermath.

*
*   *

The existence of Evil necessarily and inevitably points to the existence of the Devil. Victor Hugo, like so many other Romantics,[3] deduced from the existence of evil, "that terrible sphinx propounding a terrible riddle," the existence of an Evil Being. "It is this perfection of Evil," says the author of the novel, *les Travailleurs de la mer* (1866), "which has sometimes sufficed to incline

---

[2] Thomas Carlyle's graphic picture of Monk Sampson's vision of the Devil, in his *Past and Present* (1843), will perhaps do more to explain how the belief in the Devil grew and flourished in the Middle Ages than pages of explanatory statements.

[3] Balzac, however, could not understand how there could be two synchronously omnipotent powers, as the Lord and the Devil. He had too much faith in the wisdom of God to believe in Beelzebub. "God would be very stupid," he assures us, "to leave in this world, which he has so curiously constructed, an abominable devil whose special business it is to spoil everything for him (*l'Héritier du diable,* 1832). Alfred de Vigny similarly said that he had too much respect for God to fear the Devil.

powerful intellects to a belief in the duality of the Deity, toward that terrible *bifrons* of the Manichæans. . . . It is certain that Evil at one end proves the Evil One at the other. . . . If there is an Up," he continues, "there must be a Down; if there is Light, there must also be Darkness" (*ibid.*, II. iv. 2). Victor Hugo found an echo in Huysmans, who, in his novel, *Là-Bas,* previously mentioned, makes the following interesting statement through the mouth of Des Hermies: "Manichæism is one of the most ancient, the simplest of religions, at all events, the religion which explains best the abominable mess of the present time." This dualism is deep-rooted in the thought of man. It is suggested by our bisymmetrical bodies of right and left, and by the duality of the moral world of right and wrong and of the physical world of heat and cold, day and night, light and darkness, in which we live.[4]

Our belief in the Devil may differ somewhat from that held by our ancestors. Diabolus now shows himself perhaps no longer as a blackman with horns, hoofs and tail. Nevertheless, he is just as vivid to us as he was to the hermits of the Thebaid or the monks of the Middle Ages. What Renan said with regard to the Deity may well be applied to the Devil. When this eminent historian of religion was asked if he believed in God, he replied: "I do not know if the Divinity exists, but the Divine always exists." Whether or not the Devil exists, the Diabolical undeniably exists. But the Devil is more than a mere abstraction, an idea or a principle of evil, as he is presented by our "advanced" thinkers. The unity of all the forms and elements of evil, which still is so unmistakably real in the world, seems rather to point to a personality if not to a person. "We may not believe in a personal Devil," says Mr. Stanton Coit, "but we must believe in a devil who acts very much like a person."[5]

*
* *

Indeed, how can any man doubt the existence of the Devil? Thousands upon thousands of persons, in the Middle Ages and even later, saw him with their own eyes; and if unanimous testimony may be counted as proving anything, we must admit that the Devil is the

[4] H. Taine also deduced the existence of the Devil from the existence of evil. Cf. J. Bourdeau: *les Maîtres de la pensée contemporaine* (Paris, 1904).

[5] Stanton Colt: *The Soul of America; a Constructive Essay in the Sociology of Religion* (New York, 1914).

one person whose existence has been demonstrated beyond the slightest shadow of a doubt. How real the Devil was to St. Anthony and to Martin Luther! The first of the anchorites, upon the authority of St. Athanasius, was so tempted and tormented for twenty years by the Devil that he well-nigh lost his religion. Luther devoutly believed not only in the Devil's individuality but in his frequent appearance in physical form among men. The German reformer lived in a constant consciousness of contact with and opposition to the Devil. The founder of Protestantism affirmed that he had seen Satan with his own eyes and that he had frequently carried on a conversation with him. When Luther was studying at night in the monastery at Wittenberg, he often heard the Devil making a racket in the empty chapel below and was forced to slam his book and go to bed. The Fiend often looked over Luther's shoulder when the latter translated the Bible in the Wartburg and disputed with Diabolus in regard to the correct meaning of the Hebrew text. "The Devil," Luther assures us, "knows Scripture well and he uses it in argument." The founder of Protestantism carried on a serious controversy with the Contradictor on the subject of transubstantiation, and, in the course of the heated argument, lost his temper and hurled the inkstand at his visitor. The Devil dodged, and the ink splashed on the wall behind him. As proof of this episode, the inkstains may be seen to this day in Luther's former cell in the Wartburg.[6]

Many modern writers, who will certainly never receive canonization, are staunch believers in the Devil. E. T. A. Hoffmann, the most famous of the fantastic fictionists of Germany, held a firm belief in Beelzebub. It was a settled conviction with this writer that, when anything good befalls a man, an evil power is always lurking in the background to thwart the beneficent action. "The Devil," Hoffmann used to say, "will put his hoofs into everything, however good it is at the outset."[7] This writer lived in constant dread of the Devil. He believed that, by means of a bargain, the Evil One had obtained possession of his soul, which could no longer

[6] Luther's dispute with the Devil is very cleverly described by Népomucène Lemercier in his *Panhypocrisiade* (1819). Concerning Luther's belief in the Devil, read Wm. Edw. H. Lecky: *A History of the Rise and Influence of Rationalism in Europe* (2 vols., London, 1865).

[7] That is why one of the prayers of Charles the Fifth was: "May God do and Satan not undo."

escape eternal damnation. The poor man was persuaded that the Enemy of Mankind stood behind him while he wrote and looked over his shoulder. He so feared the Fiend that he would often awaken his wife in the night and beg her to keep watch with him and protect him, as he was sitting over his work.

Heinrich Heine, in a famous quatrain, warns us against doubt in Diabolus:

> "Mortal, mock not at the Devil,
>   Life is short and soon will fail,
> And the 'fire everlasting'
>   Is no idle fairy-tale."

The French novelist, Prosper Mérimée, who openly professed his unbelief in supernatural powers, was convinced that the Devil had much to do with the affairs of men. Théophile Gautier, sceptic and scoffer though he was, believed in the Devil. Barbey d'Aurevilly and Charles Baudelaire held firmly to the Catholic doctrine of the existence and influence of the Devil. The poet of the *Fleurs du Mal* (1857) was a staunch believer in the constant presence of the Great Enemy in this world. He laughed at his "enlightened" friends who imagined that "the Devil would one day be gobbled up" by manufactories and machines. Baudelaire had a certain feeling that an evil power existed exterior to man, since he failed to conceive how, save by means of such intervention, various sudden acts and thoughts could be explained. In a letter addressed to Flaubert in 1860, Baudelaire expressed his belief in the Devil as the origin of moral evil as follows:

"From all time I have been obsessed by the impossibility of comprehending sudden acts or thoughts of man without the hypothesis of the intervention of an Evil Power not in man himself."

In his autobiographical *Mon Cœur mis à nu*, the same writer expresses his Manichæan belief in the duality of human nature with the following words:

'There are in every man, at every hour, two simultaneous urges —one toward the Deity (spirituality), and one toward the Devil (bestiality). The invocation of God, or spirituality, is a desire to rise; that of Satan, or bestiality, is a joy in descent.'

Baudelaire also believed in hell, and laughed at the freethinkers and humanitarians of his day, who proposed to abolish hell out of

friendship for humanity. He particularly poked fun at George
Sand and, apropos of her disbelief in hell, remarked that she "had
good reason to wish to suppress hell."

Anatole France, profoundly pagan though he was, professed a
strong belief in Beelzebub and the Black Bogey (*le Livre de mon
ami*, 1885). This scoffer at all things sacred was scared by Satan.
There is a lurking suspicion that the atheist Thibault could not divest
himself of the belief in the Devil which he had imbibed with his
mother's milk. This latter-day exponent of the spirit of doubt and
denial also regretted his loss of faith in inferno and envied his
ancestors, who never questioned the reality of the unquenching fires
of hell. His poem, "la Danse des morts" (1867), ends with the
following line:

"Blessed are they who believed in hell."

Ernest Renan, who carried the spirit of critical inquiry into the
field of religion, likewise regretted his loss of belief in hell. "I would
that I knew there was a hell," he wrote; "far better that hypothesis
than that of nothingness." As he had a horror of paradise, which
he considered a place of perpetual *ennui*, he diplomatically preferred purgatory. Voltaire, who is generally considered among the
good Christians as the incarnation of unbelief, was not altogether
certain in his mind that hell did not exist. When a light-hearted
sceptic wrote him one fine morning, "I have succeeded in proving
that there is no hell," the sage of Ferney replied, "You are very
fortunate; I am far from that."

Remy de Gourmont, thoroughly godless as this deep thinker was,
manifested a passionate interest in Diabolus, and sang the praises
of Satan much in the manner of Baudelaire and Carducci. Our own
James Huneker believed in the Devil even if he denied the Deity.
His pupil, Benjamin de Casseres, is more convinced of the reality
of the Adversary than of the Almighty.[8]

This belief in the Devil on the part of freethinkers puts to shame
the doubts with regard to Evil and the Devil which we find frequently expressed by good churchmen and churchwomen in both camps
of Christianity. Happily enough, the majority of men in Christendom still hold firmly to the belief in a personal devil. Against

---

[8] Casseres expressed his belief in the Devil in his review of the present
writer's collection of *Devil Stories,* which appeared in the New York *Herald,*
of May 8, 1921.

Diabolus the Catholics yet swing their incense and the Protestants still thunder from their pulpits. In one country of Europe, at least, the Devil has not lost his legal status. According to newspaper reports, a few years ago, a Protestant pastor was sentenced at Bromberg, Poland, to eighty days imprisonment and a considerable fine for denying the existence of the Devil. The clergyman made no comment on the case beyond saying that the Devil would be glad to know that he had such fervent defenders in Poland.[9]

[9] The present writer was told a few years ago by the president of a Baptist college that he would advise any man who did not believe in a personal Devil not to join the faculty of that institution.

CHAPTER XI

THE DEVIL'S DEATH

IT has been reported from various places at various periods that the Devil is dead.[1] Scotland, among other European countries, claims to possess his tomb. A Scotch song says: "The Devil is dead and buried at Kirkcaldy." Beelzebub is believed to be buried in Brittany. When slain by St. Michael, according to an old tradition among the fisher-folk of the Breton coast, he was buried by the Archangel under the mountain which faces Mont St. Michel, and which is, therefore, called Tombelaine—*"Tumba Beleni,* the tomb of Belenus, Belus, Bel, Belial, Beelzebub" (Victor Hugo: *Quatre-vingt-treize,* III, ii. 1)[2] The demon Saracen must have died at a certain period in the past, for in the novel, *Tristan le Roux* (1850), by Dumas *fils,* he is evoked from the dead. But his resurrection is not of long duration. In the end, his human ally once more inflicts upon him such death as he must suffer, and he is again buried at Poitiers, the site of his original tomb.

Jean-Pierre Béranger, the popular French song-writer, in his satirical poem, "la Mort du Diable" (1828), gives a new and novel turn to the old legend of the death of the Devil. He is not concerned with the demise of the high and mighty personage, but with the effect it had on the conduct of the Catholic clergy. This song is a satirical attack upon Satan's supposed successors among the monks.

[1] The Devil's death forms the subject of the story, "The Devil and the Old Man" (1905), by John Masefield, reprinted in the present writer's anthology of *Devil Stories* (1921). Arthur Landsberger also used this idea as the subject of his novel entitled *Wie Satan starb* (München, 1919).

[2] Maupassant, in his story "la Légende du Mont St. Michel" (1882), has given an interesting version of the legend of the combat between the Archangel and the Archenemy, which occurred, according to a local tradition, on the famous mountain situated on the Norman coast. This story, accompanied by a critical essay, will be found in the present writer's collection of *Devil Stories* already mentioned.

Béranger was always poking fun at the priests. Even the Pontiff in the Vatican was not spared by his bold and boisterous satire. In Voltairean fashion, Béranger laughed Old Mother Church to scorn. This poem figured prominently among the pieces selected as a basis for Béranger's indictment. It was denounced by the priests as irreligious and blasphemous, and its author was declared an enemy to religion. The archbishop of Paris and the other bishops hurled their anathemas in pastoral letters against the poet of "la Mort du Diable."

The song describes the commotion and consternation caused among the Catholic clergy by the rumor of the Devil's death. The priests wail when the news of the Devil's demise reaches them. The reason for their dismay over the death of the Devil is not that they loved Lucifer so well. What worries these good men is the fact that they have thus lost their means of a livelihood. The Devil being dead, what man will now pay them to be delivered from his clutches? But Ignatius Loyola, the founder of the Order of the Jesuits, bids them to stop their wailing. He himself intends to succeed to the power of the prince of this world; and in order to be delivered from him, men will now pray and pay more than ever before. It is not easy to render in English the delicious humor and irony which this poem contains. We shall give it nevertheless in its first English translation for the benefit of the reader to whom it is not easy of access in the original.[3]

> I sing today a lay of lays,
> A glorious miracle you'll see,
> Give the great saint Ignatius praise,
> Of little saints the glory he.
> A dirty trick—if saints can trick,
> And if the truth may all be said,
> Has done the business for Old Nick,
> The Devil's dead—the Devil's dead!
>
> Old Nick went out one day to dine,
> And pledg'd the saint to drink his health,
> Aye, said the saint—and in the wine
> Some holy poison dropp'd by stealth;
> Gripes seiz'd the Devil—cruel-sick—
> He swears—he storms—and hangs his head,
> Then bursts, as bursts a heretic—
> The Devil's dead—the Devil's dead!

3 This translation appeared in the *Westminster Review,* X (1829), 210-13.

"Alas! He's dead—the friars said,—
The Devil an *Agnus* shall we sell,—
Alas! the canons cried—he's dead—
Not one *Oremus* shall we tell.
The conclave is in deep despair,
Power and the iron chest are fled.
O we have lost our Father dear,
The Devil's dead—the Devil's dead!

Love is not half so strong as fear,
For fear was constant with her gifts.
Intolerance is fading here,
Who now her blazing torch uplifts?
If man from us should once be free,
What light may beam upon his head;
God greater than the Pope shall be—
The Devil's dead—the Devil's dead!

Ignatius came—"Let me but take
His place—his right—and see; in brief—
He has made men for ages quake.
I'll make kings tremble like a leaf!
With plagues, thefts, massacres, I'll ban
Both north and south—where'er I tread;
Leave ruins both for God and man—
The Devil's dead—the Devil's dead!"

"Come, blessed one," they uttered. "Come,
We hallow thy most saintly gall"—
And now his Order—sent from Rome—
O'ershadows, darkens, curses all.
I heard a choir of angels tell
Their sympathies for man, they said,
"Ignatius is the heir of hell,
The Devil's dead—the Devil's dead!"

The reader who is perhaps inclined to be overjoyed at the report of the Devil's death should recall that Satan has a successor who is fully capable of carrying on the government of Gehenna after his death. In the words of a famous quatrain:

"The Devil is dead. He died serene,
    Though somewhat oppressed by cares;
But his wife, my friends, is a woman of mind—
    She looks after her lord's affairs."

*

* *

Moreover, the Devil's death would be the greatest of calamities for humanity. It would mean the end of all virtue, the extinction of the human race, and even the end of the world. First of all, virtue could not exist at all without vice to offset it. It is, moreover, doubtful whether men would still practise virtue if the Devil were gone. Even lacking temptation would they continue to be good without the pitchfork? No progress can be conceived without the Prince of this world. Conflict is the father of all things. It has been said that man must know the spirit of discontent if he is to advance. Moreover, with the passing of the Devil, life would simply disappear from the face of the earth. The history of the world has shown that the supposedly opposed realms of human activity personified in the Almighty and his Adversary are equally essential and eternal. Evil, no less than Good, is an indispensably necessary element in the economy of the cosmic system.

Anatole France states over and over again in his works that "Evil is the necessary counterpart of Good, as darkness is of light," and that the Devil, in whom Evil has been incorporated, is consequently immortal.

"Yes [this latterday diabolist affirms]. Evil is immortal. Satan, the genius, in whom the old theology incarnates it, will survive the last man and remain alone, seated with folded wings, upon the ruin of extinct worlds" (la Vie littéraire: "la Vertu en France," 1887).[4]

[4] Quotations in this essay are taken from the uniform English translation of the works of Anatole France published by John Lane, London and New York, 1902ff.

"Evil is necessary [he says elsewhere]. If it did not exist, neither would good. Evil is the sole potential of good. . . .

"It is thanks to Evil and sorrow that the earth is habitable and that life is worth living. We should not therefore be hard on the Devil. He is a great artist and a great *savant;* he has created at least one-half of the world. And his half is so cunningly embedded in the other that it is impossible to interfere with the first without at the same time doing a like injury to the second. Each vice you destroy has a corresponding virtue, which perishes along with it.

"I enjoyed the pleasure of seeing, one day, at a country fair, the life of St. Anthony the Great represented by marionettes. . . . Oh, how vividly it brings before us the two things working together to one end,—God's grace and the Devil's!

"St. Anthony is a great saint only because he successfully resisted the Queen of Sheba. Well, is it not obvious then that in sending the beauteous lady, . . . the Devil indispensably performed an act which was indispensably necessary to constitute his Saintship?

"Thus the marionettes confirmed me in my belief that Evil is an indispensable pre-condition of Good, and the Devil is a necessity for the moral beauty of the universe" (*le Jardin d'Epicure,* 1895).

"Evil is necessary [this author repeats himself]. It has like Good its source in human nature, and the one cannot be destroyed without the other" (*M. Bergeret à Paris,* 1901).[5]

In his autobiographical work, *le Livre de mon ami* (1884), Anatole France tells us that one day he took his baby-girl Suzanne to a Punch and Judy show, the culminating point of which was the death of the Devil.[6] This ending delighted the common crowd, which applauded the heroic act of Punch, but it saddened our philosopher, who thought that it was a great pity that the Devil had been

[5] The late James Huneker shows himself a pupil of the great French diabolist by his long encomium of the Prince of the Pit, which begins with the following: "The Devil is the mainspring of our moral system. Mock him and you mock God, who created him. Without him the world would be all light without shadow. . . ." (*Bedouins,* 1920).

[6] The Punch and Judy show invariably ends with the death of the Devil. Paine Collier, in his book, *Punch and Judy* (5th ed., London, 1870, p. 66), mentions a marionette-player who had religious scruples about making Punch kill the Devil, but the audience were so attached to the canonical ending that they hooted and mishandled him. On the origin of this traditional ending of a Punch and Judy show, see F. M. Cornford: *The Origin of the Attic Comedy* (London, 1914), p. 146.

killed. Paying no attention to Suzanne sitting by his side, he went on musing:

"The Devil being dead, good-bye to sin! Perhaps Beauty, the Devil's ally, would have to go also. Perhaps we should never more behold the flowers that enchant us; and the eyes for the love of which we would lay down our lives. What, if that is so, what in the world would become of us? Should we still be able to practise virtue? I doubt it. Punch did not sufficiently bear in mind that Evil is the necessary counterpart of Good, as darkness is of light, that virtue consists wholly of effort, and that if the Devil is no longer to fight against, the Saints will remain as much out of work as the Sinners. Life will be mortally dull. I tell you that when he killed the Devil, Punch committed an act of grave imprudence.

"Well, Pulchinello came on and made his bow, the curtain fell, and all the little boys and girls went home; but still I sat on deep in meditation. Mam'zelle Suzanne, perceiving my thoughtful mien, concluded that I was in trouble. . . . Very gently and tenderly she takes hold of my hand and asks me why I am unhappy. I confess that I am sorry that Punch has killed the Devil. Then she throws her little arms round my neck, and putting her lips to my ears, she whispers:

"'I tell you somefin: Punch, he killed the nigger, but he has not killed him for good.'"

CHAPTER XII

DIABOLUS SIMIA DEI

THE Devil is represented in Christian theology as a duplicate of the Deity. The Fiend in hell has been set up by the Church fathers as a foil to the Father in heaven. Lucifer has been limned by the Catholic Schoolmen after the Lord. The Adversary, in waging war against the Almighty, is understood to copy all of his acts and attributes. Popular tradition, moreover, asserts that the Devil, impotent to do anything original, has set his heart on aping everything created by the Deity. In Immermann's drama, *Merlin* (1832), Satan complains: *"Dass uns nichts bleibt als nachzuäffen"* (That nothing but imitating is left to us) (Prologue, 199).

The similarities between pagan and Christian belief and ritual were explained by the Church fathers as diabolical travesties of divine truths. When the early Christian missionaries discovered that the heathen rites and observances were identical with their own, they could explain the fact only by assuming that the Devil, in his efforts to pervert the truth, mimicked the exact details of the sacraments of the Lord in the mysteries of the idols. The doctors of the Church postulated the belief that, long before the advent of Christianity, Satan had put Christian ideas into the heads of the pagans in order to confound the faithful. The Church fathers assumed that, by overhearing the words of the inspired prophets, the Adversary had learned the intentions of the Almighty and had anticipated them by a series of blasphemous imitations (Justin Martyr: *Apologia* i. 54). From the identity of Mithraic and Judaic baptismal rites, Tertullian was led to declare that "Satan imitates the sacraments of God" and "goes about to apply to the worship of the idols those very things of which the administration of Christ's sacraments consists." Referring to the Mithraic eucharist, Justin Martyr also maintained that Satan had plagiarized this ceremony, causing the worshippers of Mithra to receive the consecrated bread and cup of water[1] in imitation of the followers of Christ. St. Augustine similarly saw the subtlety of Satan's power of imitation in the parallel between the observances of Christians and pagans. Even Cortés, the famous Spanish explorer, who conquered Mexico in the sixteenth century, complained that Lucifer had positively taught the Mexicans the same things which the Lord had taught the Christians. Thus the similarities in creed and cult between Christianism and paganism were interpreted by the Church as infernal counterfeits of eternal verities.

The early Christians further believed that Lucifer, in his efforts to copy the Lord, actually pronounced oracles and worked miracles among the pagans, but that when God brought his miraculous displays of power to an end, the Devil was no longer permitted to perform prodigies among the pagans, either. The Church did not doubt the supernatural power of the idols but ascribed its source to the Devil's aim to counterfeit the Deity with a view of confounding the Christians. "But the fundamental cause (*consummativa*) [of idolatry]," affirms St. Thomas Aquinas in his work, *Summa theologica* (II. ii. 94), "must be sought in the devils, who caused men to adore them under the form of idols, working in them certain things which excited their wonder and admiration." Even Edmund Spenser, writing in the sixteenth century, described the Devil as dwelling beneath the altar of an idol in a heathen temple and, in its name, uttering oracles and performing miracles.

* * *

In every other respect, Lucifer was represented by the fathers and doctors of the Church as a replica of the Lord, as the unholy counterfeiter of all things divine, playing in the world the part of "God's ape." The triceptic form, which the Devil inherited from the pagan gods of the underworld, was interpreted by the Church as his parody of the tripersonality of the Godhead. Lucifer, in imitation of the Lord, wears a long beard in the iconography of the Eastern Church. The Devil's diadem is the counterpart of the Creator's crown. As Jehovah has "principality, and power, and might and dominion" (Eph. i. 21), Satan is the possessor of "prin-

---

[1] Water was used instead of wine by certain early Christian sects.

cipalities and powers" (*ibid.*, vi. 12). If God is the father of truth, the Devil is the father of lies (John viii. 44). The sons of Belial (Jdg. xx. 13; cf. John viii. 44) parallel the children of God (John viii. 42; 1 John iii. 10).

If Spirit emanated from God, Matter was formed by the Fiend. It was a Gnostic notion to regard the whole world of objective existence as the work of the Devil. The Church adopted this view and considered all nature as the incarnation of the Evil Spirit. In fact, the Devil was looked upon down to the sixteenth century as in some sort the creator and controller of the physical order of things. The world, the flesh and the Devil are joined together in the formula of Christian baptism. Although the Catholic catechism does not contain this belief, it formed the principal doctrine of many heterodox sects. The Priscillianists, an ascetic and Gnostic sect of the fifth century, had for their central belief that the world was created by the Devil. They abstained as much as they could from all contact with the material world and rejected many foods as coming from the Devil.[2]

If God created man, Satan created woman.[3] The Manichæans held the belief that woman was fashioned by the Devil, and that the forbidden fruit with which the Serpent tempted Adam was woman herself.[4] When Adam was created (so runs the teaching of Mani), the Devil, wishing to show that he could equal and perhaps even surpass the Deity in creative power, fashioned Eve, who, in contrast to Adam, was wholly sensual, and thus soon caused Adam to sin through carnal lust. According to another Gnostic belief, Adam was likewise the handiwork of the Evil One, who fashioned him as well as Eve out of dust. Adam, however, had a spark of light in him, inasmuch as Satan, in previous struggles with the good angels, had obtained from them some elements of light

[2] Goethe and Hebbel shared this belief in the Devil as the creator of the world; consult the present writer's essay: "Des Teufels Schöpferrolle bei Goethe und Hebbel" in *Neophilologus*, vol. VI (1918-19), pp. 319-22. Anatole France, in his work, *la Rôtisserie de la Reine Pédauque* (1893), also expresses the belief that a demon has created the world.

[3] The Devil is at least the dispenser of charms to women. The famous courtesan of Alexandria maintains that if she is so beautiful it is because the Devil adorned her with all her attractions (Anatole France: *Thaïs*, 1890).

[4] The apple-story in Genesis is thus interpreted as an allegory. "Love," says Henry O'Brien in his book, *The Round Towers of Ireland* (1834), "however disguised, and how could it be more beautifully than by the scriptural penman—love, in its literal and all-absorbing seductiveness, was the simple and fascinating aberration couched under the figure of the forbidden fruit."

and passed them on into Adam's nature. Eve, on the other hand, was wholly sensual and consequently could not fail soon to bring about Adam's fall.

If the Lord created the human soul, Lucifer, according to the belief of the Albigenses, fashioned the human body as a prison for the celestial soul. Even if the upper parts of the body were created by God, its inferior parts, according to the belief of other heretical sects, were made by the Devil. The Paternians, who held this belief and who wished to render to both their creators what was theirs, indulged to their hearts' content in eating and drinking and debauching themselves.

If God is the creator of beauty, ugliness is, according to the French novelist Joris-Karl Huysmans, the Devil's handiwork (*les Foules de Lourdes,* 1906).

As heaven is the habitation of the Most High, hell is the dwelling of the Devil. The Christian hell of pitch and brimstone is the counterpart of the Hebrew heaven of gold and precious stones. The scarlet gates of Gehenna form a striking contrast to the pearly portals of paradise. The Devil, who has always wished to rival the Deity, has developed his domain in all details after the pattern of the celestial organization. Each infernal institution is copied from a corresponding eternal establishment. The diabolical monarchy was founded in opposition to the celestial kingdom. The hierarchy of hell was formed in imitation of the hierarchy of heaven. The infernal council was instituted in imitation of the celestial assembly described in the Old Testament (1 Kings xxii. 19; 2 Chr. xviii. 18; Job i. 6, ii. 1).

The malignant spirits form a contrast to the benignant spirits. The seven demons of royal rank match the seven archangels. Satan holding the keys of hell is a pendant to St. Peter, the warden of the celestial portals. The Eternity of Sorrows in hell, a creation of Chateaubriand in his novel, *les Martyrs* (1809), is the infernal counterpart to the Augustinian *æternitas felicitatis.* Hornblas, the demon, who, in the German medieval mysteries, blows the horn or Tartarean trumpet to call together the demons of hell for a session of parliament, is the diabolical counterpart of the Angel of the Last Trumpet. The functions of the fiends in hell parallel the rôles of the bright spirits in heaven. As the latter specialize in virtues, the former particularize in vices. As each angel is set over a good act, each demon is allotted an evil deed. As the angels sing hosannah in the highest, the demons pour forth pæans of praise to the Prince of the Pit. The choir of the angels in the medieval mysteries has for its counterpart a choir of demons. The spirits of hell even parody the prayers addressed to the Lord in heaven. According to Cæsarius of Heisterbach, the Devil does not even refrain from reciting in a burlesque fashion the *Paternoster* and the *Credo.* In imitation of the supernal spirits, the infernal hosts sing the *Silete* in the French medieval mysteries. Beelzebub, as chaplain to Venus, the goddess of voluptuousness, in Gil Vicente's play, *Triumpho do inverno* (1530), offers a parody of the breviary hymns for the amusement of the pious Portuguese spectators.

As the Lord works for the extension of his kingdom on earth, Lucifer also endeavors to extend his power on this planet. As the Almighty sends his angels down in order that his will be done on earth as it is in heaven, the Adversary dispatches his demons to effect his will among the children of man. The intervention of the demons in human affairs parallels that of the angels. Inasmuch as the spirits of darkness are incessantly plotting the ruin of men, the spirits of light are continually intent upon saving them. As the angels of heaven must answer to the formulas of invocation pronounced by those who have made a sacramental compact with their chief, the infernal agents can be summoned by those who have shared a sacrament with Satan. If the messengers from heaven are the guards and sentries of men, the agents of hell act as their tempters and tormentors. If the good spirit whispers good counsel into man's right ear, the evil demon whispers evil counsel into the left.

As the Lord has his elect, so Lucifer has his chosen. "The Devil has his elect" as well as the Deity, the devout George Herbert assures us. As the Creator closes a covenant with his faithful, his copyist enters into a pact with his adherents. If the bond with the Eternal is concluded with water, the pact with the Infernal is signed with blood. Satan as well as the Saviour demands from his subjects an act of deep devotion and a declaration of loyalty. *"Dæmones divinis honoribus gaudent,"* says St. Augustine (*De Civitate Dei,* x). If the Deity spreads grace on his people, the Devil distributes evil spells among his devotees. If the men of the Lord do good and practice charity, the followers of the Fiend do evil and spread hatred. As the Deity distributes crowns of gold to his elect (Rev. ii. 10; cf. 1 Pet. v. 4), the Devil in the medieval mysteries rewards his deserving demons with crowns composed, however, of far ignobler substances.

* * *

The synagogue of Satan (Rev. ii. 9) is the counterpart of the Church of God.[5] No sooner is a temple erected to the Deity than the Devil builds a chapel near by. There is a Spanish proverb to the effect that "Where God has his church, Satan will have his chapel." The Spaniards also say, "Detras de la cruz está el diablo" (Behind the Cross is the Devil). In the words of Daniel Defoe: "Wherever man erects a house of prayer, the Devil always builds a chapel."

Sweden, and the North in general, fairly swarm with the synagogues of Satan. It is believed that the Devil has a church in the village of Elfdale, situated in Sweden. The "cursed tower" of Vygla in Iceland, mentioned in Victor Hugo's juvenile novel, *Han d'Islande* (1823), was believed to be "the oratory of the Devil."

The adoration of the Devil is the obverse of the worship of the Deity. The rites of hell, mentioned in Victor Hugo's novel, just cited, correspond to the sacraments of heaven.[6] The ceremonies of the devil-worshippers were considered as blasphemous travesties of the blessed sacraments of the Church of God. Satan as well as Jehovah has his ministers (2 Cor. xi. 15), who perform his sacraments. The *magica diabolica* or *magica nigra* is in contrast to the *magica alba*. Sacred days, as is well known, are printed in the Catholic calendar with red letters, and the Devil also employs them in the books of black magic. The "Devil's mark," found on the wizards and witches, is the counterpart of the Lord's baptism. Tertullian has already said that the Devil, as the ape of the Deity, practises baptism on his subjects. The "Flying Ointment," with which the witches rub themselves in preparation for their mid-air flights to the Sabbath, is an obverse of the seventh Christian sacrament. The stick, which serves them as a steed, is, according to Arias Mon-

[5] The noted German-Polish novelist Stanislaw Przybyszewski, author of *Homo Sapiens* (1895-98), has written a work in German under the title *Die Synagogue Satans* (1897). Adolf Paul has composed a comedy entitled *Die Teufelskirche* (Berlin, 1915). The novel, *The Devil's Chapel*, has Miss Sophie Cole for its author.

[6] A description of the ritual at the infernal court was given by Hroswitha, a nun of Gandersheim in Germany, who lived in the tenth century.

tano, the diabolical counterpart to the rod of Moses and the budding rod of Aaron (Numb. xvii. 2). The Black Mass is "a blasphemous parody of the Blessed Mass." The Devil assists with the Black Mass, just as the Lord is present at the Holy Eucharist. As candles burn before the altar of God, lights are carried in front of the Devil, as he performs the rites of the Witches' Sabbath. The table and cup used in the sacrament of Satan (1 Cor. x. 21) correspond to those employed in the sacrament of the Saviour. A Basque legend tells us that the Devil makes his chalice out of the parings of finger-nails trimmed on Sundays. Another instance of the mimicry of the sanctities of the Church by "God's Ape" is the belief that the Devil exacts from the witches a kiss on an ignominious part of his body in imitation of the kiss of charity with which the early Christians greeted each other (1 Pet. v. 14).

Man can be as devout with respect to the Devil as in the worship of the Deity, says Victor Hugo in *Actes et Paroles*: "Depuis l'exil" (II. xvi). "In more ways than one," says St. Augustine, "do men sacrifice to the rebellious spirits" as well as to the Heavenly Powers. According to Biblical authority, man can drink of the cup and be a partaker of the table of Lucifer as well as of the Lord (1 Cor. x. 21). Sinners can obtain indulgences from Satan as well as from the Saviour. "There are some consciences so tender," says Victor Hugo, "that they must seek indulgences even from Beelzebub. They wish to be irreproachable even in the eyes of Satan. Sins against the Devil exist in certain morbid imaginations" (*les Travailleurs de la mer*, 1866). The sins against Satan, of which Victor Hugo writes, parallel the crimes against the Creator. The doctrines of the devils (1 Tim. iv. 1) correspond to the precepts of the priests.

As God is always nigh unto them who call upon him, so Satan always appears when summoned. "Lucifer," says Richardson in *Pamela* (1740), "always is ready to promote his work and workmen." The proverb says: "Call the Devil, and he will come or send." The Devil as well as the Deity lends his ears to the prayers addressed to him by man in need. What the Lord has refused him, man seeks to obtain from Lucifer. He may even address himself directly to the Devil. Northern belief leans to the idea that man has a better chance of getting a hearing in hell than in heaven.

There is a significant saying among the Danish and Prussian peasants to the effect that you may obtain a favor by calling on the Deity, but that if you wish to be sure of getting what you want, you must deal with the Devil. An ancient tradition exists in Northern Europe that the Antecessor, as the Devil is called in a certain Swedish myth, is present to hold out promises where the Intercessor has broken all that his sponsors had made for him when the populace accepted his baptism.[7]

* * *

Satan as *simia Salvatoris* also has a mother, who, as Queen of Hell, is the exact copy of the Queen of Heaven. This *Mater tenebrarum*—Our Lady of Darkness—is the counterpart of the *Mater dolorosa*—Our Lady of Sorrows. The infernal madonna appears in the *Juttaspiel,* the most famous secular play of medieval Germany, as Lilith, Adam's original paramour. This *Mater malorum* was the first to claim that woman was essentially man's equal and left her husband on account of his old-fashioned ideas about the husband's right to be head of the family. In the Alsfeld Passion Play, dating from the beginning of the sixteenth century, this "diabo-lady" is called Höllenkrücke (hell's crutches) on account of a lameness, which forces her to walk on crutches. In James Huneker's story, "The Vision Malefic" (1920), this counterfeit madonna appears on a Christmas Eve to the organist of a Roman Catholic church in New York.

The idea of the Devil's grandmother, on the other hand, is wholly foreign to Judeo-Christian tradition.[8] It belongs to Germanic belief. Satan's grandmother is none other than Grendel's granny mentioned in *Beowulf.*[9] The Christian Devil has simply usurped the place of the Anglo-Saxon monster in his grandmother's affections as well as in the popular mind. The Devil's grandmother is called Freya in North Germany, having been named after the Scandinavian goddess. She has also been identified with Hecate, the classical goddess of magic and witchcraft (Heine: "Ich rief den Teufel und er kam," 1824).

---

[7] In Maurice Magre's recent novel, *Lucifer,* the Devil says: "I give what I undertake to give. God promises much and gives nothing."

[8] Cf. Juilius Lippert: *Christentum, Volksglaube und Volksbrauch,* Berlin, 1882, p. 561.

[9] Cf. Jacob Grimm: *Teutonic Mythology.* Transl. from the German (4 vols., London, 1880-1888), p. 986.

In a certain play by Christian Grabbe, the Devil comes up to earth because his grandmother is busied with the unpleasant task of scrubbing up hell. Says Heinrich Heine, in his *Elementargeister* (1834), "The Germans have a habit of cleaning rooms by covering the floor with hot water and rubbing it with a coarse cloth, from which result an unpleasant sound and a lukewarm vapor which render it impossible for a reasonable man to remain in the house." Heine sees in this process "why Satan had to flee from his well-heated hell into the upper world; and here, although it was a hot day in July, the poor Devil was almost frozen to death, and was only rescued by medical aid."

Sometimes the Devil's grandmother herself comes up to the world of men. This tradition accounts for the saying, "Where the Devil can do nothing, he sends an old woman." "But the old lady," Heine assures us, "is usually in hell, attending to the cooking, or sitting in her red armchair; and when the Devil, weary with his day's work done, comes home, he swallows in greedy haste what she has ready for him, then lays his head in her lap and falls asleep. At which time, the old lady hums a song which begins with these words:

'In Thume, in Thum
Many roses bloom,
Roses red as blood'."

The German poet also tells us that when the poor imp of hell cannot sleep, the good old dame lulls him to rest by reading to him the Berlin *Evangelical Church Gazette*.

The Germans also knew of "the giant's old grandmother" and of "the mother or grandmother of earth." The Romans similarly had a mother or grandmother of ghosts.[10] The Devil's grandmother is in reality a degraded form of the Germanic goddess of fertility and domestic activity, whose symbols were the pitch-fork, the plough, the broom and the spindle.[11] This association accounts for the prominent part these implements play in medieval demonology. The witch, who was a degraded priestess of the ancient goddess of fertility, used the broom as a mount when she rode through the air to the Witches' Sabbath. The Devil himself is often represented with a pitch-fork or a broom in his hands. The Devil's pitch-fork is not the forked scepter of Pluto, to which a tine has later been

[10] Cf. Sir James Frazer: *The Golden Bough* (*London*, 1890-1915), VIII. 94, 96, 107.

[11] Cf. Karl Pearson: *The Chances of Death and Other Studies in Evolution* (2 vols., London, 1897), II, 28.

added, as is commonly assumed. It is the ancient symbol of fertility, which is still employed as a fertility charm by the Hindus in India and the Zuñi and Aztec Indians of North America and Mexico. A related symbol is the trident of Poseidon or Neptune. The Devil often carried a besom on the medieval stage. This fact leads Mr. Chambers[12] to identify the Devil in some English mystery-plays with the chimney-sweep in others, especially since both are black-faced.[13]

We do not know much about the Devil's grandfather, but in a well known German fairy-tale he is called Old Night, and Beelzebub swears by his grandfather's horns in Charles Deulin's story, "le Grand choleur" (1874).

* * *

The Devil, in imitation of the Deity, will toward the end of days send his son to men. Antichrist as the foil of Christ (2 Thess. ii. 3-10) will, according to Bellarmine, Suarez, Malvenda and *tutti quanti*, be born of a Babylonian virgin and the Devil, just as Christ was born of a Palestinian virgin and the Holy Ghost.

It is thus evident that the Devil has always been striving to equal the Deity in each and every detail of character and conduct. The designation of *simia Dei* given Diabolus by the Church fathers is thus well deserved.[14]

[12] E. K. Chambers: *The Mediæval Stage* (2 vols., Oxford, 1903), I, 214-5.

[13] On the German legends of the Devil's grandmother, the reader is referred first of all to the two articles by Eduard Lehmann: "Fandens oldemov" in *Dania. Tidsskrift dansk sprog og litteratur samt folkeminder*, vol. VIII (1901), pp. 179-94, and "Teufels Grossmutter" in the *Archiv für Religionswissenschaft*, vol. VIII (1905), pp. 411-30. The following books and magazine articles will be of further interest: Saintine: *la Mythologie du Rhin et les contes de la Mère-Grand* (1862); A. Götze: "Des Teufels Grossmutter" in the *Zeitschrift für deutsche Wortforschung*, vol. VII (1905-6), pp. 28-35; and Isabel C. Chamberlain: "The Devil's Grandmother" in the *Journal of American Folk-Lore*, vol. XIII (1900), pp. 278-80.

[14] The idea of Satan as a parody of God will also be found in Mark Twain's posthumous romance, *The Mysterious Stranger*. For further discussion of the subject of *Diabolus simia Dei, Satan simia Salvatoris, Lilith simia Mariæ* and *dæmones simæ angelorum*, the reader is referred to the present writer's monograph, *Der Teufel in den deutschen geistlichen Spielen des Mittelalters und der Reformationszeit* (Göttingen, 1915), pp. 128ff.

CHAPTER XIII

THE WAR FOR THE WORLD

AS the ruler of Heaven and the ruler of Hell are pitted against each other in an eternal combat for the mastery of the world, it is really a wonder that our earth, which, in this perennial war, has been constantly hurled to and fro between the two contending powers, has not long ago been shattered to pieces.

In this war for the world, it is man who is actually the bone of contention. The rivalry between the Eternal and the Infernal to win this planet has for its aim the possession of the human race, which is thus pulled in two different directions. The Lord tries his best to lift man upward, and Lucifer does his worst to drag him downward.

As soon as the Devil learned that the seats which he and his angels had vacated in heaven would be occupied by a new generation, of whom Adam and Eve were to be the parents, he determined to balk the sacred will of the Deity in regard to the destiny of man. From the moment Adam was created, he was tempted and tormented by Satan in body and soul. No sooner was Adam formed out of clay, so runs a Russian legend, than Diabolus, profiting by a moment when the Lord's dog was not watching, thrust seventy diseases into him. When Adam was given a woman, through her, Satan, disguised as a serpent, tempted him to sin, thus driving both of them out of Eden. By this master-stroke, Satan succeeded in wheedling out of God the assignment of the human race as his property. According to St. Augustine, man is condemned by the original sin and has become the Devil's legitimate prey. Satan thus turned man away from the path leading to Paradise and put him on the high-road to Hell. In this way, he clipped man's wings so that he could not fly upward to fill the vacant seats in the celestial choir-stalls.

Encouraged by his first success, Satan continued to sow the seeds of sin in the newly formed earth. He induced Cain to murder Abel and even incited him to hurl stones on his brother's prostrate form. Satan survived the Flood by hiding in Noah's Ark and was thus enabled to renew violence in the drunken curses of Noah. The Tempter again used woman as an accomplice. It was by working upon both the curiosity and jealousy of Noraita,[1] Noah's wife, that he managed to get on board the Ark. But he repaid her hospitality by treachery. There is an ancient tradition that, after having smuggled himself as a stowaway into Noah's Ark, Satan tried to sink it in order to do away with the human race for ever. This infernal project, however, was defeated, and the human race was saved by the hedgehog, who stuffed himself into the hole which the Devil had bored in the floor of the Ark.

Satan exhibited great activity in biblical times. He accused Abraham, and induced the Lord to test the patriarch by ordering him to sacrifice his son Isaac.[2] He was even bold enough to attempt to carry the body of Moses off to hell when the great Jewish lawgiver died, and fought over it with his old enemy, the archangel Michael. But the commander-in-chief of the heavenly militia, the hero of heaven, as this affair is recorded in the Epistle of Jude, did not bring any railing accusation against him, leaving it to the Almighty to rebuke his Adversary. Satan tempted Job in body and mind after having asked the Lord to put the poor man in his power. He indicted the Jews to their God and obtained through Ahasuerus the decree of annihilation against them in the days of Esther.[3] But the Fiend was finally foiled, and the Jews were delivered from death through the vigilance of Mordecai.

Descending to earth to destroy the deeds of the Devil (1 John iii. 8), the Son of God was continually harassed and hampered in his mission by the hosts of hell. Satan, in his efforts to frustrate the providential purposes, persuaded the rabbis to persecute Jesus. After having failed with promises of power to win Jesus away from the Lord (Luke iv. 1-13; Mark i. 13), just as he had pre-

[1] In other versions, the name of Noah's wife is Noria or Naamah.

[2] Cf. Louis Ginzberg: *The Legends of the Jews* (4 vols., Philadelphia, 1909-25), I, 272.

[3] *Ibid.*, IV, 415.

viously failed with Buddha and Zoroaster, he planned his death and, to this end, induced Judas to betray his Master (John xiii. 2). When Jesus died on the Cross, Satan was jubilant; and, ignorant of the real character of his victim, even dared to try to carry his soul off to hell. Satan, however, had no reason for rejoicing over this success. The death of the Saviour spelled the Devil's defeat. The kingdom of Satan was overthrown by the vicarious death of Christ on the Cross at Calvary.[4] In the execution of his mission, Jesus, according to the old interpretation of several biblical passages (Acts ii. 31; Eph. iv. 8-10; Rom. x. 7; and especially 1 Pet. iii. 19), descended after his burial to hell, broke open its gates, set free its prisoners and put its ruler into "everlasting chains" (Jude 6; cf. 2 Pet. ii. 4). This act was performed "as a special punishment for his audacity in tempting and persecuting our Lord on earth or for some other unfathomable intention of the Lord for the salvation of his Church and his elect" (Suarez: *De angelis;* cf. also Gregory: *Moralium libri xxv*). The events of Christ's descent to hell are recorded in full detail in the apocryphal Descensus Christi ad Inferos, which forms the second part of the Evangelium Nicodemi (3rd cent.). This tradition took a strong hold on the popular mind and was considerably elaborated by the medieval poets and playwrights.[5] The medieval English poem *The Harrowing of Hell* is a poetical treatment of this subject. The descent of Christ to hell forms an important part of the medieval mystery-plays of all European countries.[6]

The belief in Christ's Descent to Hell forms part of the Apostolic Creed. Many Protestant sects, however, have abandoned this belief and struck the words "He descended into Hell" from their creed. This denial of Christ's descent to hell is considered pure heresy by Bishop Thomas Bilson, who, in his *Survey of Christ's Suffering for Man's Redemption, and of His Descent to Hell* (1504), opposes the Puritan doctrine that Jesus suffered the pains of hell in his soul on the cross, and maintains that Christ actually went to hell "to destroy the Devil's kingdom."

---

[4] The poet Cumberland treated the subject of Satan's overthrow at Calvary in his poem *Calvary* (1792).

[5] Christ's Descent to Hell has in modern times been poetically treated by W. W. Lord in his poem, *Christ in Hades* (1851).

[6] On the medieval stage, the Devil was often represented with a chain around his neck and with fetters on hands and legs, which symbolized his captivity.

* * *

It would be wrong, however, for man to consider himself thus delivered from the Devil forever. Honesty compels us to admit that Satan's imprisonment in hell has in no way stopped his activity on earth. In fact, we can still see his tail wriggling in the world. It is all too evident that the Devil still enjoys the liberty of walking up and down the earth to molest mankind. The trier of men's souls, the tempter, is just as much "on the job" now, as he was in the days of Job. Although sealed at the bottom of the bottomless pit, his evil influence on the affairs of man has not suffered any diminution. The world's experiences of the past dozen or so of years should certainly uproot any belief we may have cherished that Satan is bound and sealed in some hellish solitude where he is superintending the tortures of the non-elect among humanity (Book of Enoch x. 37). The consensus of opinion among fundamentalist folk would be that the Evil Spirit now more than ever roams about on earth, "seeking whom he may devour" (1 Pet. v. 8).

The Princedom of the Air, far from being overthrown by the vicarious death of Christ, seems, indeed, to have been in commission all through the ages down to the present day. The conduct of men and women in this world has never changed. Satan still lurks in the best and strongest of hearts and directs and controls men's minds and wills. This fact has led many thoughtful men to maintain that, as far as mankind is concerned, the Incarnation has been of no avail. If certain Protestant sects teach the truth by contending that Christ put into men's hands the power to resist the Tempter, it is evident, from all we know about human history from the death of Christ to this day, that very few men ever have availed themselves of this power.

It would almost seem that in this war for the world, the victory lies not with the Saviour but with Satan. Is Diabolus not still the prince of this world (John xii. 31, xiv. 30, xvi. 11; Eph. ii. 2, vi. 12), nay even the god of this world—*deus hujus sæculi* (2 Cor. iv. 4)? Do we not infer from another biblical passage that the authority over the world has been delivered to Satan, who can give it to whomsoever he will (Luke iv. 6)? The earth is recognized by the Church as the Devil's property. The chief ceremony in the consecration of a church is the expulsion of the Devil from the building. The demons thus driven from the interior of the church perch themselves on its roof. This idea accounts for the gargoyles on the exterior of medieval cathedrals. The custom which prevailed in olden times of immuring a child in a new building is explained by the necessity of paying a purchase price to the Devil for the land on which it was erected.[7] The Reformation in no way disputed the Devil's authority over this world. Martin Luther saw in Satan a real living power, who was incessantly working in human affairs. In the eyes of the German reformer, the Devil was the good Lord's hangman, and the instrument of the Almighty's anger and punishment. His famous hymn "Ein' feste Burg" (1529) breathes from the beginning to the end with the conviction of Satan's great power in the world. The English reformer, John Wycliffe, in his treatise, *De dominio divino* (c. 1375), goes as far as to imply that here on earth God must obey the Devil. Anatole France, sceptic though he is, assures us that "the Old Enemy, the Spirit that denies, still holds such power in the spiritual world that even God must reckon with him. I will go further: that God, who fears him, has made him his steward" (*la Rôtisserie de la Reine Pédauque,* 1893).

But, one may ask, do we not have scriptural sanction and orthodox authority for the belief that Christ conquered hell? This question refers to the Christian theory of salvation, which may thus be briefly summarized: All men, by reason of the Fall, became the rightful and exclusive property of Satan; and it would have been unjust on the part of the Deity to take from the Devil by violence that which was in reality his due. Satan, however, was willing to relinquish his claim to the human race on condition that Jesus should be given to him as the ransom price of humanity. But Heaven outwitted Hell in the bargain for man's redemption. When Satan got the price, he found that he could not keep it. In demanding Christ as payment, he did not know the dual nature of his price; and, as Rufinus so aptly puts it, in swallowing the bait (the humanity), he was tortured by the hook (the divinity) and was only too glad to relinquish both.[8] Whether by fair dealing or foul,

---

[7] A custom prevailed in England to hang consecrated palm crosses over the doors on Palm Sunday and put them into the purses in order to drive the devil out; cf. Wilhelm Mannhardt: *Baumkultus* (Berlin, 1875), pp. 291-92.

[8] *The Devil's Lawsuit* written in the fourteenth century by the lawyer, Jacobus de Theramo, gives an excellent idea of the medieval interpretation of the Christian scheme of salvation. The evolution of the theory of salvation in the Church is thoroughly presented in Hastings Rashdoll's *The Idea of Atonement in Christian Theology* (London, 1919).

you will say, the fact remains that, through the death of the Saviour, man was redeemed from the power of Satan, and the victory was won by Heaven over Hell.

If we look at the world with open eyes, however, we cannot help believing that the contrary comes nearer to the truth. The ecclesiastics themselves believe that, in the eternal conflict between the Deity and the Devil for supremacy in this world, the latter gradually has been gaining the upper hand. The *Malleus malefi-carum,*[9] a large volume on the procedure in witchcraft cases, written by two Dominican Inquisitors appointed by Pope Innocent VIII, who, on December 4, 1484, issued the fatal bull against witchcraft, the famous "Summis desiderantes," contains the singular avowal that the Devil is constantly gaining ground, or, in other words, that the Deity is constantly losing ground; that man, who was destined to go to heaven, is rather headed downward. If such was the condition of affairs in the Middle Ages when the Church was supreme, how great must be the Devil's power over men today? It was a comparatively easy matter for man in the Middle Ages to make his escape from the jaws of Hell. The Catholic Church by its holy offices and blessed sacraments offered weapons of protection against the assaults of the enemy of mankind. The Devil was routed by the recitation of an *Ave Maria* or with a few drops of holy water.[10]

The monks exorcised the demons by singing the breviary hymns at vespers. The sign of the Cross was considered the surest defence against the snares and stratagems of malignant spirits. The very mention of the Lord often sufficed to put to flight the fiends of hell. But Satan, as Bret Harte remarks in his story, "The Devil and the Broker" (1867), is no longer scared by any holy signs. "The Christians," Voltaire said already a century and a half ago, "have lost the power to expel the Devil by the sign of the Cross." Indeed, Beelzebub no longer shudders behind his mask when the Cross confronts him, nor does he shrink from the test of holy water.

[9] An English translation of this "Witch-Hammer," published in 1489, recently appeared in England under the ægis of the Reverend Montague Summers, an exponent of medievalism in modern times. A German translation of this book appeared in Berlin in 1905.

[10] The story by Rabelais about the Devil in the holy-water basin is well known to all acquainted with the writings of that monk. A play entitled *le Diable dans un bénitier* written by Clémence Robert appeared in the fifties of the last century. The book, *le Diable dans le bénitier* (1926) by G. de la Fouchardière, the clever "columnist of the Paris daily, *l'Oeuvre,* may well be called the Gospel according to Satan.

Furthermore, the saints in heaven gave succor to the penitent sinners. The Mother of God mediated between the evil-doer who prostrated himself at her feet and the wrath of the Lord provoked by his guilt. Even in his very last hour, the Catholic could escape Satan's clutches, no matter how closely he had been identified with him, by means of a skilfully added sum of pious externalities. But the Reformation robbed the saints of the power of intervention on behalf of the sinners and abolished all the ceremonies supposed to send Satan away from his victims. The German Reformer, Martin Luther, antagonized with all his might what he called the unbusiness-like and demoralizing relations of the Catholic Church to the powers of Heaven. In the Protestant Church, the Devil must have his pay, and the Devil's pay is the soul of the sinner. Thus, ever since the days of the Reformation, Satan's power in this world has considerably increased.

It is fully in conformity with the Christian creed when we see the paw of the Devil rather than the hand of the Deity in the affairs of men. The Church has always taught that the evil influence has a stronger hold upon mankind than the good influence. It is a part of the doctrinal system of the Church that Satan can and actually does exercise over man a greater power than God— physical as well as moral. The direction of human destinies lies in the hands of the Devil rather than of the Deity. "C'est le diable qui tient les fils qui nous remuent," affirms the French poet, Charles Baudelaire. It is the Prince of the Pit who pulls the human puppets on this stage which we call the earth. The whole world lies in his grasp. He has bruised man's head. Apart from a few elect individuals, the whole human race, according to the Calvinistic creed, is doomed to hell.

* * *

Many theories have been advanced. to bring into harmony scriptual authority and practical experience. The Franciscans believed that the Fiend was in fact fettered for a full thousand years (Rev. xx. 2), but that after his millenary captivity, he was let loose again from hell to "deceive the nations" (Rev. xx. 3).[11]   Certain demon-

[11] The French novelist, Maurice Magre, published a pseudo-medieval play, *l'An mille,* which deals with the current belief toward the end of the tenth century in the imminent second coming of Christ and the end of the world, which are to follow, according to Christian eschatology, the liberation of Satan from his millenary bondage. In this play, the harsh and pitiless fanaticism of the monks, the medieval spokesmen of the Deity, is opposed to the longings and aspirations of youth, which are encouraged by the wizard, who is the mouth-piece of the Devil.

ologists taught that it was only the Devil who was laid in chains by Christ, but that the demons have retained full liberty to go up to earth in order to carry out the plans of their chief. The effect on the affairs of men, however, is unchanged inasmuch as the Devil directs his work from his dungeon and effects his will among men through millions of messengers, who carry his commands to the ends of the earth with the rapidity of a flash of lightning.

*
* *

The demonologists further maintain that even the other great devils, for the most part, keep in a mystical seclusion and appear upon earth only in cases of the greatest urgency or when compelled to do so by conjuration. But they each have a number of legions of lesser devils at their disposal, who are their agents on earth. Certain grand devils have under them as many as twenty, thirty, forty or even fifty legions of inferior spirits; and each legion is composed of six thousand six hundred and sixty-six demons. The monarch of hell himself has myriads of myrmidons, whom he sends out as his recruiting agents to the four corners of the earth to turn men's minds and steps downward instead of upward. The Devil, in his war with the Deity for the possession of the human race, has developed a monstrous passion for catching souls. He directs all his efforts toward enlarging his kingdom (*Dr. Faustus* v. 40).

The messengers of hell aim to counteract the messengers of heaven. When man's guardian angel whispers good counsel into his right ear, a demon is always near to whisper evil counsel into his left ear. The angel and the demon thus carry on a debate across man's brain over the merits and demerits of a certain act. He who advances the stronger arguments wins. In the Catholic Church, namely, each act of man is accounted for by the whispering of either a good or a bad angel. From the days when Athanasius related the life of St. Anthony in devil-fighting heroics, man's evil thoughts and acts have always been considered by the theologians as the machinations of the evil spirits.

In addition to prompting men to sin by whispering evil counsel into their ears, the demons also enter into their bodies to possess their souls. It is a part of the doctrinal system of the Church that the Devil has the power to enter both men and beasts, but can be driven from his human habitation by the conjuration of the pious.

Indeed, a man's piety was judged by the power he had to drive the Devil out. It was believed that the Devil slipped into the body of a man together with the food he swallowed.[12] One interesting feature of diabolical possession is that, though always on the watch to aid the evil-doers, the Devil, having entered the body of a person, proceeds to reveal his victim's secret sins. The stories of demoniac possession are numerous, from that of Mary of Magdala, who harbored at least seven demons in her heart (Luke viii. 2), to the nuns of Loudun, who received frequent visits from the evil powers in the year of our Lord sixteen hundred and thirty-three.[13]

On the other hand, the demons of hell can be conquered by man and imprisoned in black bottles. This conception of a demon enclosed in a phial of black glass hails from the Orient.[14] The Asiatics believed that, by abstinence and special prayers, evil spirits could be reduced into obedience and imprisoned. This tradition is frequently found in esoteric works and forms a part of the Solomonic lore. In the cabalistic *Vinculum spirituum,* a book of Eastern origin, it is said that Solomon discovered, by means of a certain learned volume, the valuable secret of inclosing in a bottle of black glass three millions of infernal spirits, with seventy-two of their kings, of whom Beleh was the chief, Beliar (*alias* Belial) the second, and Asmodeus the third. Solomon afterwards cast the bottle into a deep well near Babylon. Fortunately for the contents, the Babylonians, hoping to find a treasure in the well, descended into it, broke the bottle, thus permitting the emancipated demons to return to their ordinary element.[15] The art of imprisoning an evil spirit in a phial of black glass is also mentioned by Gervase of Tilbury, Gerson, Ariosto, Agrippa, Bodin and Palingenius. The *motif* of a demon

[12] Cf. Julius Lippert: *Christentum, Volksglaube und Volksbrauch* (Berlin, 1882), p. 561.

[13] The reader will find a good account in English of this most interesting case of diabolical possession in modern times in the article "The Devils of Loudun," *National Review,* vol. XI (London, 1860), pp. 70-93, which is an unsigned review of the book in four volumes entitled *Histoire du merveilleux dans les temps modernes* by Louis Figuier, which appeared that year in Paris.

[14] Naturally, there can be no question of a bottle in the early form of this belief. Glass was not known in the desert. We need but refer to the story of Aeolus and his bag of winds. The Asiatics imprisoned the demons in goatskins. Anybody can see that wind comes out of a black "goatskin" cloud. In Abyssinia, the Abuna blows a skin full of his breath, which is then tied up, and with a puff from which priests are ordained in that country.

[15] Cf. *The Little Key of Rabbi Solomon, containing the Names, Seals and Characters of the Seventy-Two Spirits with whom he held Converse, also the Art Almadel of Rabbi Solomon, carefully copied by "Raphael."* London, 1879.

enclosed in a liquid container occurs also in the tale of the Fisherman and the Djinn,[16] which will be found in the *Arabian Nights* and which was also treated by the German poet Klopstock in his poem "Wintermärchen" (1778).

This legend of an imprisoned demon was introduced into Spain from the East by the Moors and finally acclimated to find a place in local traditions. From Spain it spread over the whole of Europe. This idea will be found in the work of the Spaniard Luis Velez de Guevara called *El Diablo Cojuelo* (1641), from whom Alain LeSage borrowed both title and plot for his work *le Diable boiteux* (1707). This *motif* has also been employed by Fouqué in his tale *Das Galgenmännlein* (1810), by Fernan Caballero in her version of the Andalusian legend, "The Devil's Mother-in-Law" (1859), and by Robert Louis Stevenson, in his story, "The Bottle Imp" (1891.)

* * *

The demons of hell tempt men of all classes and callings. They do not distinguish between prince and pauper, philosopher and fool. "It must not be thought," assures us Charles Baudelaire, "that the Devil tempts only men of genius. He doubtless scorns imbeciles, but he does not disdain their assistance. Quite the contrary, he founds great hopes on them." Although aiming to bring all men to destruction, the demons feel a particular delight in leading a good man to sin. Their greatest triumph, as Brother Palemon says in Anatole France's novel, *Thais* (1890), is "to sow black and bitter thoughts in the heart of a good man." Among all good people it is the priests whom the Devil persecutes most, because they teach, as the French master has said, that "God takes delight in seeing his creatures languish in penitence and abstain from his most precious gifts" (*les Dieux ont soif*, 1912). Even within the sacred walls of the monasteries and convents, the holy men and women are not safe against Satan's snares (2 Tim. ii. 26). "The Devil is more busy in the monasteries," we are told by Joris-Karl Huysmans, in his novel, *En route* (1895), "than in the cities, as he has a harder job on hand." Another reason for his greater activity in cloisters than in clubs and class-rooms is that he prefers to work among priests rather than among laymen. The priests cannot find safety from Satan's snares even at the very altar. In Alphonse Daudet's story,

[16] Djinns, jinns or genii are the chief race of spirits (some good, some malignant) with which Arabian mythology has peopled the world. See Arno Paul Eichler: *Die Dschinn, Teufel und Engel im Koran.* Berlin, 1928.

"les Trois messes basses" (1869), we learn how the Devil, assuming the form of the little clerk Garrigou, describes to the officiating priest the magnificent meal that is awaiting him at the castle after he has read the three masses and, by ringing a little bell, seems to say constantly, "Hurry up, hurry up, the sooner we finish here, the sooner will we be at table." The priest cannot get his mind off the excellent dishes; he hurries through the holy service, swallowing words, jumping over passages until he is finally through and, with a sigh of relief, says "'*Ite missa est.*" He eats that night so much that he dies without having repented of his sin. He is not admitted to heaven until he has read three hundred masses in his own chapel in presence of all who have sinned through his fault for the one mass that he has stolen. One can still hear all this in the chapel on Christmas night.

On the other hand, Satan often renders good services to the clergymen. In fact, the Fiend seems to be rather fond of the gentlemen of the cloth and seeks their company a good deal. It is told that a Scotch minister was riding home one day through a wood when Satan called out to him, and warned him not to eat a poisoned chicken which his wife was ignorantly cooking for his supper. Diabolus has often substituted for many a preacher who was prevented from preaching his sermon on a Sunday morning. Lord Morley recently told the French story of the monk who was a particular friend of the Devil. One Sunday morning, the monk was too ill to preach, and as Diabolus chanced to appear in the sacristy for a chat with his frocked friend, the latter asked that obliging person to occupy his pulpit for the special edification of his congregation. The Devil preached a most masterly sermon, covering himself with shame and confusion. "How now?" said the monk when the Devil came down, "you have pretty nearly ruined yourself with that sermon."—"Oh! dear no," replied the Devil, "no harm done, no harm done; there was no unction in it."[16a] As may be seen from this story, the Devil's speech to St. Guthlac, the Irish St. Anthony, is not the only instance extant of a diabolical sermon. Diabolus is said to have preached a sermon, among others, in the church of North Berwick, and has occupied pulpits in other countries than England. In fact, the Fiend is famed as a pulpit orator. Satan's general oratorical ability renders further comment superfluous. Lord

[16a] Quoted from by Mr. John O'London in the New York *Times Book Review* for 1921.

Brougham, as we know, recommended Satan's speeches to barristers and parliamentarians.

The Devil is also a frequent visitor in nunneries. But he often finds his match among the holy women. Father Eisen, in his book, *Ancient Origin of the Festival of the Body of Christ,* tells us that the sister nuns of Cornelia Juliana often heard in her cell a prodigious noise caused by the frequent fights she had with the Fiend, whom she would seize and thrash with all her might, trampling him under foot and bitterly reviling him.[17]

It will perhaps be permitted us to offer here in full a very interesting Provençal legend about the temptation of a nun, retold a quarter-century ago in English verses by a Manchester poet, B. H. Berti:

"The good folks in Provence the story oft tell,
How the Devil once tapt at a Nun's holy cell,
    When began the night-raven to croak;—
In a Monk's cowl his horns and black features he veil'd,
His huge cloven feet and fork'd tail were conceal'd
    In a long spreading sanctify'd cloak.

" 'Father Peter is come to absolve thee of sin';
Said the arch-fiend, and stifled a horrible grin,
    'Confession and tears I require!'
The Nun drew the latch;—in the cell-bolt he came,
His garments flew off in a blue sulph'rous flame,
    His eyes roll'd like meteors of fire.

"With terror she shriek'd at his horns and his tail:—
'In the name of the Virgin! thy purpose reveal;
    'O Jesu! preserve my poor soul!'
With long ave-maries the fiend seem'd dismay'd,
Full of wrath he breath'd forth noxious steams, and display'd
    In his black iron claws a red scroll.

" 'Thy soul's all I want—these few articles sign,
'And ev'ry delight of this life shall be thine,
    'All hell to thy pleasure shall kneel!'
'O fie! prince of darkness, 'tis not quite polite
'To pay court to a lady, in such a sad fright;
    'Prithee take off that strange deshabillé!'

[17] A very beautiful medieval legend about the Devil in a nunnery will be found in the collection of stories published by Mr. F. O. Mann under the title *The Devil in a Nunnery and Other Medieval Tales* (1914). This story has also been reprinted in the present writer's anthology of *Devil Stories* (New York: Knopf, 1921).

"The demon then vanish'd, and shortly up sprung,
Strangely alter'd indeed, he was comely and young,
   In a dress quite cut out *à-la-mode*:—
'Well, you're something at last, you look handsome and spruce;
'And now, my dear Devil, the writings produce,
   'Let us see what new joys they forebode!

" 'Hey day, fourteen years! why the time is too short,
'These walls while I live can yield frolic and sport,
   'Then away with thyself and thy bond!'
'Go to,' said the tempter, 'to sign prithee haste;
'Fly, fly from these cloisters, and true pleasure taste
   'Midst my vot'ries, who form the *beau monde!*'

" 'Dear Sir, you're outbid, and your tongue's of no use;
'In transports the purest this world can produce
   'Friar Lewis and I nightly revel!
'Take your blood-written scroll; take your curst scarlet bait!'
'Ah!' mutter'd the fiend, and went shaking his pate,
   'A Nun has more wit than the Devil!' "

*
* *

The emissaries of heaven and the emissaries of hell frequently engage in a pugilistic battle over the souls of men at their death, similar to that carried on by Michael and Satan over the body of Moses (Jude 9).[18] According to medieval tradition the two parties contending for our souls often resort to gambling as a means of settling their disputes. In the pseudo-medieval mystery-play *le Prince des sots* (1830) by Gérard de Nerval, an angel throws dice with the Devil, with human souls as the stakes. The angel cheats, through excess of zeal, with the object of taking back as many of his friends as possible into Paradise. The Devil in the end loses his temper, calls the angel "great gawky fellow, sly fool," and threatens, if he catches him again at his tricks, to pull every feather out of his wings, so that he will be unable to fly back to his Master.

---

[18] The devils and angels are often shown in the Italian plays in conflict over the souls of mortals, with varying success, according to the virtues of the souls in question. In the play *The Virgin Martyr* by Massinger and Dekker (1622), a struggle between the good and the bad angel, who followed a man through life, is continued over his soul after his death. Good and evil demons were also wont to fight over the souls of mortals in the drama of the Buddhists. In Edouard d'Anglemont's poem, "l'Ame du Moine" (1829), the Devil fights, near the old abbey of Saint-Ouen situated on the banks of the Robec river, over the soul of an unworthy monk, who has just died, with his guardian angel, who maintains that the monk repented when he was on the point of death. Robert sans Peur, the Duke of Normandy, arbitrates between the two parties, and decides in favor of the angel.

Baudelaire, in his story, "le Joueur généreux" (1864), tells how he himself gambled with the Devil for his own soul.[18a] Satan is famed as the greatest gambler ever known upon or under the earth.[19] He taught the Roman soldiers how to cast lots for the raiment of Jesus (John xix. 24). Old Nick invented playing cards, which are therefore often called the Devil's Bible; and it is he also who invented dice, which are sometimes termed the Devil's bones.[20] Mr. H. G. Wells, in his novel *The Undying Fire* (1919), has Diabolus play chess with the Deity in heaven.

*
* *

Satan, on account of his search for souls, has often been portrayed in popular legend as a fisherman. There is a long poem entitled "The Devil Fishing," from which we will quote the first three stanzas:

"The Devil sat by the river's side,
    The stream of Time, where you'll always find him—,
Casting his line in the rushing tide
    And landing the fish on the bank behind him.

"He sat at his ease in a cozy nook,
    And was filling his basket very fast;
While you might have seen that his deadly hook
    Was differently baited for every cast.

"He caught 'em as fast as a man could count;
    Little or big, it was all the same.
One bait was a cheque for a round amount;
    An assemblyman nabbed it, and out he came."

*
* *

The Devil was wont to carry off the souls that belonged to him

[18a] There is an allegory representing Satan playing with a man for the latter's soul in Carl Militz's *Die Schauspieler*. Illustrations by Moritz Retzsch. The title and text are printed in German, French and English.

[19] An excellent story about Beelzebub as a golf player is Charles Deulin's "The Devil's Round" (1874), reprinted in the collection of *Devil Stories* already mentioned.

[20] In Edouard d'Anglemont's legend, "la Partie· de dés" (1833), Satan plays dice, in the ruins of the monastery of Saint-Benoît-sur-Loire, with the saint over a manor which has been bequeathed to the abbey and over the possession of which the two have long disputed with each other. The Devil shows a pair-royal of six, but the abbot is not dismayed and produces a pair-royal of seven.—As a dice player, Satan is the successor to Woden.

in a basket, as may be noted on the doorway of the Cathedral of Fribourg in Switzerland, where he is represented with a pig's head, a crook in his hand, and a rag-picker's basket on his back.[21] He was so certain of his prey that he was accustomed to leave his basket open. When he observed, however, that many souls managed to run off, he put a heavy cover and a good padlock on the box. But the cover did not prevent the souls from escaping. Aided by the rosy fingers of the cherubs, they found a way of sifting through the wicker-work of the basket. When the Devil realized his loss of souls, he slew a dromederay, and with the skin of the hump contrived a leather sack, into which he crammed as many souls as he possibly could find. "It is usually in Upper Egypt," says Victor Hugo, who has incorporated this legend in his beautiful story of the Bold Pecopin (in *le Rhin*, 1842), "by the shores of the Red Sea, after going his rounds among pagans and unbelievers, that the Devil fills his leather bag." But one day as he was promenading on the shore of the Red Sea, St. Medard saw Satan carrying on his back a bag full of damned souls. The heart of the saint was filled with compassion for the poor souls, and he quickly slit the Devil's bag open, whereupon the souls scrambled for liberty:

"Away went the Quaker.—Away went the Baker,
Away went the Friar—that fine fat Ghost,
    Whose marrow Old Nick had intended to pick
Dressed like a Woodcock, and served on toast!

"Away went the nice little Cardinal's Niece
And the pretty *Grisettes,* and the Dons from Spain,
    And the Corsair's crew, and the coin clipping Jew,
And they scamper'd, like lamplighters, over the plain!"
    —From *The Ingoldsby Legends, or Mirth and Marvels.*

In the medieval mystery plays, each demon is represented as bringing an individual soul and narrating the sin which condemned it to hell. In many plays, a long procession of such souls is shown, representing all classes and professions, from princes to paupers. Among the sinners whom the demons in the medieval drama carry off to hell, amidst the clattering of caldrons, we meet peers and

[21] The conception of the Devil carrying lost souls to hell, common to all forms of medieval literature, may be traced back as far as the apocryphal Vision of St. Paul (4th cent.). The Devil inherited his basket from Thor, who carried a basket slung over his shoulders when he went on his journeys among men.

peasants, dukes and dustment, admirals and artisans, bishops and boilermakers, millionaires and milliners, judges and jobbers. In the Redentin Easter Play of 1484, a priest who has been dragged into hell is able, by the vapor of incense and by his curses, to drive even the Devil into a corner so that he is only too glad to let his victim go. In his distribution of punishments to representatives of the various classes, Lucifer pronounces the severest penalties on the cheating craftsmen. The tavern-keeper who fails on earth to give a full measure of beer to his customers is certain in hell to be offered a hot beverage composed of oil, molten lead, pitch and sulphur.

It may thus be seen that the war for the world between the Almighty and the Adversary is still waging as strong as ever, and that Satan has not wholly been subdued by the Saviour. The jaws of hell are still open to swallow the sinners, and the Church is right in continuing to threaten us with pitch and brimstone.

The eternal combat between the Deity and the Devil will not end, according to Catholic tradition, until the second coming of Christ, who will accomplish on this occasion what he has left uncompleted when he first trod on this earth. At the consummation of things, Satan and his cohorts will be defeated by the hosts of heaven in a final combat and locked up eternally in hell, the portals of which will never open again to permit the demons to harass humanity. May this day be near. Amen.

CHAPTER XIV

THE SYNAGOGUE OF SATAN

THE Synagogue of Satan is of greater antiquity and potency than the Church of God. The fear of a malign being was earlier in its operation and more powerful in its appeal among primitive peoples than the love of a benign being. Fear, it should be remembered, was the first incentive of religious worship. Propitiation of harmful powers was the first phase of all sacrificial rites. This is perhaps the meaning of the old Gnostic tradition that when Solomon was summoned from his tomb and asked, "Who first named the name of God?" he answered, "The Devil."

Furthermore, every religion that preceded Christianity was a form of devil-worship in the eyes of the new faith. The early Christians actually believed that all pagans were devil-worshippers inasmuch as all pagan gods were in Christian eyes disguised demons who caused themselves to be adored under different names in different countries. It was believed that the spirits of hell took the form of idols, working through them, as St. Thomas Aquinas said, certain marvels which excited the wonder and admiration of their worshippers (*Summa theologica* II.ii.94).

This viewpoint was not confined to the Christians. It has ever been a custom among men to send to the Devil all who do not belong to their own particular caste, class or cult. Each nation or religion has always claimed the Deity for itself and assigned the Devil to other nations and religions. Zoroaster described alien worshippers as children of the Devas, which, in biblical parlance, is equivalent to sons of Belial. The Greeks ascribed the origin of the Scythian race to the Devil, while to Jewish eyes all Gentile races were demonic. In considering other religions as "devilish," Christianity did nothing more than accept the belief of its parent faith. If this viewpoint were confirmed, it would be safe to say

that the believers in Beelzebub outnumber to this day the worshippers of the Blessed Lord. The Christians, as far as numerical
strength is concerned, play even now a rather insignificant part
as compared with the followers of other religions, since only a
fourth of the population of this earth is Christian.

The belief in the eternal damnation of all non-Christians is not
greatly stressed nowadays. But the medieval Church was emphatic
in its assertion that all who did not seek salvation in its bosom
served Satan. Romance and history combined in representing those
outside the pale of the Church as the personal vassals of Satan,
who worked his deceptions among them. Jews, Turks and heretics,
in addition to the heathen, were believed in all Christian lands to
be allies of the infernal powers. The Jews were supposed by the
Christians to worship the Devil and to accumulate their wealth with
his aid. The Jewish synagogues were regarded by Christians as
temples of Satan. The belief that every Jew wears horns has
persisted in certain Christian circles to the present day. In the
opinion of Emmanuel Malynski, a contemporary Polish-French
writer, the Talmud has been inspired by the Spirit of Evil.

The Saracens were also regarded in the Middle Ages as living
under the yoke of the demons, with whom they are even identified
in *le Charroi de Nîmes,* one of the French medieval epic poems
called *chansons de geste.* The Devil and the Turk were commonly
thought in the Middle Ages to be closely related and often joined
together. Martin Luther also called all Turks devils.

Similarly, in the eyes of the Catholic Church, heretics were
the spawn of Satan. Heresy was traced by the Church to the blow-
ing of Beelzebub's bellows into the ears of humanity. The Albigenses were called by the Catholics "members of the Devil,"
and the Waldenses were considered confederates of the powers of
hell.

When the Church, at the advent of the Reformation, was divided
against itself, each part accused the other of serving Satan. Catholics and Protestants never wearied in accusing each other of being
influenced by the spirits of hell. Priests taught that Protestants
were devil-worshippers and magicians (Samuel Harsnett: *Declaration of Egregious Popish Impostures,* 1603). The French Huguenots, among other Protestant bodies, were believed by the Catholics
to be on intimate terms with the Devil.

The Protestants, on their part, stoutly maintained that the

Catholics were in the service of Satan. The Reformers attributed the miracles of the Catholic saints to an infernal origin, just as the Jews had believed the miracles of Christ to have been performed with the aid of Beelzebub (Matt. xii.24). The Calvinist Calfhill, in his answer to Martiall's *Treatise of the Cross* (1564), maintained that the Catholics were in reality serving Satan, while they believed that they worshipped the Lord. Martin Luther similarly considered the Catholic Church as an emanation of the Evil Spirit. The Roman Catholic and Apostolic Church was, in his eyes, the whole host of wickedness spoken of in the Book of Revelation. "Alongside of God's sacred Church," the German reformer affirmed, "the Devil has built his chapel, and keeps up in it his ape-like play with holy water" and other Catholic ceremonies.[1] The Protestant leaders supposed Roman ecclesiaticism to be tainted by a connection with the powers of hell. They saw the Devil, in his traditional form of horns, hoof and tail, standing with an immense bellows behind the Pope, the cardinals and the other prelates of the Roman Church, and filling them with hostile plans against the reformed teachings. Luther meant no metaphor when he described the Catholic clergy as the Devil's priests, and the monk's hood as the proper garment of Satan himself; and Melanchthon was deeply in earnest when he called the Papists the slavish imitators of magicians and necromancers whom he termed the agents of hell. The Jesuits were considered as the most "devilish" of all Catholic monks. Phineas Fletcher, in his poem, *The Apollyonists* (1627), identified the Jesuits with the spirits of hell by naming them after the biblical demon, Apollyon. In Béranger's belief, the Jesuits even outdo the demons of darkness in wickedness. The Pontiff in the Vatican himself was accused of diabolical relations in the writings of the Protestants. He was believed to have been crowned by Satan and to represent hell rather than heaven on earth. Others went so far as to maintain that the Pontiff of Rome and the Prince of the Pit were identical. Still others saw in the head of the Roman Church Antichrist in person.[2]

[1] Victor Hugo, in his novel *les Travailleurs de la mer* (1866), deduced from the idea that Satan had taken a fancy to the Catholics and sought their company a great deal the belief that the Devil was more Catholic than Protestant.

[2] The pope is described as Antichrist in Leconte de Lisle's poem "la Mort du moine" (1895). An interesting story about the relation between the head of the hierarchy of hell and the head of the Catholic hierarchy is Richard Garnett's "The Demon Pope" (1888), reprinted in the present writer's anthology of *Devil Stories* (1921).

The Protestant sects, warring among themselves, accused each other of connections with the powers of darkness. The Lutherans gave the Calvinists the rather unflattering name of "white devils." The Methodists considered the Presbyterians as devil-worshippers. "I perceive that your God is my devil," said John Wesley, the founder of free-will Methodism, to George Whitefield, the leader of the Calvinistic Methodists, one day in the course of an argument about predestination. The poet Swinburne considered all Puritans agents of hell. Judge Rutherford, the present head of "Russellism," declared the whole organized Church, Protestant as well as Papist, to be "Satan's organization." Thus not only all non-Christians but even the Christians themselves, if we are to credit their invectives against each other, belong to the Devil rather than the Deity.

* * *

Apart from this diabolization of other men's deities as a result of denominational differences and sectarian strife, there actually were within the Church, down to the thirteenth century, many heretical sects, who fully deserved the term of devil-worshippers.[3] Among the groups who continued within Christianity the traditions of Persian Magianism, Gnosticism and Manichæism, we may mention the Priscillianists of Spain, the Paulicians, the Bogomiles, the Catharists, and the Albigenses. The German Luciferians, of the thirteenth century, expressed their adoration for Lucifer in the belief that he had been unjustly banished from heaven and pronounced anathema against St. Michael, his conqueror. The French woman novelist, George Sand, puts her belief in the unjust treatment dealt out to the Devil by his celestial comrades into the mouth of the followers of Johann Huss in Bohemia, whom she designates as Lollards, a term really applied to the followers of Wycliffe. In her novel, *Consuelo* (1842-43), she tells us that

"In the opinion of the Lollards, Satan was not the enemy of

[3] The Devil has always counted his admirers and adorers even among the orthodox Christians. Many devout church folk, wishing to be on good terms with both parties, offer their allegiance to both the Lord and Lucifer. An English preacher of American extraction, M. D. Conway, tells of a Christian lady residing in Hampshire, England, who made her children bow their heads whenever they mentioned the name of the Devil. When asked the reason for her queer conduct, she replied: "It is safer." He also relates the story of a French peasant woman who was found one day in a church kneeling before a marble group. When she was warned by the priest that she was worshipping the wrong figure, namely, Beelzebub, she replied: "Never mind, it is well to have friends on both sides." (*Cf.* M. D. Conway: *Demonology and Devil-Lore,* 2 vols., London, 1879, II, 13.)

the human race, but, on the contrary, its protector and patron. They held that he was a victim of injustice and jealousy. According to them, the archangel Michael and the other celestial powers who had precipitated him into the abyss, were the real demons, while Lucifer, Beelzebub, Ashtaroth, Astarte, and all the monsters of hell, were innocence and light themselves. They believed that the reign of Michael and his glorious host would soon come to an end, and that the Devil would be restored and reinstated in heaven with his accursed myrmidons. They paid him an impious worship and accosted each other by saying, *Celui à qui on a fait tort te salue* —that is to say, He who has been misunderstood and unjustly condemned, salute thee—that is, protect and assist thee."

Among contemporary devil-worshippers we will mention the Yezidis, a sect living in ancient Assyria, on the slopes of the mountain called Djebel Makub, who still worship the Devil as creator of the world and author of evil, the black Jews in Cochin, British India, and the Voodoos of the West Indies and Haiti. There are infernal cults also in the North of China, in Africa, near Lake Tschad, in the South of India, in the Solomon Islands, and in the New Hebrides.[3a]

* * *

The members of the witch-cult were equally, though perhaps less justly, regarded as devil-worshippers by the Church. It is generally believed that the Witches' Sabbath, as the reunion of Satan and his worshippers was called, applied particularly to the members of the gentler sex, had no basis in reality. The general assumption among the enemies of the Catholic Church is that medieval witchcraft was an invention of the Inquisition. Modern historical research, however, has established the fact that witchcraft was not wholly an imaginary affair, but had its foundation in solid reality.[4] It should be added, though, that the mass of superstition built around it had its inception in the imagination of demented hags taken and tormented by the Inquisition.

The witch-cult was a lineal descendant of the old indigenous heathen religions that covered Europe before the advent of Christianity and that were not easily wiped out by the religion imported from the East. Even for many centuries after the conversion of the European peoples to Christianity, the new faith was only a

---

[3a] On the Yezidis, consult Isga Joseph's thesis, *Devil-Worship*. (Boston, 1919.) See also R. M. Macdonall's article "Solomon Islands and the New Hebrides" in *Cornhill's Magazine*, vol. LXIV (1928), pp. 178-92.

[4] The historicity of the Witches' Sabbath is maintained by Miss Alice Murray in her well documented thesis, *The Witch-Cult in Western Europe* (Oxford, 1921).

thin veneer. In many districts, the masses refused for a long time
to abandon their pagan rites. Men and women, in particular living
far from the advanced areas, tenaciously clung to their ancient
beliefs and observances. Inasmuch as the Christians identified the
old indigenous gods with the devils and evil spirits of the new
religion, their ritual was decreed as devil-worship, and their priests
and priestesses were branded as wizards and witches. The rites
of ancient worship, which now came to be known as witch-cults,
were chiefly devoted to the fertility of field, fold and family and
by their "obscenity" scandalized the people whose very ancestors
had practised the same ceremonies in pagan times.

The witch-cult may thus be considered as primarily a survival
of the old fertility ritual. In fact, we can discover in the Witches'
Sabbath many vestigial remains of the old fertility worship. The
Devil of the Witches' Sabbath is successor to the ancient god, who
may be recognized, in a degenerate form, by all the disguises which
he assumed at these nocturnal ceremonies. It is well known that,
on such occasions, the Devil appeared most frequently in the form
of a goat, the animal sacred to Priapus, the Greek god of vegetal and
animal fertility. The goat also served as the witch's steed when she
repaired to the Sabbath. The broom or stick which was likewise
employed by her as a mount and which was also ridden in the
dances of the Witches' Sabbath, is similarly a fertility symbol.[5]
Furthermore, the unholy ecstasy and unlicensed revelry with which
the Witches' Sabbath terminated should be explained as a survival
of the physical unions which formed part of the ancient fertility
worship.

Next to the fertility rites, the ancient fire-worship may be recognized in the Witches' Sabbath. The witches worshipped their
god as the universal father and protector, and such paternal attributes are generally applied to the ancient sun-divinity. Fire figured
prominently at the Witches' Sabbath, as it did in all pre-Christian
festivals. The torches, with which the gathering-places of the
witches were lighted, had their origin in the Beltane and solar
festivals. The worshippers held candles to the Devil when he
performed certain rites, and thus the expression originated, "to
hold a candle to the Devil." A candle was also carried in the witch-

---

[5] The broom, however, may also represent the sweeping storm, which was
the habitation of the Devil. On the medieval stage, the Devil was often represented with a besom in his hand.

cult by the Devil himself, frequently on his head, in his quality as Lucifer.

The witch-cult was also brought into connection with the weird superstition of the wild hunt, the rout of restless, wandering spirits, which was spread in all the European countries.[6] The witches repaired to their Sabbath on air-minded brooms or goats, just as the avenging maidens of Woden flew through the night air on magic steeds or in the form of swans. The Devil, who conveyed the women to their midnight convocations, was the successor to the Wild Huntsman. Popular belief mentions Diana, the goddess of the hunt in classical mythology, and Herodias, the wicked woman of biblical history, as leaders in this nocturnal air-flight. The canon "Episcopi," of the ninth century, had already associated the Latin goddess and the Judean queen with the women who flew at midnight through the air. The *Malleus maleficarum* or *Witch Hammer* written by the two inquisitors, H. Institoris and J. Sprenger, in Germany toward the end of the fifteenth century, also mentioned Diana and Herodias as leading the wild women during their nocturnal trips in mid-air by the order of the Devil. No lesser persons than Albertus Magnus and Alexander of Hales put their faith in this superstition. Turrecremata, the Spanish commentator, who lived in the fifteenth century, expressed his doubts as to this belief, on the ground that Diana never existed and that Herodias was in all likelihood not permitted to leave hell in order to join the midnight air-processions.

The witch-queen Herodias, the Wandering Jewess, the counterpart of the Wandering Jew in Christian mythology, who leads the midnight revels of devils and witches in medieval superstition, is not, as is generally assumed, the wife of Herod Antipas and the mother of Salome. The idea that both mother and daughter were afflicted with the curse of eternal wandering because of their sinful love for the Baptist, which we find in Heinrich Heine's poem *Atta Troll* (ch.xix), has no foundation in popular belief. The Herodias who figures as leader of the medieval wild hunt is Mariamne, the wife of Herod the Great. She is believed to have brought down upon herself the wrath of the Lord for her contemptuous treatment of the Magi, when they passed Jerusalem on their way to the

[6] Consult H. Plischke's thesis, *Die Sage vom wilden Heere* (Eilenburg, 1914). A beautiful description of the wild army will be found in Heine's poem *Atta Troll* (1842). In Bürger's ballad, "Der wilde Jäger" (1786), the poet gives expression to his indignation over the oppression exercised by some nobles upon their subjects.

manger of Christ. It is said that she refused to go to the window to see them, pretending that she was busy sweeping the room. For this reason, she was doomed to wander through the air at night riding on a broom-stick. Legend thus links her with Epiphany Day, and on the eve of this day, which, in the South of Germany, is not very much different from Shrove Tuesday or Carnival Day, Herodias-Berchta is led in procession through the streets riding on a broom-stick.[7] This fact points to an identification of the Judean queen with the Germanic goddess Berchta (Perchta, Bertha or Hertha), who, it will be remembered, is an appellation given in Southern Germany and in Switzerland to a spiritual being who probably corresponds to the Hulda (Holda or Holla) of Northern Germany. Frau Holda (Holde or Holle) is, in reality, an old goddess, indeed the chief goddess Frigg or Frija, the queen of heaven, the goddess of marriage, as Mother Earth is the goddess of agriculture, fertility, and growth. Friday is named after this goddess. In the country districts of Germany to this day, all marriages are celebrated on Friday. Holda signifies "the gracious, the benign one." This Frigaholda—even that name appears in an old manuscript—is the patroness of spinning maidens. She punishes idleness and slovenliness in spinning, and rewards diligence and care. During the "Twelve Nights," the distaff and spindle were not to be touched on pain of inviting the wrath of Holda.[8]

In Thuringia, Frau Holda or Holla rides with the wild hunt on Walpurgis Night. In other parts of Germany, an image of this goddess, on her flying bed of snow, is still cursed, scourged, and burnt as Herodias. Thus the Judean queen, after having been identified with the ancient Germanic goddess, was assigned to be a companion to Diana, the savage goddess of hunting in Roman mythology, who, in medieval belief, assumed the character of a witch, and both were turned into wandering spirits eternally engaged in a wild hunt.[9]

[7] Consult MacCallum's article "The Great Blessing," in the periodical *Asia* for July, 1927, for Greek Orthodox customs on Epiphany Day, the festival of the baptism of Jesus. In Italy, the peasants, who do not understand the Greek term *epiphania*, have turned it into a fairy or witch Befana, just as an English sailor calls Bellerophon, Billy Ruffian. This Befana, who in Italian popular belief has been identified with Diana, wanders in the winter nights much in the manner of Odin in Scandinavian mythology.

[8] See B. Waschnitius: *Percht, Holda und verwante Gestalten.* Wien, 1913. (Sitzungsberichte der Wiener Akademie der Wissenschaften.)

[9] For further study of the legend of Herodias, consult Jacob Grimm: *Teutonic Mythology.* Transl. from the 6th edition of the German by J. S.

Medieval witchcraft is likewise a survival of pre-Christian magic. It may perhaps be traced, as Gustav Freytag suggests, to the cult of a group of dark demons, who figured in the paganism of the old Nords and who were represented as engaged in an eternal war against the bright deities.[10] The priests of these gloomy gods performed their sacred rites by night and sacrificed to their tutelary spirits dark-colored animals of all kinds. These priests also possessed the power, through the magic agency of their gods, to blast crops and to destroy flocks and herds. Similar beliefs seemed also to exist in ancient Rome. Pliny tells us that in his country laws were enacted against injury to crops by "fascination." The medieval witch or wizard was supposed to possess the power to harm both beast and man. In popular belief, the Devil and the sorcerer or sorceress united in a contract of witchcraft, as the term was understood in the Middle Ages,[11] joined their various powers of doing evil to inflict calamities upon the persons and property, the fortune and fame, of innocent human beings. The witch was especially dreaded in the Middle Ages. She was known as a compounder of philters and poisons, a caster of spells, a wicked woman, and a hideous hag.

The Devil also bestowed his power of physical tergiversation upon the witch and warlock, who thus could transform themselves into all sorts of animals. French witches generally changed themselves into wildcats, whereas the British witches preferred to be transformed into hares.[12] The wizards liked to crawl into the skins of wolves, but, at certain of their assemblies, they also changed themselves into stags, which explains the origin of the expression "stag parties."

The witch organization permeated the lower classes in France,

Stallybrass. London, 1880-88; Karl Simrock: *Handbuch der deutschen Mythologie mit Einschluss der nordischen.* 5 Aufl. Bonn, 1878; E. K. Chambers: *The Mediæval Stage.* Oxford, 1903.

[10] *Cf.* Gustav Freytag: *The Devil in Germany During the Sixteenth Century.* Transl. from the German by Wm. A. Hervey (New York, 1893), pp. 7-8. This essay originally formed the second chapter of the second volume of *Bilder aus der deutschen Vergangenheit* (1859).

[11] The contract of witchcraft differed from the regular devil-compact in so far as it was not witnessed by an instrument written and sealed. The witches and their companions went over to the worship of the Devil and acknowledged him as their lord merely by giving him the oath of submission or by performing a certain act of homage, such as a kiss *in tergo,* a regular ceremony, it was believed, of such infernal vassalage.

[12] Witches can also transform animals into human beings. A witch changes her cat into a cavalier in Théophile Gautier's poem *Albertus* (1832).

MACBETH CONSULTING THE WITCHES

Germany and England. The French historian, Jules Michelet, in his book, *la Sorcière* (1862),[13] attributed the spread of witchcraft among the lower masses to the despair of the poor at finding that even the Church, long their friend and protector, had become feudal and tyrannical, even more tyrannical than their lay oppressors. He saw in the Witches' Sabbath the first glimpses of women's rights, of the equality of sexes, and, in fact, of all modern social reforms. The Black Mass was, in his opinion, "the protest of the oppressed masses, the symbol of the approaching freedom, the communion of rebellion." This author represents magic and sorcery as Nature's protest against the Church's proscriptions and the final victory of *terra mater* after centuries of struggles and atrocious persecutions.

The predominance of women over men in the witch-cult is easily explained by the fact that women are more conservative than men and hold more firmly to ancient beliefs and traditions. Jules Michelet, however, maintains that so many members of the weaker sex surrendered themselves to Satanism in medieval times for the reason that Satan lifted woman from the low position in which she had been held by the Church. His portrait of the medieval witch contains more poetry than history. In his opinion, she is the forerunner of the modern social reformer and natural scientist. She had neither father nor mother, nor son, nor husband, nor family. She was a marvel, an aerolith, alighted no one knew whence. Her place of abode was in spots impracticable, in a forest of brambles, on a wild moor where thorn and thistle forbade approach. She passed the night under an old cromlech. If any one found her there, she was isolated by the common dread; she was surrounded, as it were, by a ring of fire, and yet she was a woman. This very life of hers, dreadful though it appeared, tightened and braced her woman's energy. "You may see her endowed with two gifts. One is the inspiration of lucid frenzy, which, in its several degrees, becomes poesy, second sight, depth of insight, cunning simplicity of speech, the power especially of believing in yourself through all your delusions. . . . From this gift flows the other, the sublime power of unaided conception." But now the witch has nothing to say. "Her ashes have been scattered to the winds." She has perished, chiefly by the progress of those very sciences which be-

[13] Mr. A. R. Allinson has translated this book into English under the title, *The Sorceress, a Study in Middle Age Superstition*. The translation appeared in 1904 in Paris.

WITCHES CELEBRATING WALPURGIS NIGHT
By Franz Simm.

gan with her through the physician, the naturalist, for whom she had once toiled.

The witch groups were organized in worshipping congregations governed by boards known as "covens." The leader was believed to have divine inspiration by his followers, diabolic inspiration by outsiders. He was called the Devil, and in the ceremonial processions he brought up the rear, thus giving rise to the old saying, "the Devil take the hindermost." Mr. R. Lowe Thompson, in his recently published book, *The History of the Devil,* maintains that the leader in the witch-cult was first a magician—a magician disguised as an animal with horns and tail, who afterwards became a priest. When, in his later rôle as a god, he was dethroned by Christianity and driven underground, he turned into the lord of the underworld and king of the dead and finally into the Devil, as the medieval witch knew him. The Reverend Montague Summers in his recent book, *The History of Witchcraft and Demonology,* maintains that the Devil "was present in person for the hideous adoration of his besotted worshippers.[13a]

According to popular belief, the witch repaired to her secret tryst with Satan in the following manner: She removed every stitch of clothing, sat down on a broom stick, took three swallows from a liquid contained in a black bottle, immediately flew up the chimney and was gone. If she employed the goat as a mount, the witch anointed her body with a certain oil which endowed her with the power to fly through the air with the rapidity of a flash of lightning.

The meetings of the witches were held at fixed spots, chiefly in desolate heaths and hills (like the Broken or Blocksberg in Germany[14]), sometimes near the water and often at some old stand-

[13a] The book of this English clergyman represents wholly the medieval point of view. Mr. Summers shows himself in his work as an uncompromising inquisitor who would be only too glad to send heretics and "witches" to the stake if the secular authorities still executed the decrees of the Holy Office." See also his book *The Geography of Witchcraft.* (London, 1927).

[14] Brocken is the Roman Mons Bructerus, the highest peak in the Harz mountains, in fact in Northern Germany. It is 3,745 feet above the sea-level. Old tradition has it that on this mountain witches, devils and all uncanny creatures meet for a great revelry on the night between April 30 and May 1. This tradition seems to go back to the old heathen spring festival, which the early Christians considered as "devilish." Goethe selected the Brocken for the place of one of the scenes in *Faust,* a fact which has greatly added to the popularity of this mountain. Its summit may now be reached during the summer months by a mountain railway, starting from Wernigerode. In winter the ascent, necessarily on foot, is sometimes difficult on account of the snow which often reaches a depth of several feet. Blocksberg is the popular name for the Brocken.

ing stone or megalithic monument. All around the meeting-place boiling cauldrons served as torches.

Spanish witches did not congregate, according to popular belief, in their own country, but across the seas in South America. Spain was too holy to permit a Witches' Sabbath to be held on its soil. The Spanish witches, unlike their sisters in other countries, did not mount on brooms or goats to fly to their revels with the devils, but repaired to their trans-Atlantic meeting-place in boats which sailed so fast that in three hours they travelled across the ocean and back again without ever being detected by their unsuspecting husbands. They must necessarily have had a strong wind at their command, for it was none other than the Devil himself who bellied out the sails of their boats (Prosper Mérimée: *les Sorcières espagnoles,* 1829).

The main reunions of the witches occurred on May Eve (April 30), which was sometimes known as Toodmas in Great Britain and as Walpurgis Night in Germany,[14a] and on November Eve (October 31), called Hallowe'en. As a later addition, midway between these nights of power, we have witches' gatherings on Candlemas (February 2), and on Lammas, otherwise called the Gule of August (August 1). At each of the great assemblies, there were two gatherings. One was the "Sabbath,"[14b] a public meeting of all the witches in the district, who feasted, danced and celebrated their rites, worshipped their god, and indulged in all sorts of orgies. The other meeting, the "esbat," which was not open to the public, was a sort of business council at which the affairs of the cult were discussed by the officials, and the more esoteric rites were carried out by skilled hands. These secret ceremonies included blood sacrifices of creatures—such as a cat, a dog, a red cock, or an unbaptized child. In addition to the four great assemblies, smaller gatherings were held every week. It was believed that the devil-

[14a] Walpurga was an English saint, who accompanied her uncle St. Boniface to Germany in the eighth century to aid him in the foundation of religious houses. Her commemoration day fell on the 1st of May, the date of the great heathen spring festival, which was decried by the early Christians as devil-worship. In consequence, by a strange irony of coincidence, the name of the good saint became associated with that "unholy carnival" into which the Christian imagination transformed the May Day ceremonies. See the scene "Walpurgisnacht" in the First Part of Goethe's *Faust.*

[14b] The word "Sabbath," it should be remembered, has no relation to the Jewish day of rest, but is most probably derived from the French word *s'esbattre,* which means "to frolic." In contrast to the old Puritan Sabbath, the Witches' Sabbath contained elements of joy.

THE WITCHES' SABBATH. (After Picart)

worshippers met on Thursdays to forestall the Mohammedans, who gathered for the adoration of their god on Fridays; of the Jews, who observed their day of rest on Saturdays; and of the Christians, who worshipped the Lord on Sundays.[15]

The main part of the ritual of a Witches' Sabbath consisted of hymns and prayers addressed to the Devil.[16] When the religious rites were ended, the feast commenced, all partaking of the choicest wines and the most delicious meats. Salt is said never to have been used in the witch ceremonies. The Devil, as heir of the ancient death-demons, appears in all European folk-lore as a hater of salt, the agent of preservation. Salt was used in the Middle Ages in the rites of exorcism. In the Catholic Church, a child is still given salt at baptism in order to drive out the Devil. "When I am at table and feel no hunger," we are told by Richalmus, a Cistercian monk, abbot of Schoenthal in Württemberg, who lived in the first part of the thirteenth century, "as soon as I take a little salt, the appetite, of which the Devil robbed me, returns; when my appetite disappears again after a while, I take salt again, and I am again hungry."

The feast was followed by lively dances accompanied by the music of violins, flutes, citterns, hautboys, tambourines and bagpipes. The feasts and dances led up to ecstasies and orgies of a rather promiscuous kind. It was believed that each and every witch had ceremonial union with the Devil, as her lord and master. These "Satanic stunts" reached their climax when "a Jew was married to a toad" (Alexander Pushkin: "The Hussar," 1833).

* * *

The fact is worth noting that the Church did not start its campaign of extermination against the witch-cult until the end of the Middle Ages.[17] In the first centuries of the Christian era, the Church ignored this secret survival of ancient paganism and refused to put any credence in the confused mass of superstition that

[15] The matter summarized in this paragraph has been taken chiefly from the books by Miss Murray and by Mr. Thompson. *Cf.* also the present writer's review of Mr. Thompson's book, which appeared in the *Sewanee Review,* of October, 1929.

[16] The music of the Witches' Sabbath was probably not of the best. The choir could hardly be expected to be composed of trained and well modulated voices. In Victor Hugo's novel, *Han d'Islande* (1823), it is said that "Beelzebub's punishment is frightful indeed if he is condemned to hear the chorus of the women of Drontheim once a week."

[17] Jules Michelet unhesitatingly asserted that the witch first appeared in the "age of despair" engendered by the gentry of the Church.

gathered around witchcraft as a nucleus. An episcopal document of the ninth century reprimanded the belief, current among credulous folk, in the nocturnal mid-air trips undertaken by wild women at the order of the Devil. It was not until several centuries afterwards that the Church revealed its full faith in these superstitions and persecuted all whom she suspected of participating in revels which she had previously declared to be sheer phantasms. "After the Church itself stiffened into a hierarchy," writes Gustav Freytag, "after the unlimited pretensions of the popes drove many a stout heart to heresy, after more than one nation became stultified under the domination of the mendicant friars, then this superstition gradually developed in the Church into a well-grounded and deep-rooted belief. Whatever passed as devilish was wiped out in bloody persecution."[18]

After the famous and fatal bull "Summis desiderantes" issued by Innocent VIII in 1484, a burning of witches began in all European countries that continued, with interruptions, until far into the eighteenth century. The witch-hunt abated somewhat during the Reformation period, Catholics and Protestants being then deeply engrossed in persecuting each other. It was, however, soon revived and raged with greater fury than ever. Catholics and Calvinists vied with each other in burning the greater number of witches for the greater glory of God. The Puritans carried the witch-hunt into the New World. The witch-hangings at Salem and in other American towns form a dark chapter in the history of the New Continent.

Thanks to the heroic efforts of a Cornelius Agrippa, a Johannes Wierus and a Friedrich Spee, the belief in witchcraft gradually disappeared in the various European countries. Holland abolished witch persecution in 1610; Geneva in 1632, Sweden in 1649, and England in 1682. The last judicial execution for witchcraft in Europe took place in Poland in 1793, when two old women were burned at the stake. In one European country, witchcraft still has a legal status. Ireland even now recognizes witchcraft as an offence against the law. In the Commission of Peace, the newly appointed magistrate is empowered to take cognizance, among other crimes, of "Witchcraft, Inchantment, Sorcery, Magic Arts."[19]

[18] Gustav Freytag, *op. cit.*, p. 9.

[19] *Cf.* St. John D. Seymour: *Irish Demonology and Witchcraft* (New York, 1913), p. 248.

The belief in witchcraft, however, has not wholly disappeared even in the twentieth century. An unbelievably wide-spread condition of superstition and sorcery still exists in many European countries. It is generally known that faith in witchcraft and fear of the evil eye are prevalent among certain uneducated classes in small European towns. An incident that recently occurred at Bordeaux, in France, shows that the belief in witchcraft has made headway even in the advanced modern cities. In our own country, "Voodooism" is manifestly a lineal descendant of medieval witchcraft. The "hex murders" in a small Pennsylvania town not so long ago furnished sufficient proof that the witch, in the United States, has not passed out of the realm of belief with the Salem persecutions. Witchcraft, however, is not limited to remote towns in the United States. It has repeatedly come to light even in our centers of civilization. In New York, in Chicago and in most of the big cities of this country, there are thousands of persons, mostly of foreign extraction, who still believe in and practice the arts of witchcraft. The fear of the evil-eye, which prevails among many classes in our big cities, has been brought over primarily from Italy, where this superstition still counts thousands upon thousands of believers. In Naples, the *jettatore,* as the owner of the evil eye is called, is so feared that, at his approach, a street is rapidly emptied of men, women and children. In India, China, Turkey, and Greece, there exists a belief that the evil eye affects also horses and cattle. The persistence of the belief in the evil eye shows with what tenacity old beliefs and ancient superstitions will continue to exist through the ages.[20]

[20] The matter of medieval witchcraft is avowedly treated summarily in this book. The reader, who is interested in this subject, is referred to the works by Miss Murray and Mr. Thompson already mentioned, and especially to Professor G. L. Kittredge's thorough work *Witchcraft in Old and New England,* which has just been published. Among German studies on the subject we will mention the following: W. G. Soldan: *Geschichte der Hexenprozesse* (1843, 3. Aufl. 2 Bde. 1912); Johann Diefenbach: *Der Hexenwahn* (1886). A curious little book on the Witches' Sabbath is *le Sabbat des Sorciers* by Bourneville and E. Teinturier, which appeared in the *Bibliothèque diabolique* (2nd ed., 1890). Of particular interest is the book *Là-Bas* by the French novelist Joris-Karl Huysmans (1891), which was originally intended by its author as a serious study rather than a novel. In the journal *Echo de Paris,* where it first ran in serial form, it had as subtitle "Etude sur le satanisme." *Là-Bas* is a store-house of occult sciences. We learn in it all about ecclesiology, liturgy, astrology, theurgy, therapy, alchemy, sorcery, necromancy, sadism, vampirism, incubism, succubism, and all other varieties of black magic, in addition to somewhat more conventional subjects, ranging from painting to cooking. In this book, we are also told the history of Gilles de Rais, who was a leader in the medieval witch-cult, we are instructed in regard to the

* * *

Nor is devil-worship wholly extinct in modern times. Contemporary Satanism, however, is not historic, but ecclectic. It is not directly connected with medieval witchcraft, although it borrowed many elements from the cult. In contrast to the medieval witch-cult, modern Satanism is practiced by the cultured classes in the European capitals. Huysmans in his novel *Là-Bas* affirms that "the cult of Satan still survives in France as in the other principal European countries and that it has not been unknown even in England during the past hundred years."[21] The English critic, Mr. Arthur Symons, who certainly cannot be accused of credulity, maintains that "all but the most horrible practices of the sacrilegious magic of the Middle Ages are yet performed from time to time in a secrecy which is all but absolute."[22] The Reverend Mr. Montague Summers likewise asserts that "Satanists yet celebrate the Black Mass in London, Brighton, Paris, Lyons, Bruges, Berlin, Milan, and alas! in Rome itself. . . . Often they seem to concentrate their vile energies in quiet cathedral cities of England, France and Italy."[23]

Although Huysmans' presentation of modern Satanism is offered in the form of fiction, the impression must not be gained that it was evolved out of the author's imagination. As a naturalist, Huysmans relied for his material wholly on observation and documentation. He must have read hundreds of folios and collected mountains of notes in the preparation of his book, which Léon Bloy calls a cataclysm of documents. Huysmans supplemented his reading by personal observation. For several years previous to the publication of his novel, he zealously frequented the circles of the Rosicrucians, Illuminists,[24] spiritualists and other occultists of the

meaning of the sacrifice of Melchizedek, and we are informed concerning the person of Antichrist and the teaching of Paracelsus. This frightful book, as it has aptly been called, also appeared a few years ago in this country in an abbreviated English translation but was driven under cover immediately upon its publication.

[21] Huysmans reiterated his firm belief in the existence of the Satanic cult in the prefatory essay he contributed to Jules Bois's book, *le Satanisme et la magie* (1895).

[22] *Cf.* Arthur Symons: *Figures of Several Centuries* (London, 1916), p. 296, and *The Symbolist Movement in Literature* (London, 1919), p. 257.

[23] Montague Summers: *The History of Witchcraft and Demonology.* London, 1926.

[24] The original "Illuminati" were a secret mystical sect which sprang up in Bavaria under the leadership of Adam Weishaupt in the latter part of the eighteenth century, and which found adherents also in France. Secret societies

type of the Marquis de Guaita, who, in 1888, founded the neo-Rosicrucian Society of Paris, and Joséphin Péladan, who assumed the title of Sar and who dabbled in all sorts of diabolism. The bulk of his information with regard to modern Satanism was furnished Huysmans by the ex-abbé Boullan, of Lyons, to whom he addressed himself in a letter during the preparation of his novel, stating that he wished proofs of Satanism "in order to be able to affirm that the Devil existed, that he reigned, that the power he had in the Middle Ages had not diminished and that he still was the absolute Master, the Omniarch." This ex-abbé, who figures in *Là-Bas* under the most flattering aspects as Dr. Johannès, an exorcist, was well competent to furnish the desired information, inasmuch as he himself committed the acts which he attributed to others. He hoodwinked Huysmans with regard to his own work, presenting himself as an exorcist and a victim of the machinations of certain unfrocked priests, to whom he ascribed the very deeds committed by himself. The principal proofs of the existence of a cult of Satan furnished by Boullan to Huysmans were the frequent thefts of consecrated wafers throughout France, which, as he maintained, were employed in the celebration of the Black Mass.

The description of the Black Mass, which forms the central episode of *Là-Bas* and which is so marvelously painted in all of its revolting details, has been derived from the manuals of the Inquisition and the reports of the parliamentarians, and supplemented by a study of the life of Vintras, a wonder-worker, who was charged by two former members of his sect with the celebration of the Black Mass.[25] Remy de Gourmont also helped the author in his documentation on the tradition of the Black Mass. But Gourmont soon lost interest in these investigations, having finally arrived at the conclusion that no such diabolical ceremony had ever been celebrated in the Middle Ages, and left Huysmans to construct unaided the unsavory episodes of his novel.[26] Johanny Bricaud, who knew Huysmans personally, maintains, however, that the

were extremely numerous in that country and "Illuminism" of various kinds took particular hold of men's minds during the period just prior to the Revolution. *Cf.* J. P. L. de la Roche du Moine, Marquis de Luchet: *Essai sur la secte des Illuminés.* Paris, 1789.

[25] On the machinations of Boullan and Vintras and other men of their stamp, see Jules Bois: *les Petites religions de Paris* (1894).

[26] Remy de Gourmont's essay on Huysmans' *Là-Bas* entitled "le Paganism éternel" in his book of essays *la Culture des idées* (1900) is very interesting in the light of our discussion.

novelist actually assisted at a Black Mass in the rue de Sèvres, the street in which he lived,[27] although he may have drawn largely on his documentation for many of the most diabolical diversions connected with this ceremony. The reader cannot bring himself to believe that practices of this kind still exist in modern times—from the horrible profanation of the Eucharist, with which the Black Mass begins, to the atrocious and promiscuous orgies, with which it ends. It is also doubtful whether a woman of the type of Mme Chantelouve exists even in the Bohemian quarters of Paris. The contemporary cult of Satan is primarily a diabolism of debauchery. The principal part of the modern Black Mass consists of sexual perversions of all kinds. The materialist Des Hermies in *Là-Bas* reveals a deep insight into human nature when, with regard to Durtal's description of the Black Mass supposedly celebrated in Paris, he remarks: "Je suis sûr qu'en invoquant Belzébuth, ils pensent aux prélibations charnelles" (I am certain that in invoking Beelzebub, they only think of carnal prelibations).[28]

Huysmans, following the lead of other ultra-Catholic writers, includes the Masons among the devil-worshippers in his novel *Là-Bas*. But especially in his preface to Jules Bois's study on Satanism, he expresses his belief that the Masons worship the Devil, although he calls them Luciferians in contrast to the Satanists and thus renders them slightly less odious than other devil-worshippers.

[27] *Cf.* Johanny Bricaud: *J. K. Huysmans et le Satanisme* (1913), p. 16.

[28] Mr. Harry Kemp, in an article contributed to the Sunday edition of the New York *World,* of August 2, 1914, described the activities of a Satanic cult in London, which he claimed had even spread to this country.
It is not the object of this book to go at length into the matter of modern devil-worship in France, but the reader, who is interested in this question, will find ample material in the following books and magazine articles: Alexandre Erdan: *la France mystique* (1853); Charles Sauvestre: *les Congrégations religieuses dévoilées* (1867); Stanislas de Guaita: *Essais de sciences maudites* (1886). M. Jules Bois, who is at present residing in the United States, has constituted himself the historian of modern Satanism by his book *les Petites religions de Paris* (1893) and especially by his study *le Satanisme et la magie* (1895). M. Bois's views on modern Satanism are detailed by Miss Marie A. Belloc in her interview with this French writer, which appeared under the title "Satanism: Ancient and Modern" in the London monthly magazine *The Humanitarian,* vol. XI (1897), pp. 81-7, and by Thomas Walsh in his article "The Amateurs of Satan" published in the New York *Bookman,* vol. IX (1899), pp. 220-23. M. Bois has in recent years found a competitor in R. Schwæblé, who has written the novel *Chez Satan: Roman de mœurs de satanistes contemporains* (1906) and the two studies *le Satanisme flagellé; Satanistes contemporains, incubat, succubat, sadisme et satanisme* (1912), and *Chez Satan, Pages à l'Index. Possession* (1913). Johanny Bricaud, author of *J. K. Huysmans et le satanisme* (1913), already mentioned, announced for publication a study, *le Satanisme contemporain,* which apparently has not yet appeared.

The distinction between these two classes of diabolists consists in the fact that, while the Satanists worship the Devil as the spirit of evil, the Luciferians see in him the spirit of good. Huysmans has many surprises for the American reader. One may learn from him that devil-worship existed in our own country as well as in Europe, and that Americans were at the head of the two international associations for the Propagation of the Faith in the Prince of Darkness. Huysmans asserts that the "Ré-Theurgists-Optimates,"[29] founded in 1855, with headquarters in America, had for their Grand Master no less a person than the poet Longfellow, whose official title was "Grand-Prêtre du Nouveau Magisme Evocateur" (High Priest of the New Evocatory Sorcery).[30] At the head of the second diabolical organization in America stood the Southern poet General Albert Pike, who was called "le vicaire du Très-Bas, le pontife installé dans la Rome infernale" (the vicar of the Very-Low, the Pontiff installed in the Infernal Rome), by which infernal Rome was meant our good Southern town of Charleston, S. C. Albert Pike, together with the Mormon bishop John Taylor, is alleged to have introduced into France, in 1881, the so-called "Maçonnerie Palladique" (Palladic, i. e. Luciferian Masonry).[31]

The Catholics have always considered the Freemasons allies of the Devil. They are believed to have surrendered their souls to Satan, whom they worship in their rites and ceremonials. But, toward the end of the last century, Europe was literally flooded with accusations of devil-worship and immorality against the Masons. This occurred on the occasion of the papal encyclic "Humanum genus," in which the faithful were urged to "snatch from Free-masonry the mask with which it is covered, and to let it be seen what it really is." The ball was set rolling by Léo Taxil (pseud. of Gabriel-Jogand Pagès), who, in the very year of his conversion, gave to the world the first of his "complete revelations concerning Freemasonry" in two volumes called *The Brethren of the Three*

[29] This extraordinary phrase is, according to Mr. F. Legge, "apparently composed of three languages: Optimates is used by Cicero for the aristocratic, as opposed to the popular, party; Theurgos is a man who works wonders by means of the gods, . . . Ré is apparently the Egyptian sun-god Ra" ("Devil-worship and Freemasonry" in *The Contemporary Review*, vol. LXX [1896], p. 472, note).

[30] Huysmans innocently followed his authorities, who, curiously enough, confused the poet Longfellow with a Scotchman by the same name, who was said to have helped in the organization of the "New Reformed Palladium." Cf. Arthur Edward Waite: *Devil-Worship in France* (London, 1896), p. 35.

[31] *Ibid.*, pp. 32 ff.

Points (1884). This writer started his literary career as editor of *l'Anti-Clérical,* an anti-clerical paper of the lowest type, but later was converted, or reverted, to the faith of his childhood. He published his books under various pseudonyms in order to gain greater credence among his readers. He kept up this deception as long as he could, and, in the year 1897, on the eve of being exposed, publicly confessed that all his revelations about Masonic devil-worship were a hoax. Other books by this anti-Masonic writer are: *The Cult of the Grand Architect* (1886); *Sister Masons,* or *Ladies' Freemasonry* (1888); and *Are There Women in Freemasonry?* (1891). His novel, *The Devil in the Nineteenth Century,* appeared in serial form, in 1892-1895, under the pseudonym of Dr. Bataille. His *Memoirs of an ex-Palladist* were passed off as the work of an English lady, Miss Diana Vaughan, who claimed that she had seen Lucifer appearing at one of the meetings of a Masonic ladies' auxiliary as a very handsome young man, clad in a golden *maillot* and seated on a throne of diamonds.

This great accuser of the Masonic Brethren was followed by others, chief among whom were Mgr. Léon Meurin, S. J., archbishop of Port-Louis in Mauritius, author of the book entitled *The Freemasonry; The Synagogue of Satan* (1893), and Signor Domenico Margiotta, commander of a pontifical order, whose chief book of accusation against the Masons is named *The Palladism as Cult of Satan-Lucifer* (1895). Obviously Signor Margiotta does not uphold the distinction between Satanists and Luciferians marked by other writers. He received from the Pope the apostolic benediction for his denunciation of the Masons, his former associates. Other anti-Masonic writers were Paul Rosen, author of *Satan and Company* (1888), and Jean Koska (pseud. of Jules Doinel), who wrote a book with the significant title of *Lucifer Unmasked* (1895).[32]

---

[32] The reader who is interested in this Catholic-Masonic controversy, in addition to the writings of Legge and Waite already mentioned, is referred to the following books and magazine articles: Arthur Lillie: *The Worship of Satan in Modern France* (1896); Bräunlich: *Der neueste Teufelsschwindel* (1897); Charles Henri: "Der enlarvte Lucifer" in the Stuttgart Socialist monthly *Die neue Zeit,* vol. XV (1897), II, pp. 490-98 and "Satanismus und moderner Exorzismus in Frankreich," *Deutsches Protestanten-Blatt, XXX* (1897), 106-10. J. Rieks' book, *Leo XIII und der Satanskult* (Berlin, 1897) is a criticism of the attitude of the papacy toward the pretended revelations of Masonic devil-worship made by Léo Taxil and others. On Léo Taxil's attacks against Freemasonry, consult also Hermann Gruber's *Leo Taxil's Palladismus* (Berlin, 1898).

CHAPTER XV

THE DEVIL-COMPACT IN TRADITION AND BELIEF

THE tradition of the devil-compact, which figures as an important factor in demonology, is of great antiquity.[1] This notion of a bargain with Beelzebub is of Oriental origin, and is traceable as far back as the Persian sacred writings. In the Zend-Avesta, Ahriman fails in his efforts to tempt Zoroaster. But Iblis has greater success in this direction. In the *Shah-Nameh* of Firdusi,[2] this demon promises the Arabian prince Zohak to place him higher than the sun if he will sign a pact with him. The offer is accepted without much hesitation, and Iblis consecrates the pact by a kiss on both of Zohak's shoulders, from which spring forth two black serpents that no man can destroy. At last, the demon himself appears in the guise of a learned physician, and recommends that the serpents be given human brains to eat. Zohak kills his father and succeeds him on the throne, but he finally pays the penalty for the evil deeds committed by him with the demon's aid.

This Persian belief in a devil-compact forced its way into the religion of the Jews during the period of their Babylonian captivity under Zoroastrian rulers, and was transmitted by the Jews to the Christians.

The devil-compact is clearly mentioned in the Book of Enoch, the Talmud and the Kabbala and is besides evident from a number of biblical passages. The temptation of Eve in Eden may perhaps be regarded as the first germ of this idea.[3] It is evident that the ac-

[1] The first attempt to treat this subject critically is J. A. Rinneberg's study *De pactis hominum cum diabolo* (17th century).

[2] Aboul-Casem or Abul Kasim Mansur, called also Ferdoussi, Ferdausi or Ferdusi, celebrated Persian epic poet, author of the *Shah-Nameh* or *Book of Kings* (c. 941 - c. 1021).

[3] Cf. E. G. Holland: "Who was the first Faust?" *Appleton's Journal,* XIV (1875), 80-81.

count of the temptation of Jesus in the wilderness is based upon a belief in the possibility of an agreement of reciprocal obligations or relations between man and the Devil and upon the recognition of the Devil's great power in this world.[4] This idea is particularly noted in the words which Satan addresses to Jesus in showing him all the kingdoms of the world: "All these things will I give thee, if thou wilt fall down and worship me" (Matt. iv. 9; cf. Luke iv. 6-7).

The term "New Testament," which meant to the early Christians and still means, in the original Greek, the "New Contract" or the "New Covenant," furnished the theologians with additional scriptural support for the belief in the possibility of man entering into a formal contract or covenant with the Devil, who was represented by the Church fathers as the replica of the Deity. The Adversary, wishing in every respect to counterfeit the acts of the Almighty, naturally also attempts to form a compact with men.

St. Jerome accepted this belief in a devil-compact to explain the expressions "a covenant with death" and "an agreement with hell" used by the prophet Isaiah in reproaching the rulers of Jerusalem for their unconcern about the impending peril for their city. The passage runs as follows:

"Wherefore hear the word of the Lord, ye scornful men, that rule this people which is in Jerusalem. Because ye have said, We have made a covenant with death, and with hell are we at agreement; when the overflowing scourge shall pass through, it shall not come unto us: for we have made lies our refuge, and under falsehood have we hid ourselves. Therefore saith the Lord God, Behold . . . the hail shall sweep away the refuge of lies, and the waters shall overflow the hiding place. And your covenant with death shall be disannulled, and your agreement with hell shall not stand; when the overflowing scourge shall pass through, then ye shall be trodden down by it" (Is. xxviii. 14-18).

The belief in a devil-compact was supported by many other prominent Church fathers. St. Augustine treats the notion at great length. St. Basil, the Great, bishop of Cæsarea (370-379), tells in his *Dialogues* of a compact which his own servant Proterius closed with the Fiend. According to the account of this legend given in the *Alphabet of Tales,* written in fifteenth-century English, this young man sold himself to the Devil for the love of a woman.

Naturally enough, the diabolical pacts of the first centuries of our era must be taken not in the apocalyptic but in the Hellenic

[4] Cf. [Gustav] Georg Roskoff: *Geschichte des Teufels* (Leipzig, 1869), I, 201, note 9.

sense. It was purely a question of conversion to the old pagan divinities, whom the Christians had reduced to devils. Even the famous devil-compact of St. Theophilus, of the sixth century, must have differed considerably from the medieval diabolical pacts by which Diabolus won everything and his human partner nothing but the prospect of the rack or the stake.

* * *

The idea of the devil-compact penetrated from Asia into Europe through the intermediary of Byzantium, and was merged with beliefs that were similar and perhaps originally related. The old Northern demon, according to Jacob Grimm, also formed a pact with men, although he did not exact a written agreement.[5] In fact, the agreement in writing can only have originated in a period during which Roman legal forms had arrived to the peoples of the West.

It is not always possible for us to detect in folk-lore what is indigenous and what belongs to foreign nationalities. The identity of the beliefs and practices of primitive peoples the world over can be explained in two ways: If we assume that they were of independent origin, we must explain their identity by the uniformity of the human mind; but if, on the other hand, we hold to the belief of their common origin and beginnings from a common geographic center, it follows that their dissemination throughout the world must have come about through migration or mixture of races.[6]

* * *

The idea of the devil-compact among the Northern peoples included various elements. First of all, it was derived from the manner in which men negotiated in heathen times with the hearth-spirits of the most varied character. The Nords in ancient days dealt with sprites just as the farmers now treat their hired help. Terms of service were arranged by our ancestors with cobolds as with human beings. They were hired and "fired" as the need presented itself or ceased to exist. When the demons of hell assumed the heritage of the ancient household-spirits among the Northern

[5] Cf. Jacob Grimm: *Deutsche Mythologie.* 4. Aufl. Berlin 1875-78. Translated from the German (*Teutonic Mythology*) by J. S. Stallybrass. 4 vols. London, 1882-88.

[6] M. Gaster in his paper, "Folk-Lore in the Old Testament," *Folk-Lore,* XXX (1919), 75, believes that the latter view is now being more and more recognized.

peoples, they also negotiated with men agreements of mutual service and promise. They, too, served their masters for stipulated periods in return for certain rewards, chief among which were human souls. The services exacted from the demons of hell by our ancestors increased, however, in proportion to the increase of their power. When the Devil was given unlimited sway over the world, the demands placed upon him and his underlings knew no limitations.

The conception of the devil-compact can also be explained as a survival of the old blood-bond with the tutelary deity.[7] It was believed in ancient days that a bond by blood-transfusion could be formed with spiritual as well as with human beings. This will account for the part which the red vital fluid plays in the diabolical pact. The writing or signing by man of the required document with blood drawn from his own veins as earnest-money of future full payment—his soul—is an addition which grew out of a misconception of the original meaning of this covenant with the trusted divinity. The use of blood in the devil-compact to bind man's promise to the powers of hell may also be explained by the idea found in the Old Testament that strength and feeling dwelt in the blood, which was considered the seat of all life.[8] In fact, blood already played a part in the evocations of the evil spirits practised by the Jews of the post-exilic period.

The idea of the blood-signed devil-compact may also have derived a few points from the Odin cult, in which men signed acts of self-dedication to the deity by marking their arms with the spear-point. This custom was traditionally derived from the conduct of the god himself, who is said to have marked himself with a javelin point, as he neared his end while he was envisaged as a king ruling over Sweden.

The selling of a man's soul to Satan is, furthermore, of cannibalistic inception. It is vestigially of the old sacrificial cult. The divinity with whom man covenanted was supposed to absorb the soul of his human ally when he devoured his body. The psychical was a part of the physical nutrition. Man's soul was transferred to the divinity together with his flesh. This will account for the medieval belief that the demons devoured the souls of the damned

[7] Concerning the idea of the old blood-bond, see H. C. Trumbull: *The Blood Covenant.* Philadelphia, 1893.

[8] Cf. Georg Roskoff, *op. cit.,* I, 347.

in hell. This idea probably is of Oriental origin. The seven
Assyrian evil spirits had a predilection for human flesh and blood.
Ghouls and vampires belong to this class of demons. Edgar Allan
Poe, in his story "Bon-Bon" (1835), represents the demons as preparing in hell all sorts of fancy dishes made of human souls. When
the original idea of cannibalism disappeared, the pledging of the
human soul to the spirit was understood to mean the extension of
his kingdom. It was reserved for Christianity to interpret the dedi-
cation by man of his soul to his tutelary divinity as the loss of his
salvation.[9]

*
*   *

Although the Christian belief in devil-compacts goes back, as
has been shown, to the fourth century, it was not prevalent until
the Middle Ages when it took a great hold on the minds of men.
For three hundred years the idea was universal throughout the
civilized world. Pope Innocent VIII, in his famous bull, "Summis
desiderantes," issued on December 5, 1484, officially recognized the
possibility for man to form of his own free will a pact with the
powers of hell. The Reformation, which was a movement of
progress in so many respects, still increased the popular belief that
man could covenant with the demons of hell. In fact, the century
of the Reformation even brought the belief in demonology and
witchcraft to its height. According to Jean Bodin, author of *la
Démonomanie des sorciers* (1580), a Paris lawyer was hanged in
1571 for having signed a bond with the Devil. In Germany, an
edict of the Elector Augustus of Saxony of the year 1572 proclaimed the penalty of death by fire against whomsoever "in forget-
fulness of his Christian faith shall have entered into a compact, or
hold converse or intercourse, with the Devil. . . ." In England, as
late as 1643, a certain Thomas Browne was indicted before a Mid-
dlesex jury for selling his soul to an evil spirit for an annuity of
£1000 but was acquitted. This belief was also carried over to the
New World. Increase Mather, the New England preacher, likewise affirmed that many men made "cursed covenants with the
Prince of Darkness."

[9] Cf. Julius Lippert: *Christentum, Volksglaube und Volksbrauch* (Berlin,
1882), p. 563.

*

*   *

The belief as it prevailed among our medieval ancestors was to the effect that man could enter with the Devil into a compact by which he obtained from hell whatever he desired for a certain period —later fixed at twenty-four years—at the expiration of which term he was to deliver his soul to the Devil. It was supposed that Diabolus, wishing to draw man away from the Deity, assured for himself by this means man's soul while its owner was still living— *vivente corpore*, as it is related in Edgar Allan Poe's story "Bon-Bon" already mentioned. In his anxiety to obtain human souls, the Fiend felt no hesitancy in paying even hard cash for them, as it is expressed by Victor Hugo in his novel *Han d'Islande* (1823). The deed of transfer had to be written or at least signed by man with blood drawn from his own veins.

The man who wished to enter into business relations with the Devil generally applied to a Jew to act as intermediary. It was believed that only Jews could enter into communication with the Devil through the arts of magic. In the Theophilus-legend, the Jew who acts as a go-between is a sort of sorcerer who is disloyal to his own religion. When Chateaubriand, in his novel *les Martyrs* (1809), employs a Jew as an agent of hell, he also represents him as a Jew who has renounced the faith of his fathers. The zealot in one religion prefers a zealot to a liberal even in an opposing religion. In later legends, the sorcerer or sorceress, who brings about the meeting between man and the emissary of hell, is not always descended from the seed of Abraham.

In many literary works wherein is employed the tradition of a man selling his soul to Satan, the shadow, regarded as an emanation, an extension, so to say a "part," of the personality, is symbolically used for the soul. In Chamisso's *Peter Schlemihl* (1814), the title-character sells his shadow to the Devil for the purse of Fortunatus, and then, putting on the seven-leagued boots, diverts his mind from unpleasant thoughts by running about the world. Edgar Allan Poe offers an example of the identification of the shadow with the soul in "Bon-Bon." Oscar Wilde, in his tale "The Fisherman and his Soul" (1891), likewise considers the shadow of the body as the body of the soul.

Man could even sell to Satan a part of his body. Alphonse Karr, in "la Main du diable" (1855), narrates the suffering of a man who offered his right hand to the Devil in exchange for his brother's life. His brother recovered from his illness, and to fulfill his part of the agreement, he cut his right hand off and paid with his own life for the remission of his brother's.

It is further known that man could surrender to Satan not only his own soul, but also that of a person over whom he had authority. The medieval legend of the knight who sold his wife to the Devil is well known.[10]

Satan entered into the possession of man's soul when the term ran out by killing man's body. Man thus paid the penalty for his bargain with Beelzebub with violent death. The Devil usually inflicted death upon his victim by tearing his flesh with his sharp claws and teeth. It must be observed, however, that the Devil has no interest whatever in man's body. If he kills the man, it is only to obtain his soul. "When the term [of the devil-pact] is over," Victor Hugo tells us in his juvenile novel, *Han d'Islande* (1823), "the Devil destroys the body in taking the soul, just as a monkey cracks the shell to eat the nut."

The Devil, notwithstanding the great power he possesses over the bodies and minds of mortals, is, however, not potent enough to put a man to death, unless his victim has blasphemed or renounced the Lord.[11] This idea probably sprang out of the limitation imposed by the Almighty upon the power of Satan during the temptation of Job and out of the advice given the great sufferer by his well-meaning wife: "Curse God, and die" (Job ii. 9). It is only in such cases that the Devil has over men "the power of death" (Hebr. ii. 14; 1 Cor. v. 5). In view of this limitation of his power over the body of man, Diabolus exacted from his partner in the bond, which assigned the victim's soul to hell, a formal denial of the Christian faith, a rejection of Christian symbols and a renunciation of the Lord and his saints. The Devil was particularly anxious about his

[10] This medieval legend of the knight and his wife has been retold by W. Carew Hazlitt in his collection *Tales and Legends of National Origin* (London: Macmillan, 1899).

[11] In Bürgers ballad "Lenore" (1774), a young girl curses God for having robbed her of her lover William, who had fought at the side of King Frederick at the battle of Prague and died on that occasion. She is then carried off by the Devil, who appears on horseback at midnight beneath Lenore's window in the form of her lover and calls her to ride with him to their wedding-bed. Another illustration of the Devil's power over a man, who has cursed God, is furnished in Victor Hugo's ballad "les Deux archers" (1825), in which two archers, who blasphemed God, are immediately killed and carried off to hell by the Devil.

partner's repudiation of his baptism, the first sacrament which wipes away the original stain, which sacrament is man's safeguard against Satan. The man not only was expected to deny his baptism, but he had to accept another sacrament of baptism from hell. He also was forced to express a hatred for all Christians and a promise to resist all attempts to convert him.

*

*   *

The contract-stories differ as to the objects which the human party to the agreement designed to derive from it. Position, power, protection, and pleasure were for the most part the objects for which man sold his soul to Satan. Wealth and learning, which figured so frequently in the contracts formed by man with the Fiend, were intended to provide man with the power for which he craved. Man aimed often to obtain, through contact or contract with the spirits of hell, such powers as would put him in a position to accomplish things beyond the ordinary conditions of humanity. He wished to batter down the walls of natural limitations imposed upon all mortals, and thus gain mastery of the world.

As prince of this world, the Devil could without any difficulty grant even the most extravagant wishes of man. He often even promised to place his magic powers at the service of the contracting party. "It was usually by means of contracts with the Devil," says Professor Ward, "that in a number of medieval legends men were said to have obtained a full command over the objects of those passions which it was the task of the Christian religion to repress or repel. Thus they were thought to have been enabled to drink to the dregs the cup of sensual indulgence, to satisfy the cravings of earthly ambition, to glut the accursed hunger for gold and for all that gold can buy, and to gratify the desire for knowledge of all things good and evil and for the power which knowledge insures."[12]

*

*   *

Generally a pact with the Devil cost man his eternal salvation. But Diabolus often found a man who was clever enough to outwit

[12] Cf. A. W. Ward: *Old English Drama* (4th ed., Oxford, 1901), pp. xiii-xiv.

the purchaser of his soul.[13]   Although Satan is called the archdeceiver, he can easily be deceived and hoodwinked.   Popular belief, in fact, often represents the Devil as a trusting fool who is outwitted by the shallowest forms of trickery and dishonesty.   Man has no scruples about his breach of contract with Beelzebub.   He feels no hesitancy whatever in avoiding his part of the obligations mutually incurred by the two contracting parties.   In violation of the written pact, he often cheats the Devil out of his legal due by technical quibbles.   Man considers the legal document signed with his own blood as "a scrap of paper."   "But still the pact is with the Enemy," says Henry Osborne Taylor; "the man is not bound beyond the letter, and may escape by any trick.   It still is the ethics of war; we are very close to the principle that a man by strategem or narrow observance of the letter may escape the eternal retribution which God decrees conditionally and the Devil delights in."[14]

The Devil, on the other hand, is never known to have tried evading the fulfilment of his share of the agreement.   Although he is said to be a liar, Satan has never attempted to cheat his stipulators.[15] In regard to the fulfilment of his word, the father of lies has always set an example in honesty to his Christian negotiators.[16]   There is a universal belief that the Fiend invariably fulfils his part of the obligations.   It is a fact well worth noting that, although the Devil insists that his human negotiator sign the deed with his blood, he himself never has been required to sign it even in ink.   The human party to the transaction has always had full confidence in the Devil's word.   "It is peculiar to the German tradition," says Gustav Freytag, "that the Devil, in the compacts which he makes with men, endeavors to fulfil zealously and honestly the terms of agreement to the letter; the defaulter is man."[17]   But the Germans have no

[13] The Gascon, who always has had a reputation for shrewdness in France, may, in the opinion of Anatole France, safely make a pact with the Devil, "for you may be sure that it is the Devil who will be duped" (la Rôtisserie de la Reine Pédauque, 1893).

[14] Henry Osborne Taylor: The Mediæval Mind (2 vols., London, 1911), I, 489.

[15] The German writer, Grabbe, in Don Juan und Faust (1824), runs counter to popular tradition when he says, "Wer mit dem Teufel dingt, der wird betrogen" (He who negociates with the Devil is cheated).

[16] Bret Harte, in his poem "A Legend of Cologne," assures us that it has never been heard that the "Father of Lies" ever broke his word, and that the Devil has left "this position in every tradition to be taken by the 'truth-loving' Christian."

[17] Cf. Gustav Freytag: The Devil in Germany During the Sixteenth Century. Transl. from the German by Wm. A. Hervey (New Hork, 1893), p. 12.

monopoly to this belief. Already in the *Golden Legend*,[18] we find it
reported that Satan once bitterly complained of the manner in which
men try to evade their obligations towards him, whereas he always
faithfully fulfils his part of the pact. "The Christians," he complained, "are cheats; they make all sorts of promises so long as they
want me, and then leave me in the lurch, and reconcile themselves
with Christ as soon as, by my help, they have got what they want."

We can now understand why in Eugene Field's story, "Daniel
and the Devil" (1893), it seems so strange to Satan that he should
be asked for a written guarantee that he would fulfil his part of the
contract. Evidently this was the first time that the Devil had any
transaction with an American businessman, who has not even faith
in Old Nick.

*

*   *

The medieval Church itself provided man with the means of
evading the terms of his contract with the Devil. The bold con-
tractor knew full well that he could count upon the Church to save
him from the jaws of hell and force the Devil to surrender his rights
to man's soul. In fact, prior to the Reformation, the Devil was nearly
always cheated of his bargain through the instrumentalities of the
Church.

The surest way for medieval man to avoid paying the penalty of
his rash action in compacting with the powers of hell was to appeal
to the Holy Virgin, who was always ready to fight the Fiend. The
votary of the Virgin could especially count upon the Mother of all
Mercies to help him break the contract with the Enemy if he omitted
her in his general renunciation of the saints of Heaven.

The Virgin had in the Middle Ages almost as much power as
the Trinity. As has well been remarked by Karl Pearson, she was
the vindication of the right of the common folk to a goddess of their
own kind.[19] In the medieval drama, Christ gives his mother, upon
her assumption to heaven, a crown and scepter with full power
over the Devil.[20] It is the Queen of Heaven rather than her Son

[18] The *Golden Legend* (*Legenda aurea sive historia Lombardica*), a collection of stories of the saints taken partly from books partly from verbal
accounts, was compiled about 1275 by Jacobus de Voragine, a Dominican archbishop of Genoa. Longfellow has chosen this title for the second part of his
Christus: A Mystery (1873).

[19] Cf. Karl Pearson: *The Chances of Death and Other Studies in Evolution* (London, 1897), II, 351.

[20] In Ostendorfer's woodcut, the Virgin carries the keys of heaven and
hell.

who breaks the bolts and bonds of hell and binds the Enemy with all his crew.   The Blessed Virgin was a sort of valkyr or amazon, always at war with the demons to snatch the pacts and the souls of the repentant sinners from them.   The medieval poets call her for this reason Noah's Ark which carries mankind over the hell-flood.[21] The stories of the pitying interposition of the Mother of Christ on behalf of the repentant sinners are, according to Henry Osborne Taylor, among "the fragrant flowers of the mediæval spirit."[22]   The Polish writer, Ignacy Matuszewski, explains the rôle which is assigned to the Virgin in Catholic legend as a psychological atavism, a heritage of the mystic faith of the primitive peoples in the influence of the woman over the demon.[23]   In pagan times the woman already possessed power over the evil spirits.   In Hindu mythology, Kali or Durga interceded in the fight between her husband Siva and the demon Darida.   The mother of all men was told by the Lord that she could crush the serpent's head.   The predominance of drollery, however, soon altered this poetic conception of woman. It is then the old toothless hag, spindle in hand, the very sight of whom puts the Devil in flight.   The woman appears in this rôle in the medieval *fabliaux* and farces.[24]

The Blessed Virgin snatched from the jaws of hell Merlin,[25] Theophilus,[26] and Robert the Devil.[27]   In the medieval story of the

[21] In a Spanish play *Mascaron* of the thirteenth century, the Holy Virgin appears in defence of the human race against the charges brought by the demon Mascaron.

[22] Cf. Henry Osborne Taylor, *op. cit.,* I, 490.

[23] Cf. Ignacy Matuszewski: *Dyabel w poezyi* (2nd ed., Warsaw, 1899) p. 105.

[24] Read in this connection the ballad "The Devil and the Scold" in the collection *English and Scottish Ballads* (Boston: Houghton, 1858), VIII, 257-8. Joanna Southcott published anonymously in 1802 *A Dispute between the Woman and the Powers of Darkness.*

[25] Merlin, a legendary diviner, who plays a very important part in the Celtic legends and the medieval tales of chivalry as the friend of King Arthur, was, according to Cæsarius of Heisterbach, the son of a demon and a nun. Through the intervention of the Virgin, he did not follow in his father's footsteps and was finally saved from perdition.

[26] The Theophilus-legend will be treated in the next chapter.

[27] Robert the Devil, the son of a duke and duchess of Normandy, was counted among the great progeny of Satan.   He was born, according to the confession of his own mother, in answer to prayers addressed to the Devil. According to another version of this legend, the Devil was Robert's physical father.   However, when Robert learned of his diabolical descent, he turned from his father to God.   After he had repented of his misdeeds, the Blessed Virgin took pity on him, secured his pardon and had him married to the daughter of the emperor of Sicily, with whom he was in love.   During his courageous

knight who sold his spouse to Satan, the Mother of God, to whom the victim addressed herself on her way to the Devil, assumed her form and accompanied the knight in her stead to the Devil and forced him to return the deed to the knight. Many later works also represent the woman as victor over the demons of hell. Cyprian in Calderón's play, *El Mágico prodigioso* (1663), is saved through the instrumentality of a woman, whose spirit of innocence defies and defeats the Devil's power. Goethe, in *Faust* (1808-32), has woman, not a particular woman, but the Eternal Womanly—*das Ewig Weibliche*—draw Faust onward and upward in the end and redeem him from hell.[28]

*

*   *

The Devil, notwithstanding all the disappointments these commercial transactions have brought him, evidently has up to this day not renounced this poorly paying business of purchasing human souls. The shrewd dealer should realize that he possesses the human soul without any contract or any special document and without paying a penny for it. In fact, a man can surrender his soul to Satan under no necessity of signing a document. Thus Don Joan lost himself to the Devil through his bad deeds, without entering into any special contract. When a man commits a sin, he falls into the power of the Enemy. Each evil deed is an act of acquiescence to Satan's will, which is equivalent to an alliance with him. "Give up your soul to Satan's darling sins," it has been said by a clergyman, "and he will help you for a season until he has his claims carefully wound around you. When his links are carefully closed, he seizes his victim, who has no longer any power to resist." Carlyle has also said: "Follow the Devil faithfully, you are sure enough to go to the Devil; whither else can you go?"

defense of Rome against the besieging Saracens, an angel bestowed upon this penitent celestial weapons with which he was given power to rout his enemies. The medieval legend of Robert the Devil has been retold by W. Carew Hazlitt in the book already mentioned.

[28] A very interesting modern version of this idea of woman's victory over the Devil will be found in Frederick Beecher Perkins's story, *Devil-Puzzlers* (1871), which has been reprinted in the present writer's anthology of *Devil Stories* (New York: Knopf, 1921).

CHAPTER XVI

THE DEVIL-COMPACT IN LEGEND AND LITERATURE
(I)

THE tradition of the devil-compact took deep roots in popular fancy as well as in Catholic belief. It loomed up in the tenth century as the vital point of a legend and gathered around itself an enormous material. In the form of the Theophilus-legend, which, in the sixteenth century, merged into the Faust-myth, it entered the literatures of all European countries and formed the subject of poem and play, novel and short story, throughout the civilized world for full thousand years.

The story of the compact closed by Theophilus with the Devil is briefly as follows: Theophilus was a bishop's seneschal or vice-dominus, living in the sixth century, at Adana in Cilicia, Asia Minor. He was so highly esteemed by the priesthood and by the community that, upon the death of his bishop, he was considered worthy of the bishopric. But, through modesty, he declined the proferred dignity. The new bishop, to whom Theophilus was calumniated, resenting the fact that he was second choice, was only too glad to deprive him of his position in the Church. In order to recover his post, he enlisted the services of a Jewish magician, who secured for him an appointment with the Devil. Diabolus demanded of Theophilus a document signed and sealed with his own hand, in which the deposed priest promised to deliver to the Devil his own soul and in addition agreed to deny Christ and the Virgin. The day following the conclusion of the contract, the bishop honorably reinstated Theophilus in his former position. But after seven years of riotous living, realizing that his end was near, he repented of his act. For forty days and forty nights he fasted and prayed to the Blessed Virgin for pardon of his sins. She, however, first turned a deaf ear to his prayers because he had broken faith with her. But finally the Mother of all Mercies took pity on the repentant sinner. As he prostrated himself in his church at the foot of her altar at midnight, she descended from heaven, bent over him, stroked his burning brow, and assured him of pardon if he would deny the Devil and return to Christ. Mother Mary then interceded with her Son to show indulgence toward the penitent sinner. She demanded from the Devil the parchment and placed it upon the breast of Theophilus as he lay asleep in the church. Upon awakening, the repentant priest found the fatal contract, by which he had pawned his soul to Satan, and cast the document into the flames. Three days later, after having publicly proclaimed before the congregation his penitence and the miracle of his preservation, Theophilus passed gently away in blessed peace, and the Church inscribed his name on the roll of her saints as Theophilus the Penitent.[1]

The story of Theophilus was purported to have been told by his pupil, Eutychianus, as a living witness. It was translated in the ninth century from the original Greek into Latin by Paulus Diaconus, spread in a variety of versions through Eastern and Western Christendom, and became one of the treasures of saintly legend in the Western Catholic Church. This story was a stock item in medieval collections of miracles and exampla. Vincent of Beauvais inserted it in his *Speculum Historiale* and Jacobus de Voragine introduced it into his *Legenda aurea* (both manuscripts of the thirteenth century).

The first poetical treatment given the Theophilus legend was the play in Latin hexameters *Lapsus et conversio Theophili vicedomini* written in the tenth century by the first original German woman poet and dramatist, Hroswitha or Roswitha, the learned abbess of the Benedictine convent of Gandersheim. Brun von Schönbecke incorporated this legend in his poem, *Die Ehre der Maria*, composed about 1276. In this quaint poem, the contract was sealed not with blood, but with a ring, a *motif* which frequently occurs in medieval literature. Three low German and two Icelandic dramatic versions of this legend date from the fourteenth century.[2]

[1] On the Theophilus legend, see E. Sommer's Latin thesis *De Theophili cum Diabolo foedere* (Halle, 1844).

[2] For the bibliography on the low German versions of the Theophilus play, see the present writer's book, *A Historical and Bibliographical Survey of the German Religious Drama* (Pittsburgh, 1924), pp. 65-67.

THE LEGEND OF THEOPHILUS

The first poetic treatment of this legend in France is the early thirteenth-century poem of Gautier de Coincy, *le Miracle de Théophile*. It was given dramatic form in France toward the end of that century by a *trouvère* named Rutebeuf in his *Miracle de Théophile*.[3] There are also five renderings of the Theophilus legend in Spanish.

The Theophilus legend made its appearance in English about the year 1000, when Ælfric, in a *Homily on the Assumption of the Blessed Mary*, summarized it briefly with full mention of the written compact. Poetic versions of this legend are included in both the *South English Legendary* (thirteenth century) and in the *North English Homilies* (fourteenth century). There is still a third poetic version extant in Middle English. The story also appears in the *Alphabet of Tales* written in fifteenth-century English. In 1572 the priest Wiliam Forrest rhymed the legend afresh in a poem, which forms part of his work, *Life of the Blessed Virgin Mary with other Poems* and which was intended as a kind of apology for the Roman Catholic religion. A prose version of it occurs also in Thomas Heywood's *Hierarchie of the Blessed Angells* (1635).

Among the recent dramatizations of this story may be mentioned Mr. B. C. Greene's *Théophile* (1903), and A. Kingsley Porter's *The Virgin and the Clerk* (1929). The latter play is a clever work of satire, philosophy, and religion. According to Porter's interpretation of the old legend, Canon Theophilus refuses the bishopric of Adana in order to dedicate himself to the writing of a hymn to the Virgin. Unable to accomplish this task, he sells his soul in exchange for success. The roots of the soul, however, are deep, and the song to the Virgin is, after all, heard—and answered.[4]

[3] This play will be found in the first complete edition of the works of Rutebeuf prepared by Achille Jubinal in 1874, t. II, p. 231 sqq. A critical edition of Rutebeuf's *Théophile* was prepared in 1925 by an American woman, Mrs. Grace Frank. Léon Clédat has put this medieval text into a modern French version.—This interesting play also attracted the latter-day diabolist, Remy de Gourmont, who, in 1896, brought out a modern version accompanied by an excellent introductory essay.

[4] On the legend of Theophilus in medieval poetry, consult K. Plenzat's thesis, *Die Theophiluslegende in den Dichtungen des Mittelalters*. Berlin, 1926. (Germanische Studien, XLIII).—The items on the Theophilus legend in England have been drawn from Professor George Lyman Kittredge's thorough work, *Witchcraft in Old and New England* (Cambridge, Mass., 1928), p. 239. A critical edition of the later English version of the Theophilus legend, accompanied by an introduction, was published by Eugen Kölbing in the *Englische Studien*, I (1877), 16-57.

The legend of Militarius is an adaptation of that of Theophilus. It is the story of a soldier who, in order to prolong a life of pleasure, forms a bond with Beelzebub, but is finally saved and restored to salvation through the intercession of the Blessed Virgin, whom he has not named among the saints of heaven he has renounced.[5]

* * *

The idea of the devil-compact was also introduced into the medieval legend of St. Cyprian, which Calderón, the greatest of Spanish dramatists, took, in the seventeenth century, for the subject of his lyrical play, *El Mágico prodigioso*. In this version, Cyprian, of Antioch, a great philosopher and a very expert magician, is in love with Justina, a damsel living in his native city. She is of high birth and great beauty, and, moreover, is an ardent Christian. He tries in many ways to win her love, and she, in just as many ways, resists his every effort. As a last resort, Cyprian sells his soul to the Devil, who promises to put Justina in his possession. But finding that the Devil has no power over the fair Christian, who renders all his temptations impotent by calling on God, Cyprian will no longer have anything to do with a weak devil, is converted to the stronger power, received into the Church, and dies the death of a martyr with Justina, in the reign of the Roman Emperor Diocletian (284-305).

The contract between the Devil and Cyprian is first mentioned in the *Golden Legend,* where the agreement is verbal. In Calderón's drama, however, the pact between the Devil and Cyprian is signed with blood. Comparing Goethe's play with that of Calderón, we find that the two have in common the point that the demon is not in a position to perform his exact engagements, and consequently loses out in the end. The two plays differ in the fact that Cyprian gives himself to the Devil to have and to hold with a definite desire as the incentive, but Faust closes a contract with the Devil in order to obtain such general objects as strength, self-development and enjoyment.[6]

[5] The legend of Militarius was treated by Gotefridus Thenesis (Gottfried von Thienen) in a narrative written in leonine hexameters, of which a specimen is given by Professor Karl Alexander von Reichlin-Meldegg in his study on the subject. A critical edition of this poem will be found in the volume published by Dr. Robert Petsch and entitled *Gehalt und Form* (Dortmund, 1925).

[6] Concerning the parallels between the Cyprian-legend and the Faust-saga, consult Sánchez Antonio Moguel: *Memoria acerca de "El Mágico prodigioso" de Calderón y en especial sobre las relaciones de este drama con el "Fausto" de Goethe,* Madrid, 1881. This work was translated into French by J. G. Magnabel (Paris, 1883), and into German by Johannes Fastenrath (Leipzig, 1882). See also Zahn: *Cyprian von Antiochien und die deutsche Faustsage,* Erlangen, 1882.

*
* *

Many other legends of devil-compacts will be found in medieval writings. Among the good deeds of St. Wulfric, the hermit of Haselbury in Dorset, who died in 1154, we find that on a certain occasion he forced the return of a contract signed with the Devil by a Northern man who, under stress of poverty, had formed an alliance with hell, but who later repented and appealed for help to the pious hermit. Walter Map, writing in the same century, tells of Eudo, a rich young baron, who, after having been reduced to poverty by extravagance, closed a pact with the Devil and grew rich by robbery and murder. But he at last repented of his rash act, and sought out the Bishop of Beauvais, whom he found beyond the walls of the city near a great pyre that had been kindled to burn a witch. The wrathful bishop imposed upon him the penance of leaping upon this pyre. Eudo straightway obeyed and was burned to death.[7]

Among the legendary figures believed to have closed a compact with the Devil we may also mention Zytho, who lived in Bohemia in the fifteenth century, and Twardowski, the Polish equivalent of the German Faust, who is said to have been a contemporary of the wizard of Wittenberg. Twardowski made rather unusual demands upon the Devil, requiring the latter to build a house for him out of poppy-seeds and to cover it with a roof composed of the beards of Jews. It should be added that he had his specifications fulfilled and was finally carried off to hell through the chimney of his curiously constructed house.[8]

*
* *

The legend of the devil-compact attaches itself also to a great number of historic personages. Among philosophers and scientists

Professor James Geddes has recently brought out an excellent critical edition of Calderón's play for American classes. The influence of Calderòn's drama is evident in Jules Lemaitre's story, "la Vierge sarrasine" (1889), in which, by the purity of a young and innocent girl, the Devil is driven out of a statue of the Black Virgin, which he inhabited.

[7] These two instances of medieval pacts have been taken from Professor Kittredge's book already mentioned.

[8] Mr. Sutherland-Edwards has interpreted the legend of Twardowski for English readers in his article "The Faust Legend," *Macmillan Magazine*, XXXIV (1876), 268-75. Among the poetical versions of this legend, Mickiewicz's *Pani Twardowska* (1822) is best known. Other Polish poets, who treated this subject, are Korsak, Zielinski, Groza, Szujski, Kaminski, Kraszewski and the Czech Vrchlicky.

who were said to have sold their souls to Satan, for one consideration or another, are included Socrates, Apollonius of Tyana, Apul-
eius, Roger Bacon, Raymond Lulle, Lully or Lullus, Scaliger, Cornelius Agrippa, Paracelsus, Nostradamus, Servetus, Giordano
Bruno, and Galileo. Of the theologians and religious reformers
reputed to have entered into a pact with hell, we may mention Tri-
themius, Luther, Melanchthon and Calvin. Among the magicians
and thaumaturgists believed to have leagued themselves with Lucifer, Simon Magus of biblical times and Jean de Fontenelle of the
fifteenth century are best known. Among the men of the eighteenth
century who were suspected of traffic with the infernal powers, we
may include Cagliostro, a clever Italian student of the occult and
magician, and the Duke of Luxembourg, the famous general of the
imperial army and Marshal of France, the companion and successor
of Condé and the opponent of William of Orange. The compact,
which the Duke was believed to have concluded with the Devil,
was given to the public full and complete in every paragraph.

Even the popes were not free from the suspicion of dealing
with the Devil. An English poem of the fourteenth century ascribed
the signing of a Satanic pact to Pope Cælestinus, who died in 432.
The story of Gerbert (Sylvester II) and his pact with the Devil,
by means of which the eminent medieval *savant* attained to the
summit of earthly ambition at the cost of his immortal soul, is
familiar to all who may be acquainted with medieval writings. It
will be found in the *Gesta Regum* (twelfth century) of William of
Malmesbury, from whom both Robert Holkot and Vincent of Beauvais borrowed it. This story also appears in the vernacular in the
fifteenth-century *Alphabet of Tales* already mentioned, and is re-
peated by Bishop Pilkington, who lived in the following century.
In Walter Map's account of Gerbert's ascension to the seat of Peter,
Gerbert's supernatural protector is Meridiana, a fairy, in whom
Professor Kittredge recognizes a feminine form of the *dæmonium
meridianum* or Midday Demon.[9] Others thought that Gerbert had
sold his soul to Satan not in return for the papacy, but in order to
obtain from the Devil a knowledge of physics, arithmetic and music.
Gerbert, as well as two distinguished Englishmen, Roger Bacon
and Bishop Grosseteste, was popularly credited with the invention

[9] George Lyman Kittredge, *op. cit.*, p. 240.

of a magical speaking head of brass.[10]   Another illustrious occupant of St. Peter's Chair, Gregory VII, was also believed to have sold himself to the Devil, and to have paid the last penalty for his familiarity with the Fiend.   The Popes Paul II and the notorious Alexander VI (Rodrigo Borgia),[11] were likewise supposed to have held commerce with the powers of hell.

*
* *

The story of Dr. Faustus is the most famous version of the legend of the devil-compact. Johannes Faustus, a laborious student, has drained dry the sources of intellectual satisfaction to be found in the various ordinary departments of human knowledge. Wearied and worried, but unsated, the voracious student turns to magic, and finally conjures up the demon Mephistopheles. With this demon Faust enters into a contract, binding Faust to surrender his body and soul to Mephistopheles at the end of twenty-four years and reciprocally binding Mephistopheles to be at Faust's command during that period, providing for him during that quarter-century his fill of miraculous exploits and sensual delights.

The legend of Dr. Faustus, as compared with that of Theophilus, shows the contrast between Protestantism and Catholicism with regard to the devil-compact. The arch-deacon of Adana, as we have seen, succeeded, through the intervention of the Blessed Virgin, in escaping his punishment for daring to deal with the Devil. But the wizard of Wittenberg was duly carried off to Hell by way of payment at the expiration of the bond. The Church, which forfeited its power at the Reformation, could not aid the man who had mortgaged his soul to Mephistopheles. Faust had to meet with the traditional doom. He was irrevocably damned, lost and fallen into the power of the Devil. The friend of the Fiend belonged to Hell.[12]

[10] The legend of Sylvester II will be found in J. von Döllinger's book, *Die Papstfabeln des Mittelalters*, Stuttgart, 1863, second edition, 1890, English translation (*Fables Respecting the Popes of the Middle Ages*), London 1871. A brief account of this legend will also be found in Paul Carus's interesting book, *The History of the Devil and the Idea of Evil* (Chicago, 1900).

[11] A good biography of this pope is F. L. Glaser's book, *Pope Alexander VI*. The infernal pact of this pontifical Faust has been treated by Barnabe Barnes in his play, *The Devil's Charter, or a Tragedy Containing the Life and Death of Pope Alexander VI* (1607). This play is the first attempt, after Marlowe's *Dr. Faustus*, to make a devil-motif the basis of a serious drama.

[12] A very interesting Protestant version of the devil-compact is the play, "The Bottomless Sack," written by Hans Sachs, a friend of Luther, on October 15, 1563. An English translation of this farce will be found in William Leighton's *Merry Tales and Shrovetide Plays by Hans Sachs* (London, 1910), pp. 210-15.

It should be added, however, that in the Faust legend the devil-compact is not the *root* but the *fruit* of Faust's sin, which consists in the abandonment of sacred for secular learning. The Faust legend is the creation of orthodox Protestantism, which, through it, expresses disapproval of the humanistic movement of its day. In fact, Faust had that interest in secular learning and that love of the beauty of the ancients which was common to all men of the Renaissance. He shared with the humanists of his day the wish to know all things, to do all things and to enjoy all things. Faust pays, by the forfeit of his soul, not so much for the foul pact with the Enemy of Mankind as for his revolt against the Word of God. The oldest Faust-book represents its hero as selling his soul to Satan solely in order to augment his learning and to comprehend that which cannot be known by the natural faculties of man. It is said of Faust in this book that he resolved "to search into all the deep things of heaven and of earth." Marlowe's play, *Dr. Faustus*, based on this account of Faust's life, also has its protagonist consign himself to the Devil in order to obtain from him a deeper understanding of the mysterious operations or secrets of natural laws. It was G. R. Widmann, in his Faust-book, who added the search for sensuous enjoyments to the conditions of the contract drawn up between Faust and the Fiend.

Faust may be considered a counterpart of Luther. Both Luther and Faust broke away from Rome. Luther drew nearer to the Lord; Faust looked to Lucifer for aid. Both Luther and Faust had dealings with the Devil. Luther warded off the Devil in the Wartburg by throwing an inkstand at his head; Faust summoned the Devil and admitted him into his cell. Both Luther and Faust had a thirst for knowledge. Luther loved sacred lore; Faust preferred secular learning. Both Luther and Faust disapproved of the celibacy of the clergy. Luther married; Faust sought sensual delights out of wedlock. Luther was victorious over the Devil; Faust finally fell into the Devil's clutches.

*
* *

The historicity of Faust has long been doubted. So much legend has been woven about his stark figure that historians have been hard put to arrive at the truth. On the strength of the testimony

of a few contemporaries, however, it is now generally accepted that
Faust was an historical person, having lived during the first half of
the sixteenth century. He was born in Kundling (Knittlingen)
near Bretten, the birth place of Melanchthon, between 1480 and
1490, studied at the University of Cracow, and died, about the year
1549, in Staufen (Breisgau).

Faust appeared to his contemporaries as a doubtful wizard and
a charlatan. According to their testimony, he was an eccentric
fellow who supported himself by going about the country and passing himself off on the credulous folk as a great sorcerer and necromancer. He either hinted mysteriously or boasted openly of his
knowledge of the occult, and the common folk of his day readily
accepted his stories. Faust styled himself Magus Secundus Magister
Georgius Sabellicus Faustus Junior and even assumed the title
of Philosophus Philosophorum. He was accompanied by a younger
man named Wagner, whom he called his famulus, and by a black
dog trained to fetch him food, also called a famulus. Since both—
his assistant and his dog—bore the same enigmatical name, might
they not be one and the same—an embodied demon contrived by
this master of *Schwarzkunst* or black magic?

When Faust met with a violent death toward the middle of the
sixteenth century, it was believed that the wicked wizard had been
carried off by the Devil, with whom he had concluded a compact,
and who had helped him to perform the supernatural acts. Legend
later elaborated the details of Faust's magic deeds and sad end. It
was said that he had studied at the University of Wittenberg and
come in contact with Martin Luther. It was reported that in 1525
he had incurred opprobrium by bestriding a barrel in Auerbach's
wine-cellar at Leipzig. Rumor had it also that, when the period of
the fatal contract between Faust and the Fiend was ended, the
demons appeared at midnight and beckoned Faust to follow them.
The next morning his body, torn limb from limb, was found lying
on a dunghill in the village of Rimlich, near the town of Wittenberg.
A number of his contemporaries, among them Melanchthon and
Johann Wier, believed that the Devil had wrung Faust's neck.
Johann Gast affirmed that Faust had been strangled by the Devil.
This Protestant minister of Basle also recorded that Faust's "corpse

lay face downward on the bier all the time, though it was turned over five times."[13]

About forty years after Faust's death, his story was first told in a popular chap-book entitled *Historia von D. Johann Fausten* and printed by Johann Spiess in the year 1587 at Frankfort-on-the-Main. This work was the basis of a long series of popular books on Faust, chief among which figures Widmann's account published in 1599.

* * *

Christopher Marlowe, a predecessor of Shakespeare, is the first great dramatist who was attracted to the Faust legend. His powerful drama, *The Tragical History of Dr. Faustus* (c. 1589), is founded on an English translation, which appeared within less than two years after the publication of the original Frankfort Faust-book and which was entitled *History of the Damnable Life and Deserved Death of Dr. John Faustus.*[14]

Marlowe's play follows in spirit and in details the popular account of Faust's character and career. The devil-compact is its central point and chief motive. Marlowe took the legend as he found it and turned it into a grim tragedy of sin and damnation. He did not give his play any philosophical interpretation, but it is pregnant with the old warning: "For what shall it profit a man, if he shall gain the whole world, and lose his own soul?" (Mark viii. 36). If Calderón's *El Mágico prodigioso* already mentioned

---

[13]On the Faust legend, see H. Düntzer: *Die Faustsage* (1846); Peter: *Literatur der Faustsage* (1851); K. Engel: *Literatur der Faustsage von 1510-1873* (1874); Karl Kiesewetter: *Faust in der Geschichte und Tradition* (1893); P. Ristelhuber: *Faust dans l'histoire et dans la légende; essai sur l'humanisme superstitieux du XVIe siécle et les récits du pacte diabolique* (1863); E. Faligan :*Histoire de la légende de Faust* (1888); P. Saintyves: *la Légende du Docteur Faust in Collection d'Epopées et Légendes* (1926); V. Errante: *il Mito di Faust dal personaggio al poema di Goethe* (Bologna, 1924); "The Devil and Dr. Faustus," *Cornhill Magazine*, XIV (1866), 687-701; J. Oxenford: "Faust, Dramatic and Legendary," *Belgravia I* (1867), 188-90; Henry Schütz Wilson: "Facts and Fancies about Faust" (in his *Studies in History, Legend and Literature*, 1884); Henry Sutherland Edwards: *The Faust Legend; its Origin and Development from the Living Faustus of the First Century to the Faust of Goethe* (1886); James Hain Friswell: "Dr. John Faustus" (in his *Varia; Readings from Rare Books*, 1886); and Gabriel W. Gilbert: "The Legend of Faust and Mephistopheles," *The Mentor*, XVII, (1929), 1-14. R. A. Redford draws an interesting parallel between Faust and Prospero in his article, "Shakespeare and the Faust Legend," *Gentleman's Magazine*, CCLXXXV (1898), 547-66. The best critical study on the subject is H. G. Meek's *Johann Faust: The Man and the Myth* (London, 1930).

[14] A modernized edition of this Faust-book has been brought out by William Rose and published, in 1925, in the Broadway Translations. See W. E. P. Pantin's article "The Sources of Marlowe's *Dr. Faustus," Academy*, XXXI (1887), 449.

can be considered an apotheosis of the Catholic dogma of free-will, Marlowe's *Dr. Faustus* is the poetic illustration of Protestant fatalism. Marlowe makes the Devil finally victorious. Faust has his period of power and pleasure by the Devil's aid, but the Devil must have his pay, and his pay is the soul of his ally. Faust technically repents, but not until his lease of enjoyment is run out, and Hell stands pyrotechnically agape. The sincerity of this kind of repentance, caused by the necessity of discharging a poignantly unpleasant debt, may well be questioned. There is actually no trace of regret for entering the infernal compact until punishment is impending; and then, by a stupendous touch of irony, Faust is dragged away to Hell just as his parched lips twist to shriek, in terror-stricken babblement, that sugared and langorous verse which Ovid whispered in Corinna's arms at the summit of life's felicity: "O lente, lente, currite noctis equi!"

Marlowe is at his unrivalled best in rehandling the legend of Faust. The scene of Faust's soliloquy as he awaits the stroke of midnight, which shall end the twenty-four years and bring his self-imposed doom, is impressive in its intensity and deservedly ranks among the finest specimens of poetic composition in any language.

Soon after its appearance, Marlowe's *Dr. Faustus,* together with other English plays, was brought over to Germany by strolling bands of English comedians, who performed it early in the seventeenth century in various German cities. The subject was soon taken up by companies of German actors, who followed Marlowe's play on broad lines. In this way, the dramatic form of the Faust legend was shaped in Germany for almost two hundred years. The Faust play, in a great variety of forms, continued as a popular item in the repertoires of the theatrical companies of Germany, until it was crowded off the stage by the French classical drama, which was considered the epitome of all excellence. The Faust-theme fell into the hands of travelling showmen, who amused the young with their marionettes. In this way, through a long procession of puppet-plays, handed down by tradition through generations of showmen, the Faust-story retained its popularity until almost to our own

[15] As we shall see later, Goethe first became acquainted with the Faust subject in the form of a puppet-play. On the popular Faust drama, see K. Engel: *Das Volksschauspiel von Doktor Johann Faust,* 2. Aufl., Oldenburg, 1882. This author has also published several volumes of old puppet-plays, among which will be found texts of Faust marionette-plays, Otto Schade's edition of the Faust puppet-play, first published in 1856, has been reprinted in the Insel-Bücherei No. 125.

days.[15]   The following is the plot of a Faust puppet-play as summarized by Bielschowsky in his *Life of Goethe:*

"An investigator, unsatisfied by all his learning and deep meditation, consigns himself to the Devil, in order, through him, to acquire all sciences and arts, all treasures and enjoyments of the world, and for a period of time to feel like God.   This he does, so far as lies within the Devil's power.   Faust travels with the Devil through the world, becomes a magician, who has power over the living and dead, and tastes every kind of pleasure, even that of living at a ducal court, where he calls up the dead and wins the heart of the princess, until finally, sated with everything, though not satisfied, he repents and turns in earnest prayer to God.   At this critical moment the Devil brings him Helena.[16]   Captivated by her beauty, Faust gives up all pious thoughts of repentance, rushes toward her and embraces her.   In his arms she is transformed into a Fury, and, robbed of earthly enjoyment and heavenly bliss, he is dragged away to Hell."[17]

* * *

Lessing was the first to point out the poetic possibilities of the Faust legend.   In his opposition to the vapid imitations of the French tragedies, and with the aim of showing what power lay in the old German popular plays, he essayed the subject of Faust in 1759 but never finished it.   Lessing wished to turn the conclusion of his play to Faust's salvation.   He would not permit his hero to fall into the power of the Devil.   In the century of enlightenment, in which Lessing lived, love of secular learning, even error and heresy, were no longer considered crimes.   Referring to the desire of knowledge and the love of truth which, in the century of the Reformation, constituted Faust's sin, Lessing wrote: "God has not given man the noblest of impulses to make him unhappy."   The story of Faust's condemnation to hell was, in Lessing's opinion, immoral and hence untrue.   In his proposed Faust play, the devils, in anger at losing their prey, were to be beaten back by the angels with the words: "Ye shall not prevail!"

The subject of Faust was essayed by many other German writers in the latter half of the eighteenth century.   The new interest and new attraction that the Faust legend had for those men Bielschowsky explains by the striking similarity of that period to the Renaissance epoch.   The poet-painter Friedrich Müller, known in Germany as

[16] Helena was the wife of Menelaus, a woman of surpassing beauty, who was carried off to Troy by Paris and thus became the cause of the Trojan Wars (*Iliad* iii. 165).

[17] Albert Bielschowsky *Goethe*. 2 vols. 1895 and 1903. New German edition. München, 1929. *Life of Goethe*. Translated from the German by William A. Cooper (3 vols., New York, 1905-08), III, 251-2.

Maler Müller and also as *Teufelsmaler* Müller, who worked on this material in 1776 to 1778, wished in his *Fausts Leben dramatisiert* to employ the Faust legend as a satirical portrait of the age. The Faust dramas by Julius Graf von Soden and Johann Friedrich Schink also merit attention.

Friedrich Maximilian Klinger's philosophical work, *Fausts Leben, Taten und Höllenfahrt* (1791), is less a novel than a political pamphlet.[18] It may aptly be called a devil's-eye view of human history. In his novel, Klinger follows that version of the Faust legend which identified the famous magician Johannes Faust of the chap-books with Hans Fust or Johannes Faust, a goldsmith and member of a rich burgher-family of Mayence, who was the financial backer and partner of Gutenberg, the inventor of the art of printing. The two partners were suspected of meddling with forbidden books of magic, and of performing evil witchery. They were also accused of plunging into sorcerous formulæ in a quest for the magic stone of the old philosophers and for their lost secret of transforming cheap metals into gold. Faust, who later obtained the machinery from Gutenberg and set up a printing press in Paris, was especially considered a magician and a servant of Satan. The red letters, which he used in the colophons at the close of his earliest printed volumes, were interpreted by his contemporaries as proof of the black art which originated the works so easily produced by him. The multiplication of the Bible considered especially dangerous and sinful by the Catholics also contributed to the diabolical reputation of the Paris printer.

In Klinger's novel, Faust is a superman superb in his spirit of rebellion against "all the old-established customs of society." He is the incarnation of the Romantic revolt against all social and moral laws that hold men in chains. Faust sells himself to Satan not to obtain from him wealth or physical enjoyment but in order to learn from him "the secrets of human destiny and the reason for moral evil in the world." And for Faust the Devil can invent no greater agony than to keep him ignorant of the very problems that torment him. Faust's own personal sufferings concern him less than man's moral misery. He has great faith in the goodness of man. "You

[18] On this work consult G. J. Pfeiffer's study, *F. Klinger's "Faust." Eine literarhistorische Untersuchung*. Würzburg, 1890. Klinger's *Faust* was translated by George Borrow and published in London in 1825. A later issue of this translation was published by Kent in 1864. The translator took considerable liberties with the text.

will avow to me," he says to the Devil, "that man is the apple of the eye of him whom I now no longer must name." But the Demon replies: "Then I will return to hell a convicted liar, and give thee back the bond which thou wilt presently sign with thy blood." Thereupon the Devil makes a wager with Faust to prove to him the utter corruption of man; and to this end drags him into an endless course across Europe at the dawn of the Renaissance. Faust visits the Germany of Frederick III, the France of Louis XI and the Italy of the Borgias. The Devil has no difficulty in proving to his companion that man, far from needing a Devil to tempt him to evil, puts the very Devil to blush by his evil deeds. He shows Faust that, in this God-governed world, "evil arises from good," predicts that the art of printing, with which its inventor intended to benefit mankind, would turn out to be an instrument of evil, by converting the small stream, which had previously poisoned the human mind, into a tremendous flood. Faust, who considered himself to be the benefactor of mankind by his discovery of printing, later destined to become the right handmaiden of our civilization, is disappointed and disillusioned, seeing the seeds of good he tried to sow among men already turned into disasters, and proudly accepts eternal damnation. He feels no regret in quitting the earth after having found that it surpasses Hell in wickedness.

* * *

Goethe, the greatest son of that century and the stoutest champion of its new ideas, next took hold of the Faust myth. In his hands, it has become the most poetical expression of the eternal combat between good and evil in the heart of man. The impression of the Faust legend gained from a puppet-play seen when a boy in Frankfort remained with him to the day of his death. He began working on the material in 1772 and finished the first draft in 1775. His Faust-fragment appeared in 1790, the First Part of the poem in 1808, and the Second Part posthumously in 1832.

Goethe follows the first Faust-book in ascribing to his hero the thirst for knowledge as the primary motive of his compact with Hell. The Goethean Faust, "recognizing the vanity of abstract learning and intuition, but eager to the point of frenzy to understand and possess the world, makes a pact with the Spirit of Negation, so as to throw himself into the experimental forms of learning." Goethe deviates from the legend,

however, on two important points. First he substitutes for
a fixed period—the traditional quarter-century—the agreement that
Faust is to be the Devil's property at any moment whatsoever, when
Faust shall be brought to the point of saying to the ecstatic moment,
"Bleibe doch; du bist so schön." The moment of complete and for-
getful self-satisfaction is the price of his damnation.[19] Secondly,
following the lead of Lessing, Goethe represents his hero in the end
as saved from perdition by Gretchen and triumphantly borne aloft
by angels, leaving Mephistopheles crestfallen and defeated.[20] The
Devil thought to lure Faust with the woman, but he lost him through
her influence. Thus Mephistopheles becomes the power which e'er
designs the bad and e'er accomplishes the good.

Through Goethe's poem, the Faust legend has obtained a place
second to no other in the poetic literature of the world. The diabolical parts of Goethe's poem influenced the imagination of the poets
and playwrights in all European countries. Among his German
imitators may be mentioned E. A. F. Klingemann, who wrote a
tragedy (1815), Nikolaus Lenau, also a tragedy (1838), and Heinrich Heine, a ballet (1851). Christian Grabbe brought together
Don Juan and Faust in his drama written in 1824.

* * *

The tradition of the original Don Juan Tenorio, who lived in
the fourteenth century and who is said to have been the associate of
King Pedro the Cruel of Castille, contains, notwithstanding what
has been said in the previous chapter, the element of a diabolical
pact.[21] But the Devil is absent in the earlier versions of the legend.
As all know, who are acquainted with Don Juan in play and opera,

[19] Cf. Alexander R. Hohlfeld's very interesting article, "Pact and Wager
in Goethe's *Faust*," *Modern Philology*, XVIII (1920-21), 1513-36. Read also
Ludwig Nader: "Zum Pakt in Goethes *Faust*," *Zeitschrift für Deutschkunde*,
XXXVII (1923), No. 3 and Otto Pniower: "Der Teufelspakt in *Faust*,"
Jahrbuch der Goethe-Gesellschaft, VIII (1922).

[20] The question as to whether or not Goethe was indebted to Lessing for
the "happy" ending of his poem has recently been revived by Ernst Bergmann
in his article "Ist die 'Rettung' des Goetheschen *Faust* auf Lessings Faust-
Fragmente zurückzuführen?" *Jarbuch des Braunschweigischen Geschichts-
vereins*, 2. Folge, Bd. 2 (1929).

[21] The first definite appearance of Don Juan Tenorio in literary fiction
dates back to the *Burlador de Sevilla y Convidado de Piedra*, by Gabriel Tellez
(1571-1648), better known under the name of Tirso de Molina, first published at
Barcelona in 1630. The typical seducer appears in the folk-lore of many
countries, but the Spaniard presented the character so masterfully that it is
accepted as a Spanish conception. Don Juan is also the hero of Molière and
Mozart, of Byron and Shaw. Bernard Shaw's *Man and Superman* (1905)
contains an interlude in the form of a dream on the theme of Don Juan and
the Devil.

it is the Dead Guest, the Commander, who is the executor of the divine sentence against the arch-seducer and mocker. In later versions, however, this character is represented as the Devil in disguise, who helps Don Juan in his numberless conquests of women and who accepts the invitation to the banquet to put an end to his career of seduction. Thus in the play, *The Rest of Don Juan*, by Henry Morford (1848), a continuation of Byron's *Don Juan* (1819-24), we find the following ending: One night, at a banquet, a tall dark stranger enters the room and beckons Don Juan away. The two depart together while the lights burn blue and the guests smell brimstone. On the morrow, Don Juan's body is found in a cemetery.

In Rostand's last play *la Dernière nuit de Don Juan* (written in 1911), the Devil, having appeared at Don Juan's banquet to drag the arch-seducer to the bottomless pit, grants his request to return to earth and live ten years longer. When this period has passed, the Devil again appears as a showman with a Punch and Judy box, and summons the shades of the one thousand and three ladies of Don Juan's traditional affairs in order to confuse and confound the host. He asks Don Juan to name the women he has seduced, but this most hardened of rakes has truly known none of them. The cynical lover seduced them when they were ready, and was accepted because he offered himself most frequently. He has had all the women but never possessed one single woman. Then the Devil at last discloses the punishment which he has reserved for him. Not for such as Don Juan exists the flaming pit, to which sinners of the type of Nero and Heliogabalus are condemned! There is another hell for such a sorry and trivial fool. Don Juan shall be a Pulchinello for all eternity. The proud Spaniard begs mercy and asks for the eternal fire. But the Devil inexorably replies that he has reserved the eternal theater for him. At the Devil's behest, Don Juan, he who believed himself to be the irresistible lover, the wickedest sinner, appears, bowing, and scraping and grimacing absurdly, as a puppet, on the Punch and Judy stage, which the Devil, in the guise of the showman, brought with him at the beginning of the play.[22]

[22] The definitive study on the Don Juan legend is the Paris thesis by Georges Gendarme de Bévotte, *la Légende de Don Juan; son évolution dans la littérature; des origines au Romantisme* (1906). For further study of this subject, particularly in the post-Romantic period, the reader is referred to the following books and articles: Francisco Augustin: *Don Juan en el teatro, en la novela y en la vida;* con un estudio preliminar sobre la vejez de Don Juan, por el Dr. Gregorio Marañon, Madrid, 1928; S. M. Waxman: "The Don Juan

Karl Immermann's *Merlin* (1832) is perhaps the greatest attempt by a German to write a Faust in imitation of Goethe. This play is a kind of appendage to the Second Part of the Goethan poem, replacing Mephistopheles by Merlin.[23]

*
* *

The influence of Goethe's *Faust* did not make itself sufficiently felt in France until this poem found a worthy translator in the person of Gérard de Nerval, who, in 1828, when he was hardly out of his teens, brought out a French version of the Goethean poem that surprised and enchanted the great German himself. Gérard de Nerval has the great merit of winning the French public for this great German poem, which passed unnoticed among his countrymen in previous translations. Gérard de Nerval's version enjoyed the enthusiastic admiration of the French public and became the Gospel of the French Romantics.[24]

Gérard de Nerval's translation of Goethe's *Faust* gave the impetus to a very great number of adaptations of this poem on the French stage. Among the numerous dramatic adaptations, we will point out the following plays: *l'Amour et la mort,* a play first presented at the Variétés theater on September 6, 1828. This drama contains a witch-scene, in which the Devil is evoked by a sorceress. In another play, *Une nuit de Paris,* given in March, 1829, at the Vaudeville theater, a naive young man, son of a retired court-recorder, on the point of getting married and ready to pay his bachelor's debts, permits himself to be dragged into all sorts of debaucheries by a Mephistopheles in human form. The play, *le Cousin de Faust,* presented the same month at the Gaîté theater, shows by its very title, the influence of the Goethean poem. It need scarcely be said that this statement also holds good with regard to

Legend in Literature," *The Journal of American Folk-Lore,* vol. XXI, April-September, 1908. An interesting article on this subject, written from the psycho-analytic point of view, appeared in the magazine, *Psyche and Eros,* vol. II (1929), No. 2. On Russian versions of the Don Juan tradition, see C. A. Manning's article in the *Publications of the Modern Language Association of America,* vol. XXXVIII (1923), No. 3, especially pp. 485-91.

[23] Concerning Immermann's debt to Goethe, consult Otto Volkart's article, "Immermanns *Merlin* und Goethe's *Faust,*" *Westfälisches Magazin,* N. F., 2. Jg. (1910). On this play, see also Ottakar Fischer: *Zu Immermanns "Merlin"* (1909); Herman Hamann: "Das Rätsel in Immermanns *Merlin,*" *Neue Jahrbücher für Wissenschaft und Jugendbildung,* Bd. I (1925); Karl Schultze-Jahde: "Zu Immermanns *Merlin,*" *Zeitschrift für Deutschkunde* (1925).

[24] On Goethe's influence in France, cf. F. Baldensperger: *Goethe en France; étude de littérature comparée* (Paris, 1904; second edition, 1920); and Pierre Lasserre: *Faust en France* (1929).

Jean Lesguillon's drama, *Méphistophélès, ou le Diable et la jeune Fille,* played at the Panthéon theater in 1832, in which the Devil is caught in his own traps.

Among the other imitations of Goethe's *Faust,* we may mention Emmanuel Arago's Faust-play, produced about 1832, which contains a cohort of demons and witches presided over by Mephistopheles, reminiscent of the Walpurgis-Night in the German poem, and Eugène Robin's dramatic poem, *Livia* (1835), in which the title-character loves Faust for a short time previous to the expiration of his compact. Mephisto puts Livia's love to test by offering her Faust's love in return for the salvation of her soul. Livia loves Faust sufficiently to sign the pact of perdition in her turn. But when Mephistopheles appears to seize her, he finds her dead, with the angel Emmanuel watching by her side.

A rather interesting French adaptation of Goethe's *Faust* is the play by Eugène Scribe and de Saint-Georges, *la Nuit de Walpurgis,* with its subtitle "comédie politique du temps présent," which was presented at the Gymnase theater in 1850. In this comedy, Mephistopheles takes by the hand the Faust of the rue Saint-Denis, the politician Morin, and leads him into the midst of the Witches' Sabbath of 1848.[25]

*
* *

What attracted Gérard de Nerval so powerfully to *Faust* was its devil-myth. The character that appealed to him in this drama was not the wizard of Wittenberg, but his *spiritus familiaris.* In Gérard de Nerval's opinion, which he expresses in the preface to the first edition of his translation of *Faust,* the real hero of this poem was not Faust but Mephistopheles. Gérard de Nerval was discerning enough to discover the fact that Goethe did not conceive of the Devil in the form of a hideous phantom, as he is usually represented to children; but that, on the contrary, he has portrayed him as the Evil Being par excellence, before whom all other poetic personifications of Evil were only novices, hardly worthy to be the minions of Mephistopheles.

The scene in *Faust* that drew its best French translator so irresistibly to Germany was the narration of the prank that the Devil played on the students in Auerbach's Cellar. Gérard de

---

[25] On this play, see the *Journal des Débats* of June 17, 1850. Mephistopheles plays a rôle also in Edouard Grenier's *Jacqueline Bonhomme,* with its subtitle "tragédie moderne" (1879).

Nerval longed to visit the spot that had witnessed this famous feat, and, as soon as his means permitted him, hurried to Leipzig so that he might lean his elbow on the table from which Mephistopheles had the glowing wine gush forth amidst flaming jets to the utter amazement of the revellers. *"Plus heureux que nous,"* wrote Théophile Gautier in 1867 in his recollections of his poor friend, who had hanged himself twelve years previously, *"il s'est assis accoudé sur la table d'où Méphistophélès faisait jaillir avec une forêt des fusées de vin incendiaires."* [26]

When Gérard later sought inspiration in Goethe's *Faust* for his own works, he imitated only the diabolical parts of the play, such as the conjuration of the Devil, the devil-compact, and the evocation by the Devil of the beauties of antiquity.

The first play which Gérard de Nerval planned already showed the influence of Goethe's *Faust.* The pseudo-medieval mystery-play, *le Prince des sots* (1830), with its blazing mouth of Hell surmounted by a Paradise of starry azure, reveals reminiscences of the Prologue in the Goethean poem. This French play has for its subject the arrival of a company of jugglers at a feudal castle under the pretext of giving a performance, but in reality for the purpose of rescuing a fair lady held in durance vile by a tyrannical husband or father.

The minor plot, which is a play within a play, tells of an angel, who descends from the azure sphere and throws dice with the Devil, with human souls as the stakes. The angel cheats, through excess of zeal, with the object of taking back as many of his friends as possible into Paradise. The Devil in the end loses his temper, calls the angel "great gawky fellow, sly fool," and threatens, if he catches him again at his tricks, to pull every feather out of his wings, so that he would be unable to fly back to his Master. The quarrel grows bitter, and leads to a row, under cover of which the lover, protected by the Prince of Fools, succeeds in carrying off his lady fair.[27]

[26] Théophile Gautier: *Portraits et souvenirs littéraires.* Paris, 1875.

[27] The synopsis of this play has been given after Gautier's account of it in his *Histoire du Romantisme* (1874). M. Aristide Marie in his study, *Gérard de Nerval, le poète et l'homme* (Paris, 1914), p. 368, n. 22, maintains that Gautier's memory failed him in his account of the plot of this play. It is not with the Devil but with a juggler placed at the entrance to Hell-mouth that the angel plays the game of dice. Gérard de Nerval, who could not have the play performed, changed it later into a novel, which was published after the original manuscript by L. Ulbach in *la Nouvelle Revue* for 1887.

Gérard de Nerval's second play, *Nicolas Flamel,* written the same year, bears a still stronger impression of Goethe's *Faust.* The scene in which Satan appears to Flamel on the tower of the Church of Saint-Jacques is an evident imitation of the apparition of Mephistopheles in Faust's study.[28]

Nicolas Flamel, a man of genius, has been ruined by his alchemistic researches. In his "despair of never attaining," he takes the decision to sell his soul to Satan. Ambition drives him to enter into a pact with the powers of hell. Having been unsuccessful in soaring to the heights, he now contemplates plunging himself to the depths. His decision, however, is actuated not by his material misery so much as by his thirst for learning. He is anxious to be freed from the chains which bind the human mind. He expects from the Devil not material rewards so much as the ability to know all and to comprehend all. He summons Satan and offers to sign away his soul. But the Devil is not content with the scholar's soul. He demands the inclusion of Flamel's wife in the pact for fear that, through her piety, she may in the end obtain her husband's pardon from Heaven and thus snatch his soul from Hell. Flamel, as a good husband, balks at this condition. He is willing to forfeit his own soul as payment for services received, but he will not jeopardize his spouse's soul in the bargain. Satan, however, is stubborn on this point. He will have both or none at all. In the end, as Flamel is hard pressed by his creditors, he expresses his willingness to hand over his beloved wife as well as himself to the Devil.

The long drawn-out negotiations furnish several occasions for the Devil to expound his philosophy. Satan shows himself in this play as a thorough-going dualist. He expresses the idea of two co-equal and co-eternal powers continually engaged in a war for the

[28] The substitution of the tower of the Church of St. Jacques de la Boucherie for the scholar's laboratory of alchemy is due to the fact that the name of the protagonist of this play is historically linked with this church. Nicolas Flamel, a member of the University of Paris and a librarian, who died in 1417, is one of the most famous persons buried in the Church of St. Jacques. He left a great sum of money to this church, and his effigy, together with that of his wife, used to be seen kneeling at the Virgin's feet in the tympanum of the porch. Nicolas Flamel was venerated by the alchemists as their patron for having, as it was believed, discovered the philosopher's stone. His house in the Rue des Ecrivains was searched several times in order to find some indication of his secret. In the selection of the church tower as the place of temptation we may perhaps also see a reminiscence of the temptation of Christ on the pinnacle of the Temple (Matt. iv. 5; Luke iv. 9). On Nicolas Flamel, see Maurice Magre's recently published work, *Magiciens et Illuminés.*

mastery of the world. The two antagonists—Deus and Diabolus—
he maintains, are equal in glory and grandeur, but man, standing
between them, is inferior to either of them. The Mighty Abyss,
he tells Flamel, has as much beauty as the High Mountain. The
ugly, he claims, is that which has neither height nor depth. The
bad lies not at the ends, but in the middle. Men should prefer Hell
or Heaven rather than earth for a sojourn.

Nicolas Flamel finally becomes conscious of Satan's sophistry.
In the end, the specious arguments advanced by the Devil open his
victim's eyes. Flamel realizes that true happiness lies not on the
heights nor in the depths, but mid-way, amidst the sacred and
familiar things of the earth. He finally decides to act in the
spirit of Aristotle's "Golden Mean" and according to the Latin
proverb: *"Medio tutissimus ibis,"* refuses to sign the pact, abandons
his ambitions, and returns to his desk to earn his living with his
pen.[29]

[29] This "drame chronique" was left unfinished by its author. Two small
fragments of this play appeared in the *Mercure de France au XIXe siècle* for
1831. The conclusion is given in the résumé after a recent English translation,
which appeared in the *Dublin Magazine,* I (1923-24), 503-512. Its author,
Seumas O'Sullivan, has added a final scene.

CHAPTER XVII

THE DEVIL-COMPACT IN LEGEND AND LITERATURE
II

THE Faust legend occupied the mind of Gérard de Nerval during a long period of his literary activity. In Germany he explored all popular traditions in regard to Faust, even down to the puppet-plays. The oldest Faust-book of 1587, which he read in connection with his translation of the First Part of Goethe's *Faust*, is printed at the end of his translation of the Second Part of this poem (1840).

Gérard de Nerval cherished for many years the project of a French adaptation of the Faust legend. He left behind a manuscript fragment of a Faust play, containing the first act and the beginning of the second act. The manuscript is interrupted at the point where Mephistopheles counsels Faust to forget Margaret for the beautiful courtesans of antiquity, Helena,[30] Cleopatra[31] and Aspasia.[32]

Gérard de Nerval abandoned the project of finishing this play of Faust when a copy of Klinger's work already mentioned finally fell into his hands. This philosophical novel was well known to the French public. It was translated into French six years after its first publication and again in 1808 and 1823. Among the dramatizations of this novel in France may be mentioned *les Aventures de Faust et sa descente aux enfers* by de Saur and de Saint-Génies, which was produced for the first time in 1825, and M. E. Théaulon's lyrical play *Faust,* first produced on October 27, 1827.

[30] On Helena, see note 16.

[31] Cleopatra was the last queen of Egypt. Her beauty fascinated Cæsar and Antony.

[32] Aspasia, the famous courtesan of antiquity, was the mistress of Pericles and the friend of all the writers and philosophers of her time, especially of Socrates. See "Pericles and Artaxerxes" in Plutarch's *Lives.*

The story of the latter play is as follows: The protagonist, a young and melancholy *savant*, inventor of the art of printing, sells himself to the Devil because the father of the beautiful Marguerite hesitates to give him his daughter in marriage. Fortunately the girl is protected by the statue of a woman saint, endowed with miraculous powers. With her iron arm, she forces Mephistopheles to return the infernal pact.

The *Faust* of Klinger deeply impressed Gérard de Nerval when, as a school-boy, he caught sight of it on a bookstall along the banks of the Seine. He turned its leaves, but could not purchase it for lack of sufficient pocket-money. When he returned the following day, he found that it had been sold. He searched for a copy of this book for almost thirty years, and when he finally discovered it in the library of his friend Monselet, his joy knew no bounds. He forthwith set out to employ this novel as a model for the long contemplated play on the old Faust legend, leaving the play based on the first Faust chap-book unfinished, and published it in 1851, under the following title: *l'Imagier de Harlem ou la Découverte de l'imprimerie.*

Though principally an adaptation of Klinger's novel, this play also contains several reminiscences from the Second Part of Goethe's *Faust*. The similarity of the plots in the works of Klinger and Gérard de Nerval is very striking. Both Klinger's hero and Gérard de Nerval's protagonist discovered the art of printing, but this discovery plays a much smaller part in the German novel than in the French play based upon it. Why Gérard de Nerval replaced Johann Faust by Laurens Coster of Harlem, Holland, one of the reputed inventors of printing, is difficult to explain. Did he wish to return the credit for the discovery of printing to the Dutchman, for whom his counrymen had long claimed the glory of the invention of this art?[33] Or did he simply wish to bring an element of originality into a work which is otherwise merely a mosaic of borrowings? The question is not easy to answer.

Gérard de Nerval's play of the printer of Harlem has for its principal plot the invention of printing, and its central idea is the fact that the Devil takes hold of this discovery and makes of it one of his tools to ruin mankind. Satan, assuming the form and language of a Machiavelli who is more Machiavellian than his proto-

---

[33] On the question as to who really was the inventor of printing, see Aloys Bömer: "Noch eimmal: Coster und Gutenberg oder nur Gutenberg?" *Zentralblatt für Bibliothekswesen,* Bd. XLVI (1929), nos. 1-2.

type, enlightens Coster on the lamentable consequences of his invention. He takes him on a tour of the European capitals to show him how the tyrants of the earth turn his invention into a tool for the oppression of the masses. He also evokes for his companion a panorama of history to show him the fatal fruits of his discovery. At the court of Frederick III at Aix-la-Chapelle, Satan applies Coster's invention to the printing of paper money.[34]

Gérard de Nerval's principal originality consists in the creation of his diabolical personages. Klinger's Leviathan, as well as Goethe's Mephistopheles, is effaced in this play behind a Satan with several avatars. The Devil does not show himself here in *propia persona*. He tempts, perverts, and leads men astray under endless incarnations. The chamberlain of the Archduke of Austria, who answers to the name of Blocksberg,[35] is the first of Satan's seven avatars. The most original diabolical personage in this play is a sort of phantom of beauty named Alilah, who appears under various and ambiguous forms. She shows herself to Coster as Aspasia,[36] as the Imperia,[37] as the Lady of Beaujeu,[38] and finally as a Muse. Coster permits himself to be held under the spell of this phantasmal woman for a dozen years, but in the end this ally of the Devil is herself instrumental in his salvation.

The *motif* of the devil-pact also appears in two stories generally attributed to Gérard de Nerval. In "les Deux notes" (1831), Satan appears to propose an insidious pact to Paganini, the famous Italian violinist, and in "Ugolino" (1833), we meet a lunatic virtuoso, who sells his own soul and that of his young child in order to obtain from Satan a miraculous violin.

*
* *

As in Gérard de Nerval's case, what all other French Romantics seized upon in Goethe's great poem was its medieval sorcery. Its philosophical and symbolical contents escaped them as they did its best translator. What interested them most in *Faust* were its fan-

[34] Those of us who lived in Europe after the Great War, during the currency-inflation period, will heartily agree that paper money was the Devil's own invention.

[35] Blocksberg is the popular name for the Brocken, which is the German mount of witches.

[36] On Aspasia, see note 32.

[37] The Imperia (1455-1511) was an Italian courtesan, who enjoyed great celebrity during the pontificates of Julius II and Leon X.

[38] The Lady of Beaujeu (1460-1522) is Anne of France, daughter of Louis XI, and wife of Pierre de Bourbon, who was lord of Beaujeu when he married her. She was very famous for her beauty and wit.

tastic parts. Thus George Sand counted *Faust* among the great
fantastic plays in her "Essai sur le drame fantastique: Goethe,
Byron, Mickiewicz" (1839).

Faust, especially in its diabolical aspects, strongly influenced
French imagination during the Romantic period. Mephistopheles
with his *rictus infernal* was the rage of the Romantics. These
children of the Revolution, with their strong swayings toward
Satanism, went wild over the wit of this Mocker of Mankind. They
almost deified the Devil and actually swore by Mephistopheles and
the Walpurgis Night. Painters devoted their talents to transferring
this "Satanism" to their canvases. Delacroix painted the Walpurgis
Night, and Louis Boulanger the Witches' Sabbath. The great
Romantic composer, Berlioz, in his *Damnation* de Faust (1846),
based on Gérard de Nerval's version, knew how to bring out the
diabolical element in the Goethean poem, the appeal of which its
French translator rendered so well into French. This opera is the
full expression of Romantic music. It contains, as Gautier has
well remarked, what Gounod's lacks—the diabolical irony of negation, which is the chief trait of Mephistopheles's character.

The influence of Goethe's *Faust,* insofar as its devil-compact
is concerned, is evident in many poems, novels and short stories not
only of the Romantic period but also in later times. We will refer
to a few of the French works of the last century which particularly
show reminiscences of the Goethean poem.[39]

Théophile Gautier's poem *Albertus* (1832) is a sort of sardonic
burlesque upon *Faust* and certain Romantic works which were
tinged with medievalism. This poem has been called by its author
"half diabolical, half fashionable." It certainly is semi-supernatural
and semi-sensual, fantastic and funereal, impertinent and indecent.
This "theological legend," as its subtitle runs, was written completely in the spirit of a period which was revelling in everything
connected with metamorphoses, black arts, devil-compacts and
Witches' Sabbaths.

Albertus, a young Italian painter, offers his soul to Satan for
the possession of Veronica, a wicked woman and hideous hag, who,
by means of magic, has succeeded in transforming herself into a
marvelously beautiful young girl, but who in his very arms changes
again to her original form. At this sight Albertus is seized with

---

[39] The *Légendes françaises* (1829) and the *Nouvelles légendes* (1833) by
Edouard d'Anglemont contain several legends figuring a devil-compact.

terror. The blood in his veins runs cold. He wishes to escape, but he cannot free himself from her cold and clammy arms. He belongs to her through a rash word uttered in the madness of delirium.

Albertus is forced to accompany Veronica to the Witches' Sabbath. They mount two broomsticks, bridled and saddled, which carry them through the air to the infernal tryst. Now they reach their destination.

"The place was lighted by a flame, casting a blue light like that of a blazing punch. It was an open spot within the forest's depths. Wizards in their gowns and witches nude astride upon their goats adown the four corners of the world arrived at once. Investigators into sciences occult, Fausts of every land, magi of every rite, dark-faced gypsies, and rabbis red-haired, cabalists, diviners, hermeceutists black as ink and asthmatically gasping—not one of them failed to appear at the meeting place" (XI).[40]

All wait for Satan who is to preside *in propia persona* over the ceremonies.

"At last he came; but no devil of sulphur and of aspect terrific; no devil old-fashioned, but the dandiest of fiends, wearing imperial and slight moustache, twirling his cane as well as could have done a boulevard swell. You could have sworn he's just come from a performance of *Robert the Devil* or *The Temptation*, or had been attending some assembly fashionable. He limped like Byron (but no worse than he), and with his haughty mien, his aristocratic looks, and his exquisite talent for tying his cravat, in every drawing-room a sensation he would have made" (CXIV).

Gautier now amuses himself by composing the grand symphony of the adepts of Satan. When the concert is finished, the dancing begins. Poor Albertus is the unwilling spectator of the most monstrous diabolical diversions. In the midst of the ceremonies, the Devil sneezes. The odor of the company is too strong for his fashionable nostrils. "God bless you," Albertus says courteously. No sooner has he uttered these words when the whole frightful pageant disappears. Devil, demons, wizards, witches, all vanish into the air. Albertus feels sharp claws and teeth tear his flesh. His shrieks avail him not. The next morning, peasants find on the Appian road, near Rome, a man's body, with broken thighs and twisted neck.[41]

[40] Quotations taken from the subscription set, in 24 volumes, of the works of Théophile Gautier in English, edited by F. C. Sumichrast and published by C. T. Brainard Publ. Co., Boston and New York, 1903.

[41] Reminescences of *Albertus* will be found in the description of the Black Mass in Oscar Wilde's story, "The Fisherman and his Soul" (1891).

The story, *l'Amour et le Grimoire,* originally called *le Nouveau Faust et la Nouvelle Marguerite, ou Comment je me suis donné au Diable* (1832), by Charles Nodier, is likewise a burlesque of *Faust.* In it, Nodier brings down Goethe's lofty poem to the level of a very ordinary *bourgeois* affair.

Maxime, who tells the story in the first person, summons Satan and offers his soul to the Devil on condition that the latter bring to his room at midnight a certain Marguerite, to whom the young man has taken a passing fancy. Satan, however, turns a deaf ear and refuses to submit to the beck and call of a mere school-boy who has by chance got hold of a grimoire (book of conjurations). By a curious coincidence, the girl appears in his room without the aid of the Devil. A friend of the young man, who has succeeded in persuading Marguerite to elope with him, has sent her up to the room of her would-be seducer there, in hiding, to await the morning coach. Maxime's anxiety not to betray a trusting friend shows that he is too good a man to sell his soul to Satan.

Charles Nodier's story, "la Combe de l'homme mort" (1833), based on a sixteenth century legend of a bargain with Beelzebub, shows many reminiscences of the Faust story. On the eve of All Saints' Day in the year fifteen hundred and sixty-one, the Devil seized a man riding along the road and bore him off thirty leagues to a narrow valley in the Jura mountains. Many years ago this man had murdered an old hermit in order to obtain his wealth, after having won his confidence through hypocritical piety; and when trapped by the villagers and threatened with death, he had sold his soul to Satan in exchange for a thirty years' respite. The contract was written in Satan's scrawl on a slip of paper stained with blood and marked with five black finger-nails like a royal seal.

The man was as eager for knowledge as he was for wealth. After having escaped punishment through the aid of the Devil, he studied at the Universities of Metz and Strasbourg, sat at the feet of the famous Cornelius Agrippa,[42] and obtained his doctorate in

[42] Cornelius Agrippa of Nettesheim (born in Cologne 1486, died in France 1535) was a sceptic philosopher and student of alchemy and magic, who was considered by his contemporaries a great magician and necromancer. He was also supposed to have formed a pact with the Devil, who attended him in the shape of a black dog. In the French mysteries, he himself has even been transformed into a devil. Some of his necromantic feats are recorded in Thomas Nashe's *Unfortunate Traveller* (1594). Read also Southey's ballad "Cornelius Agrippa" (1799). The best biography of Cornelius Agrippa is Henry Morley's *The Life of Cornelius Agrippa, doctor and knight, commonly called magician.* 2 vols., London, 1856.

four faculties. His reputation as a scholar spread far and wide, and he was finally called to fill a chair at the University of Heidelberg. Men and women came from the four corners of the continent to study under this professor. Satan himself, attracted by this scholar's reputation, enrolled as one of his students. The professor, by dint of his great scholarship, was soon elected rector of the celebrated German university. He possessed fame and fortune and never thought of his pact with the Devil. But Satan had a better memory than even the rector of the University of Heidelberg. At the expiration of the term, the Devil was at hand to claim fulfillment of the terms of the compact. As the rector rode one day along the highway, pleased with himself and the world, the Devil appeared, snatched him up, and brought him to the spot of the murder. When the rector ascertained his whereabouts, he was assailed by unpleasant memories. An old woman, urged on by the Evil One, helped along the poor professor's memory by a full and detailed recital of the events which had occurred thirty years before and which gave the valley its name—the Valley of the Dead Man. As he finally rushed out, anxious to disappear in the dark of the night, the Devil followed him and wrung his neck.[43]

The idea of a devil-compact occurred frequently in the literatures of the various European countries, during the first half of the last century, even in works which cannot be traced to Goethe's influence. Medievalism, which formed an important part of Romanticism in all European countries, also implied diabolism. The Devil, as is well known, occupied a position of paramount importance in medieval arts and letters. He was a prominent and popular character in the mystery-plays. The interest which Romanticism showed in

[43]It is not within the scope of this book to treat of Goethe's influence in works which do not contain the devil-compact. We will, however, refer to George Sand and Flaubert, who composed many of their works under the inspiration of the Goethean poem. George Sand's fantastic drama, *les Sept cordes de la lyre* (1839), is copied from *Faust*. Its principal character Albertus is a replica of the German philosopher. He, too, is tempted by Mephistopheles in his ambition to know and comprehend all. The Witches' Sabbath in her novel, *le Château des Déserts* (1847), is a clear imitation of the Walpurgis Night in *Faust*. Flaubert's juvenilia as well as his *Tentation de saint Antoine* (1874) likewise show many reminiscences of the Goethean poem. Louis Ménard's story, "le Diable au café" (1876), which contains a philosophical discussion between the Devil and the author, shows Goethe's conception of Mephistopheles.

medieval legend and history brought into literature magic potions, Witches' Sabbaths, devil-compacts and all other sorts of Satanism.[44] In England, the Gothic School of fiction brought diabolism into vogue as far back as the last quarter of the eighteenth century.

Horace Walpole, author of *The Castle of Otranto* (1764), was the first of a group of writers who took supernatural terrors as the principal subject of interest. He may be regarded as the founder of the Gothic and ghost-haunted fiction in England. Of greater influence on her contemporaries was Mrs. Ann Radcliffe, "the mighty magician of the *Mysteries of Udolpho*" (1794), who introduced into the popular novel deep dungeons and haunted houses, spirits and spooks.

The leader in this field of fiction, however, was Matthew Gregory Lewis, author of *Ambrosio the Monk* (1795 or 1796). In contrast to Ann Radcliffe, this novelist employed a supernaturalism which disdains all rational explanation. He introduced diabolical machinery into the popular novel, and created the so-called diabolical supernaturalism. His novel just mentioned is the final word in the English School of Terror. Lewis may be given the credit for having introduced the Devil into modern fiction. In *Ambrosio the Monk*, the Devil is not brought in with an allegorical or satirical aim, but is the leading character, the mainspring of the action. This novel may have been influenced by Jacques Cazotte's romance, *le Diable amoureux* (1772), but it advanced far beyond its model, although a sense of mystery and even of the supernatural is already to be found in the French romance. The novel, *Ambrosio the Monk*, tells the story of a licentious monk named Ambrosio, a superior of a monastery in Madrid, who delivers himself to the Devil in order to accomplish his infamous designs. He goes from crime to crime, from perjury to incest, and from rape to murder, until he is finally carried off by the Devil.

Not far behind Lewis was the Reverend Charles Robert Maturin, author of *Melmoth the Wanderer* (1820). The central episode of this novel is also a devil-compact. The unique feature of this work

[44] Thus Victor Hugo's *Notre-Dame de Paris* (1831), which is a resuscitation of medievalism, contains the medieval belief in sorcery, alchemy, the devil-compact and the Witches' Sabbath. The arch-deacon of Notre-Dame, Claude Frollo, an alchemist, if not a sorcerer, is believed to have closed a compact with the Devil. Quasimodo, the hunchbacked bell-ringer, is supposed to be a demon bound to serve the arch-deacon for a given time, at the end of which he will carry off his soul by way of payment.

is the fact that a human being solicits souls for Satan as a kind of recruiting sergeant for hell. The aim of the author, a good Irish clergyman, in writing a novel so full of horrors, was to show that any man who deals with the Devil is doomed to perdition.

The writers of these novels of wonder and terror are mostly forgotten now, but they were once famous. Walter Scott and Byron were proud to be their friends. The former praised Horace Walpole, and the latter thought *The Castle of Otranto* the most beautiful novel in the English language. Scott, Charles James Fox and Richard Sheridan likewise praised the novels of Ann Radcliffe in the warmest terms. Byron admired this woman novelist and mentioned her in *Childe Harold* (1812) together with Shakespeare, Otway and Schiller. Moore, Shelley and Keats were also under her influence. Scott called *Ambrosio the Monk* "an effort of a genius hardly ordinary." Byron likewise admired this novel, although he later satirized it in his *English Bards and Scotch Reviewers* (1809). Polidori and Shelley were so strongly impressed by this novel that they decided to try their hands at writing supernatural stories of the same sort. Mrs. Shelley was inspired by these writers to compose her *Frankenstein* (1818). Maturin also enjoyed a great reputation in his own country, even Scott and Byron exaggerating his talent.[45]

*
* *

The writers of the English School of Terror likewise left their marks on the minds of the French of the Romantic period. The novels of this school circulated all over the European continent during the first half of the past century, but took hold particularly in France. They were repeatedly translated into French and devoured by the French reading public. These romances were also redacted into dramatic and operatic form and met with great success. Berlioz furnished the music for the libretto of *Ambrosio the Monk*. Mrs. Ann Radcliffe is especially considered the literary embassadress from England to France. The horrors and terrors of these English romances had a great attraction for the French

[45] Concerning these novelists, the reader is referred to Edith Birkhead's thesis, *The Tale of Terror; a study of the Gothic romance* (London, 1921), which is a detailed and documented account of the growth of supernatural fiction in England from Horace Walpole to Wilkie Collins. Jakob Brauchli's German thesis, *Der englische Schauerroman um 1800* (Weida i. Thür., 1928), will also be consulted with profit.

nation, which had experienced the Reign of Terror, at which time it seemed, as a writer in the *Journal des Débats* so aptly expressed it, as if "Hell had vomited its inhabitants on earth.[46]

Even the leaders of the Romantic movement in France did not disdain these novels. Chateaubriand read and praised them. He speaks, in 1822, of the English "romancers of ruins and phantoms" (*Mémoires d'outre-tombe*, 1848). Nodier mentioned the English "romanesque" romances in his essay, *Du fantastique en littérature* (1832) and imitated Lewis in his story, *Iñez de las Sierras* (1837). Mérimée, in his essay on Alexander Pushkin (1868), mentions William Beckford, author of *Vathek* (1781), who was also a member of the English School of Terror. The influence of *Ambrosio the Monk* is evident in Mérimée's play "la Femme est un diable" (1825) and in his story *les Ames du purgatoire* (1834). Victor Hugo likewise admired the English novelists and tried to rival them in their own effects. His story *Han d'Islande* (1823) contains several quotations from Maturin's novel. The influence of *Ambrosio the Monk* is evident in Victor Hugo's ballad "la Légende de la Nonne" (1828) and in his novel *Notre-Dame de Paris* (1831).

Of all French Romantics, however, Balzac was the greatest admirer and imitator of the English novelists of the School of Terror. He fairly revelled in their works "like a janitress" (to employ Théophile Gautier's expression). The great French novelist refers to these English writers in several of his works. He mentions Mrs. Radcliffe in his preface to the *Histoire des Treize* (1833-34), in the episode "la Fille aux yeux d'or," which forms a part of this book, and in *la Grande Bretèche* (1832). Traces of the influence of this woman novelist may be seen in Balzac's novel, *l'Héritière de Birague* (1822). Lewis and Maturin, however, were Balzac's first masters in the art of fiction and continued to be his inspiration to the end. In *Honorine* (1836), Balzac refers to Lewis's *Ambrosio the Monk*. The Frenchman's novel, *le Vicaire des Ardennes* (1822), is for the most part an imitation of this English novel. It was seized almost in the moment of its publication and destroyed by the government, but was later reprinted under the title *le Sorcier*. Lewis's influence can also be detected in Balzac's maturer works.

[46] For the influence of the English School of Terror in France, consult Alice M. Killen's thesis, *le Roman "terrifiant" ou "roman noir" de Walpole à Anne Radcliffe et son influence sur la littérature française jusqu'en 1840* (1920; 2nd ed., 1924).

Of all the novels of the English School of Terror, *Melmoth the Wanderer* with its theme of a devil-compact left the deepest impression on the mind of Balzac. He held its author in high esteem and listed him among the poets who used the idea of an angel drawn by a demon to hell in order to refresh him with the dews of heaven (*l'Elixir de longue vie,* 1830). In a moment perhaps of undiscriminating enthusiasm, Balzac brackets the Melmoth of Maturin with the Don Juan of Molière, the Faust of Goethe, and the Manfred of Byron as "the great characters drawn by the greatest geniuses of Europe." Again, in his preface to the already quoted *Histoire des treize,* the French novelist speaks of Melmoth in the same breath with Faust and Manfred. Maturin's book, thanks to the honor which Balzac granted its author by borrowing his subject, continued to enjoy a high reputation among the French writers. Thus the novel *Ile de Feu* (1870) by Dumas *fils* recalls the thesis of *Melmoth the Wanderer.*

Balzac's novel, *le Centenaire ou les Deux Behringheld* (1832), is an imitation, almost a translation of *Melmoth the Wanderer.* The centenarian, named Behringheld, is a sorcerer born in the fifteenth century. He can live eternally, as a result of a compact concluded with the powers of hell, on condition that he shall always find new human victims and induce them to sell themselves to him. Like Melmoth, he always seeks his victims among the unfortunates of the earth; but while Melmoth, in exchange for the gifts he can bestow, asks only for the souls of his victims, Behringheld sacrifices them to the very last drop of their blood. In the end, the centenarian, deprived of his prey in the final moment, is condemned to death.

In *Melmoth réconcilié,* written by Balzac thirteen years later, Maturin's novel is given a different ending. In the English work, Melmoth's efforts to hand over the infernal pact to another person are unsuccessful and, in the end, this bondman of Beelzebub is lawfully carried off by the Devil. In Balzac's story, Melmoth, after several centuries of wandering over the face of the earth, succeeds in changing destinies with another mortal. The French novelist also alters the character of the Wanderer. Maturin's Melmoth is anxious to continue living eternally, whereas Balzac's yearns for death. The hero of Balzac possesses the power of endless life, but has not the right to lay it down at will. He has obtained, under the terms of the contract, the power to know all, to comprehend all and to do all. He is the "peer of Lucifer," the Lord of life, by virtue of the indwelling demon. He has everything that makes for happiness, but still he is unhappy. He has finally realized the biblical truth that it profits no man to gain this world at the cost of his own soul.

Melmoth, in his search for a soul, is unceasingly harried across the world by the hounds of hell. He can obtain the boon of death and the bliss of heaven only if he can find another soul to deliver to the Devil in compensation for his own. He seeks his victim among the unfortunates of the earth; but no man, even in the most abject poverty and the greatest suffering, will buy health and wealth in exchange for his soul. Wherever he turns his steps, Melmoth meets with a tragic refusal—until finally he comes to Paris. In this city, he at last finds a man who is willing to sell his soul to him for cash. The man is M. Castanier, a bank-cashier, who has forged a signature and fears arrest. The Parisian enters upon the heritage of the Irishman. But he also repents of his act, and is anxious to hand over the infernal gifts to another. This cashier, who received two million francs for his soul, now buys the soul of a broker for a few hundred thousand francs. It is now the broker's turn to get rid of his bargain, and he obtains for the small sum of ten thousand francs the soul of another man. In this manner, the price of souls sinks from day to day. The poor devil is given no rest and passes through a number of bodies until he finally lands in a mere notary's clerk, whom he carries off in the end. The secret of the infernal power, brought to earth by the Irishman Melmoth, spiritual son of the old Reverend Charles Robert Maturin, is thus lost forever.[47]

Alexandre Dumas's play, *Don Juan de Maraña ou la Chute d'un ange* (1836), though an imitation of Mérimée's story, *"les Ames du purgatoire,"* published two years previously, really goes back to Lewis's *Ambrosio the Monk*.[48] Don Juan, in company with his familiar demon enters a convent, in which Martha is on the point of death. But this fact does not confound the famous sensualist nor the demon. Martha accepts the demon's proposal to lead her to her lover, Don Juan, if she will abandon her soul to hell. Immed-

[47] Robert Louis Stevenson's "The Bottle Imp" (1891) is mainly an imitation of this novel by Balzac.

[48] There are also reminiscences in this play of Goethe, Scott and Shakespeare. Cf. Loève-Veimars' criticism of the first production of this play in a *feuilleton* of the *Journal des Débats*, May 4, 1836.

iately after signing the compact with her blood, however, she dies and escapes Don Juan's pursuits.

Don Juan de Maraña should not be confused with the famous or rather infamous Don Juan Tenorio. The former, in contrast to the latter, was not carried off to hell, but ascended to heaven. He too began as a sinner, but ended as a saint. This Don Juan de Maraña, a blasphemous, sacrilegious, adulterous assassin, dripping with the blood of countless victims, the enemy of the whole world, which he had filled with horrors and atrocities, finally repented, entered a monastery and died a saint, venerated, blessed and canonized, with an epitaph he had himself placed on his tombstone: "Here lies the worst man that ever lived."

Frédéric Soulié's novel, *les Mémoires du diable* (1837-38), although revealing influences from many authors, both French and foreign, is, as far as its subject-matter is concerned, a work primarily related to the blood-and-thunder school of English fiction and recalls especially Lewis's *Ambrosio the Monk* and Maturin's *Melmoth the Wanderer*. But, as often happens, the disciple outdoes his master. The work by Soulié in many portions is just a mass of horrors and abominations. In fact, the author reached the extreme in barbarity and monstrosity. Of his predecessors in France, Soulié is particularly indebted to LeSage, author of *le Diable boiteux* (1707), from whom he borrowed the idea of introducing into a work of satire a personage whose universal knowledge shall work out the scheme of the author and make the hero acquainted with all the vicissitudes, mysteries and hypocrisies of the human species.[49]

The idea of editing the Devil's memoirs was also not original with Frédéric Soulié. Jean Paul Richter was perhaps the first to edit *Selections from the Papers of the Devil* (1787). Wilhelm Hauff, another German Romantic author, brought out, in 1828, a series of autobiographical papers under the title *From the Memoirs of Satan*. There were others, even after Frédéric Soulié, who claimed the honor of appointment by his Satanic Majesty to edit his "journal." In 1872, J. R. Beard, a Unitarian minister, published an *Autobiography of Satan*. Another autobiography of the Devil was

---

[49] Soulié's novel, although not much read at present, was very popular in its day and frequently adapted for the stage. A phantastic drama entitled *la Sonnette du diable,* based on Soulié's novel, was written in 1849 by Anicet Bourgeois and Guerville. Paul Féval's novel, *les Mémoires du Diable* (1832), is a poor imitation of Soulié's work.

found among the posthumous works of Leonid Andreev and appeared in English under the title *Satan's Diary* (1920). Our own H. L. Mencken also favored us, in his *Book of Burlesques* (1916), with selections "From the Memoirs of the Devil." The American satirist, Oliver Bainbridge, brought *The Devil's Note-Book* to light in 1908 and had it illustrated by "Vet" Anderson.

The originality of Frédéric Soulié in this novel consists in the terms demanded by the human party to the devil-compact. Armand de Luizzi sells his soul to Satan for a rather uncommon consideration. What tempts him is not wealth, which, indeed, he possesses, nor pleasure, which he probably thinks he can procure for himself without the Devil's aid. What he wants in exchange for his soul is to know the past lives, the trials and temptations, of his fellow-men and women. As Mr. George Saintsbury, in his *History of the French Novel* (1919), well remarks, this is "a thing which a person of sense and taste would do anything, short of selling himself to the Devil, *not* to know."

The plot of this novel is based upon the idea of successive bargains between the Lords of Ronquerolles and the Prince of Darkness. A fresh one is opened whenever the last inheritor of an ancestral curse has gone to close his account. The story, as given by Mr. Saintsbury, is briefly as follows:

The new Count de Luizzi summons Satan by means of a certain little silver bell at the not most usual but sufficiently witching hour of two a. m., saying at the same time, "Come!" After a slightly trivial farce-overture of apparitions in various banal forms, Luizzi compels the Devil to show himself in his proper shape. The bargain contains, as in Melmoth's case, a redemption clause, though of a different kind. If the man can say and show, after ten years, that he has been happy, he will escape from the Devil's clutches. What Luizzi demands of the Devil in exchange for his soul is to know everything about other people, and to be permitted even to reveal and print it. In certain circumstances, he can rid himself of his ally, when unwelcome, and perform other acts at the price of forfeiting a month of his life, which naturally will abridge the ten years.

Obedient to the wishes of Satan, the Baron de Luizzi goes out into the great world, and meets with numerous adventures, all containing the principles of the great moral of this novel, which is to teach us not to trust to first appearances. For instance, he sees an old lady, who is notorious for her prudish behavior, her sanctified conduct, and her religious turn of mind; and then he falls in love with a beautiful young lady, whose levity of disposition has raised the breath of scandal to such an extent, that she is at length driven from society. The Baron summons the Devil to narrate to him the history of those two women. To his astonishment, he finds that the former was stained with every crime—an adulteress, and a wretch who had poisoned her husband; and the latter was as pure and virtuous a creature as any human being can be!

The end of the novel is the usual sudden "foreclosure" by Diabolus despite the effort, to employ the words of Mr. Saintsbury, "of no less than three Gretchens who go upwards, and of a sort of inchoate repentance on Luizzi's own part before he goes downwards."

Dumas *fils* follows his father's foot-steps across the Middle Ages and brings back that astonishing novel *Tristan le Roux* (1850), which may be counted among the most jovial parodies ever written on the pseudo-historical novel. Tristan the Red-headed, son of Gilles de Retz, evokes from the dead a demon named Saracen, who, as it seems in this instance, can be dead, and forms a pact with him, through the intermediary of a Breton sorceress, in order to obtain the love of his cousin Alix. The demon Saracen has, however, been especially commissioned by hell to effect the ruin of the Maid of Orleans.[50]

*
* *

But if French Romanticism, particularly in its employment of the devil-compact as subject-matter, is indebted to England, it amply repaid its debt to that country by influencing many of the leading English Romantics. Thus Thackeray's story, "The Painter's Bargain" (1834), was written under the influence of the French Romantics, as is admitted by the author himself in the "Divertisement to the First Edition" of his *Paris Sketch Book*

[50] Marshal Gilles de Retz or Rais (the "French Bluebeard") was a Grand Master in the medieval witch-cult and is said to have sacrificed about 150 women and children in the witch-rites. According to the theory developed by Miss Alice Murray, in *The Witch-Cult in Western Europe* (Oxford, 1921), he was the chief of the witch-group to which Joan of Arc belonged, but made no attempt to rescue her. Nine years after her death, he, too, was tried on the same charges and condemned.

(1840). It was Thackeray's good fortune to live in Paris during the wildest and most brilliant years of Romanticism; and while his attitude toward the movement and its leaders, as presented in the *Paris Sketch Book,* is not wholly sympathetic, he is indebted to it for his interest in the Devil. The Romanticism of Thackeray has been denied with great obstinacy and almost passion, for like Heinrich Heine, the chief of German Romantic ironists, he poked fun at this contemporary movement. But "to laugh at what you love," as Mr. Saintsbury has pointed out in his *History of the French Novel,* "is not only permissible, but a sign of love itself."

Thackeray's story, "The Painter's Bargain," is a dream-fantasy, in which the devil-compact is treated in a rather unusual way. The soliloquy of impieties of Simon Gambouge, a poor French painter, is acknowledged by an invisible devil, and his question, "Where are you?" is answered in the smallest of voices "S-q-u-e-e-z-e!" Immediately, after the nail has been pricked from a bladder of crimson lake in the hand of the artist, a little imp spirts out on the palette, a little blood-colored imp of expanding dimensions—as big at first, we are told, as a tadpole, then as a mouse, as a cat—when it jumps off the palette and turns a somersault. The Devil offers to help Simon Gambouge to all the good things of life for full seven years (seven is a sacred number even to Satan) in exchange for the poor painter's soul. The contract has already been drawn up by the Devil on " a sheet as big as a double *Times,* only there was a different *stamp* in the corner.

In Thackeray's earlier and poorer story, "The Devil's Wager" (1833), which was also written under the inspiration of the French Romantics, a priest, who is under a bond to Satan, finally forfeits his body and soul by reciting a prayer contrary to the express condition of the infernal contract. But by sacrificing himself, he saves his brother's soul from "those regions of fire and flames where poor sinners fry and roast in *sæcula sæculorum.*" This story is very laughable, if one can laugh at the idea of being damned.

On the other hand, Washington Irving, the first of the great American writers, seems, in his story, "The Devil and Tom Walker" (1824), to owe very little to foreign influences. Although, by his interest in popular legends, he shows his sympathy with the Romantic movement of Europe, his story is redolent of the American soil. He presents the Devil as a maker of a contract who expects his contract to be fulfilled. In this respect, Diabolus is acting according to sound American business principles. Tom Walker also shows himself a good Yankee business man in his attempt to evade payment of the contract. The Devil wins in the end, as no amount of ingenuity on the part of New England skinflints can worst him in a bargain, and Washington Irving must be put down as a realist.[51]

The redemption clause in the "Devil-Puzzlers" (1871) by the American humorist, Frederick Beecher Perkins, is rather unique. The author of this story follows an old tradition, which attaches a wager to the infernal pact. According to the terms of the contract drawn up between the "hero" of this story and the Devil, the mortal may, at the expiration of the period, be left unharmed in body and soul, provided he can put to the Devil three questions, one of which the subtle spirit cannot answer. The Devil loses because he cannot tell which is the front of a woman's bonnet. He answers the first two questions dealing with metaphysical problems, but the third, suggested by the mortal's wife, proves his undoing. This story is a specimen of the laborious methods and clumsy wit of the early American humorists.

The old tradition of the devil-compact has continued in its appeal to this day and has not failed to attract many eminent contemporary writers in all European countries. John Masefield treats this ancient tradition in his story, "The Devil and the Old Man" (1905).

Max Beerbohm's story, "Enoch Soames" (1916), is perhaps the most recent treatment of this old tradition by a prominent Englishman. Soames, a representative of the prominent literary leaders of the eighteen nineties, styling himself a Catholic diabolist, makes an extraordinary bargain with the Devil. He is willing to forfeit his soul to Satan for the privilege of visiting the British Museum a hundred years after his death to learn what posterity thinks of him. But he cannot find his name in any catalogue or index or biography, nor anywhere at all, except under the name of Beerbohm, Max, where he is mentioned in the phonetic spelling of 1992, as an

---

[51] John B. Hymer has written, in 1908, a "phantastic musical travesty" in one act on Washington Irving's story and has given it the same title.

"immajnari karrakter" in a short story by this writer. Broken-hearted, Soames then forfeits himself to his purchaser.

The French novelist, Pierre Veber, made the devil-compact the central theme of his novel *l'Homme qui vendit son âme au diable* (1918).

Maurice Magre, in his recently published work, *Lucifer* (1929), is bold enough to treat the old tradition of a devil-compact in a "modern" novel. This work is an exaltation of the pagan ideal of the enjoyment of the flesh. "The only truth is in material enjoyment," Lucifer is made to say. The novel ends, however, with the declaration that the redemption of man will come from a union, within every one of us, of Christ and Lucifer.[52]

*
* *

What first strikes the reader of all these poems and plays, novels and short stories, which employ the devil-compact, is the lack of variety in their treatment of this subject. Mr. Saintsbury, in his *History of the French Novel,* has already called attention to the monotony in the employment of this *motif* in literature. This uniformity in the literary treatment of the devil-compact, he says, is especially surprising when it is contrasted with the great variety in circumstances of the bargains with Beelzebub which are transacted daily in actual life. This fact shows us how pitiful a thing is the imagination of man after all.

What we must next gather from this mass of material, treating the *motif* of the devil-compact, is a conviction of the meanness of man. Almost invariably the Devil is represented as thwarted by trickery and treachery. In John Masefield's story already quoted, Diabolus dies in his attempt to collect his bill. Naturally, as long as mortals write the stories, the Devil is going to find it difficult to collect his debt. These literary accounts of the devil-compacts do not, as Mark Twain regrets, give Satan's side of the story. The reader cannot but admit that the Devil appears in these stories much more honest than the men with whom he has to deal. Whether Diabolus gives us ten, twenty or twenty-four years from the signing

[52] See the present writer's review of this novel in *Books Abroad,* IV (1930), 40.

of the contract, he always keeps his part of the agreement, while we have the perennial hope of swindling him after we have done our worst and enjoyed it. If the stories had been conscientiously written, all of the characters who cheated the Devil would certainly have gone to hell solely for the methods they used in saving their souls.

The Devil should be complimented at the attention given him by the best writers of all ages and languages. He should be offended perhaps at the flippant and audacious manner in which his power is flouted in this world. But he may certainly be satisfied with his influence on earth, manifested in these stories by the devilish ingenuity of the heaven-bound mortals.

All this leads us to conclude, however, that the Devil will cease to be our most formidable Reality and become only material for Romance as soon as we will have given up the hope of trying to cheat him.

CHAPTER XVIII

THE LOVES OF THE DEMONS

THE medieval superstition about the loves between demons and humans is a theological interpretation of the ancient belief in the cohabitation of gods with mortal women. The pagan deities, after they had been raised to demonhood by Christianity, still continued to seek the company of the daughters of the earth. In the Northern European countries, this medieval belief was, in addition, a survival of the old Teutonic mythology in which elves and trolls woo or abduct mortals. The mystagogues and occultists of the eighteenth century reverted to the old indigenous belief that the demons who joined themselves carnally to mortals were actually elemental spirits. "In the latter half of the eighteenth century," Anatole France tells us, "much was spoken of sylphs and salamanders, elves, gnomes, and gnomides. They are born with souls as perishable as their bodies, and they acquire immortality by commerce with the magi. . . . Demons are no other than sylphs and salamanders. They are in truth beautiful and benevolent. . . . The angels whom Enoch shows us allying themselves to women in amorous intercourse are sylphs and salamanders" (*la Rôtisserie de la Reine Pédauque*, 1893). The reader will recall in this connection Fouqué's *Undine* (1811), which is based on this belief in an amorous alliance between an elemental spirit and a man. It is the story of a beautiful water-fairy, who has no soul and who can obtain a soul only by marrying a mortal. But she gains with this soul all human sorrows. Her husband is unfaithful to her, and she kisses him dead.

The apocryphal Book of Enoch, in its elaboration of the biblical account of a union between the sons of God and the daughters of men (Gen. vi. 1-4), fully admits the possibility of physical relations between celestial and terrestrial beings. The Talmud teaches that the angels who forsook the choir-stalls of heaven for the love-beds of earth received corporeal forms so that they could be carnally joined to mortal women. The demons who descended from these fallen angels inherited the bodies of their parents, and therefore could continue seeking the company of the daughters of men. Other demons, who, in Talmudic tradition, formed a part of the six days' creation, received no corporeal forms because they were fashioned toward the end of the sixth day when the Lord was in a hurry to finish his work in order to avoid desecrating the holy Sabbath. These evil spirits, nevertheless, in the opinion of the rabbis, could avail themselves of human senses and passions by nestling in the hearts of human beings.[1] In Christian mythology, the cohabitation between ethereal and material beings offered no difficulty. The demons, although possessing no bodies, could borrow human forms whenever they wished to join themselves to mortals in amorous union.

*

* *

Medieval superstition knew of a species of demons whose special mission was to seek carnal relations with mortals. They appeared either in the form of men or of women and were consequently called *incubi* and *succubi*. The *incubus* (Latin term for the English expression "lie on") was a demon in the form of a man who haunted women in their sleep, and the *succubus* (Latin term for the English expression "lie under") was a demon in woman's guise who visited men in their dreams. The Church put its full faith in this popular superstition and persecuted all who confessed having had such carnal connections. Medieval monks and nuns stood in holy terror of these lustful demons. The French novelist, Joris-Karl Huysmans, humorously calls these imps of hell "ecclesiastical microbes," since they chiefly tormented holy men and women in the monasteries and convents.

The belief in *incubi* and *succubi* was prevalent in all European countries. Witches and wizards openly avowed their relations with these demons. Cæsarius of Heisterbach, in his *Dialogus magnus visionarum et miraculorum* (thirteenth century), records several manifestations of *incubi* and *succubi*.[2]

[1] Cf. Moncure Daniel Conway: *Demonology and Devil-Lore* (2 vols., 3rd ed., New York, 1889), II, 94.

[2] On the belief in the *incubus,* see the chapter "Die gespenstische Buhlschaft" in Erasmus Francisci's *Der höllische Proteus* (2nd ed., 1695). Professor

The delusion of these diabolical paramours did not end with the Middle Ages, that dark period of human history. It has continued to this day, especially in Catholic countries. This fact need not surprise us at all. For the Catholic, this belief, as any other belief, has been fixed *ne varietur* by the Church. Thus, in 1861, the Abbé Lecanu, writing a history of Satan, began with these words:

> "In the matter of beliefs, we must return to those of the fifteenth century; we set forth this aphorism right at the beginning, in order that those who do not feel themselves in agreement with us may not waste their time by reading us."

Father Sinistrari, of Ameno, living in the seventeenth century, gives, in his learned work on *Demoniality or, Incubi and Succubi,*[3] long and detailed accounts of these demons who assume human forms for the purpose of indulging in the vices of men. An English priest, the Reverend Father Montague Summers, who has recently brought out a critical edition of Sinistrari's work, fully shares, in this "enlightened" century, the belief in this medieval *incubus*-delusion.

In all fairness, however, it should be added that the belief in *incubi* and *succubi* is not now generally held by the Catholic priests. Anatole France, in *les Opinions de Jérôme Coignard* (1893), puts doubts into the mouth of his spokesman with regard to this medieval superstition. He has this liberal priest say:

> "It is not written in the Fathers that the Devil begets children on poor girls. All these tales of Satanic lust are disgusting imaginings, and it is a disgrace that Jesuits and Dominicans have written about them."

The psychological basis for this belief in evil spirits who visited human beings in their sleep is sufficiently clear to any person who is even superficially acquainted with the modern theory of sex-repression and the working of the subconscious mind during our sleep. Reginald Scot, as early as the sixteenth century, explained

---

George Lyman Kittredge, in his *Witchcraft in Old and New England* (1928), also has a long chapter on this subject. An interesting legend of a *succubus* will be found in E. L. Linton's *Witch Stories Collected from Scotland and England* (London, 1861).

[3] The original Latin manuscript of Sinistrari's book was discovered in 1872. It was translated into French in 1875 and into English four years later. A new English translation from the Latin, accompanied by an introduction and notes, was issued, in 1927, in London.

the common belief of his day in *incubi* and *succubi* on physiological grounds, by assuming "some euyll humour" in the mortal's physical constitution. His contemporary, Johann Schenck, a Rhenish physician, explained the *incubus* delusion as the obstruction of the vessels which connect the spleen to the stomach by the thickening of the melancholic juices, which are converted into black bile.

The medieval belief in *incubi* and *succubi* has been frequently employed in works of fiction. Balzac has treated the *succubus motif* in his story *le Succube* (1833), which tells of the tragic fate of a beautiful woman, believed by her contemporaries to be a demon who charmed men in order to lead them to their ruin. Zulma, the Mauritian, had been brought to France from Africa by gypsies and left as a young girl in a church of Tours to fill the place of a statue of the Virgin Mary which they had carried off. The priest of the church baptized her and placed her in a convent; but when she grew up, her Oriental blood asserted itself, and she yearned for the world. After having escaped from the convent with the aid of a priest, who first taught her to sin, she sank lower and lower until she menaced the morals of the town. She was accused of luring men to sin by supernatural means, condemned and sentenced to death. Joséphin Péladan's novel, *la Victoire du mari* (1889), is an interesting modern handling of the old *incubus* delusion.

*
* *

The amorous ability of the Devil himself has been doubted on theological grounds by many demonologists. Inasmuch as Satan's fall, according to tradition, was the result of his pride and envy, it has been taken for granted that an incapacity for admiration or affection was the chief characteristic of the fallen angel. Théophile Gautier, in his essay on Baudelaire (1868), clearly states that "the distinguishing feature of Satan is that he is incapable of admiration or love." In Byron's *Cain* (1821), Lucifer mocks and gibes all through, not only at love of God, but at all human love, at Cain's love for Adah and for his children, at his affection for Adam and for Abel. Moreover, misogyny is generally included in misanthropy. His hatred of woman necessarily must form a part of the arch-enemy's hatred of all mankind. Furthermore, Satan's aversion to woman is probably even greater than his enmity to man. The war between woman and the Devil dates back to the days in Eden when Satan used Eve as a tool to accomplish the fall of man, and when in revenge the Lord gave the woman the power to crush the serpent's head (Gen. iii. 15). This biblical story has justified many demonologists in affirming that dislike for the fair sex is a distinctly diabolical trait.

Certain demonologists, wishing to offer a reconciliation between the Catholic conception of the character and conduct of Satan and the popular superstition about the Fiend's fondness for the fair sex, in this respect distinguish between the Devil and his demons. Satan himself, they maintain, has no room in his heart for any affection. The rest of the demons, however, having followed their leader, in his rebellion, out of devotion to him, are not safe against the wiles of women.

The belief in Satan's sensuality presents, however, a greater difficulty from the psychological point of view. The consistency of the character of the Tempter demands his unsusceptibility to the charms of the beautiful sex. For he is certainly a poor general who depends for victory on a certain weakness of his enemy which is also his own weakness.

These objections can be answered by calling attention to the fact that Satan, in paying court to the fair daughters of this earth, need not have his heart in the affair; and, not unlike many a mortal man, he merely pretends that he has an affection for his victims. Neither is it necessary to infer from Satan's relations to mortal women that he has sexual desires. He may in such instances act only as the tempter to sin without himself feeling any emotions. In fact, the frigidity of the Fiend has been well established by tradition. The medieval witches who confessed to having had carnal connections with the Devil complained of the bitter coldness of their diabolical lover. Very remarkably unanimous on this particular are the confessions of all the witches of every country.

European folk-lore contains many instances in support of the belief that the Devil himself did not disdain dallying with the fair daughters of Eve. The strategy of Satan in his relations with the beautiful sex was simple and infallible. When he wished to dominate a woman, he first took from her her virginity. It seems that, after this first sacrifice, she could refuse him nothing more and became his very obedient slave. In his efforts to obtain the soul of a woman, Satan would not shrink from any sacrifice. For a woman this *cavaliere servente* was willing to perform any sort of service, no matter how menial, if he had hope of winning her in the end. (In this respect, Satan is again not unlike many a mortal man.) But the Devil was often duped out of his due. There is a story of a Portuguese courtesan named Lupa, whom Satan served as a waiting-maid for several years, deeming this one soul worth such long and patient labor. But she died, in spite of all this trouble, repentant and sanctified, with St. Francis and St. Anthony mounting guard at her bedside.

Satan, as this tale shows, did not limit his attentions to virtuous girls, but even courted women of loose morals. He seemed, however, to prefer to pay his devotions to married women for the reason that adultery is a greater sin than unchastity, and his aim was always high. Anatole France, speaking from the viewpoint of the credulous common folk, assures us, in his already mentioned work, *la Rôtisserie de la Reine Pédauque,* that in former times the demons "used to take a hand in domestic life in a far more intimate fashion than they do today." One of the tricks, in which the Devil indulged on his amorous adventures, was to impersonate some man of spotless character in order to besmirch his name. "Occasionally," writes Lecky, "with a still more refined malice, the Evil One assumed the appearance of some noted divine, in order to bring discredit upon his character; and an astonished maiden saw, prostrate at her feet, the form of one she knew to be a bishop, and whom she believed to be a saint."[4] Satan's power of impersonation was so great that women often gave birth to children that in miniature perfectly resembled the parish priest.

Apart from the ambiguity of such philoprogenitiveness, the procreative ability of the Devil has, however, often been called by Protestants into question, although Luther formally declared that the Devil, as the antithesis of the Deity, could beget children by virgins.[5] The Old Testament, figuratively of course, speaks of the sons and daughters of Belial, and the New Testament of the children of the Devil (Acts xiii, 10; 1 John iii, 10). Sir Thomas Browne emphasized Satan's sterility. "I could believe," said he, "that spirits use with man the act of carnality, and that in both sexes; . . . yet

[4] Wm. E. H. Lecky: *A History of the Rise and Influence of Rationalism in Europe,* 2 vols., London, 1865.

[5] Consult on this question Schubart's learned Latin treatise, *De potentia Diaboli in sensus hominum* (1748).

in both, without the possibility of generation" (*Religio Medici*, 1642). Balzac likewise affirms that the Devil "copulates but doth not engender." It is probably because he lacks children that Lucifer complains in Byron's *Cain* (1821), "My brotherhood's with those who have no children."

Many demonologists hold the belief that the offspring of demons can only assume the form of animals. "When a demon fathers a child," says Anatole France, in his already twice mentioned work, *la Rôtisserie de la Reine Pédauque,* "it takes the shape of an animal." Others assert that the children of demons can only be demons or some other uncanny creatures. According to the belief of German country folk, elves are the offspring of demons and witches.[5a] Still others maintain that the child of a demon comes into the world only in the form of a physical monster.

Hoffmann's story, "Der Teufel in Berlin" (in *Die Serapions-Brüder,* 1819-1821), has for its subject the birth of a devil-baby. Satan, however, is not the physical father of the child born to a high Prussian commercial dignitary. In this tale, it was the impression made by the Devil upon the woman during her pregnancy that produced this monster to the great consternation of his parents.

The green monster in Gérard de Nerval's story, "le Diable vert" (1849), owes its deformity to still less material causes. In the French author's story, at a police sergeant's wedding-feast, the groom drinks the wine from a bottle found in a fantastic cellar, although he knows that this liquor is possessed of the Devil. Nine months afterwards his wife gives birth to a monster who is as green as the seal of the bottle emptied by the father on the occasion of his wedding. All efforts on the part of the parents to change the color of the child's complexion are in vain. The boy remains to the day of his death just as he was at his birth, a green monster. For this reason, the author explains, it is customary among Frenchmen to send each other to the green devil—*au diable vert.*[6]

The turning-point in Hoffmann's famous work, *Die Elixiere des Teufels* (1815), comes with the birth of a demon-child, who, in this case, is the product of a demon-mother and a human father. This story goes back to the days of the Thebaid, at which period

---

[5a] In A. Petöfi's poem, "Schwert und Kette," the chain as symbol of slavery is the child of Satan and of a witch.

[6] For the correct explanation of this expression, see Littre's *Dictionnaire de la langue française.* 5 vols. Paris, 1863-77.

a certain saint obtains an elixir from the Devil. This fatal phial is later brought from the Egyptian wilderness to Europe and, after many centuries, it falls into the hands of a painter and pupil of Leonardo da Vinci, an Italian prince, who drinks it and is fired with infernal aims and ambitions. He produces amazing paintings, commits a series of atrocious crimes, and finally consummates an unlawful union with a diabolical phantom, by whom a son is born to him. At the sight of this monster, the father is seized with the most agonizing feelings of remorse. He is suffered to purchase his pardon, however, on condition that he shall continue to do penance as a wanderer on the face of the earth until the race to which he has given origin shall die out in virtuous atonement. That end must focus in the person of some descendant whose sanctity shall be as remarkable as was the original depravity of his cursed ancestor. This consummation comes in the eighteenth century in the person of Brother Medardus, who is the custodian of this elixir in a monastery in East Prussia. He also drinks it and is led to quit the cloister and commit numerous and atrocious crimes. But he repents in the end and thus brings about not only his own salvation but also that of his wandering ancestor.

The belief in a devil-baby has survived to this day among the backward peoples of Europe, as may be seen from a news item, printed in the New York *World* of February 18, 1920, about the birth of a devil in Russia.

This belief has even been transplanted to our own country. Miss Jane Addams, in an article printed in the *American Journal of Sociology,* of July, 1914, tells of the vivid interest of many old Italian women in the story of the supposed birth of a devil-baby in Chicago.[7]

The tradition of a child sprung from the union of a demon-father and a human mother was confused in the popular mind with the belief in a demon-baby placed in the bed of a lying-in woman. The demons, in imitation of the elves, were often supposed to substitute a child of their own for the human baby, which was therefore called a changeling. Thus in certain parts of France, we are informed by Victor Hugo in *les Travailleurs de la mer* (1866), the child from the union between a demon and a human mother was called *cambion,* which is the equivalent of our "changeling."

[7] This story has been revised and reprinted in the *Atlantic Classics,* 2nd series, Boston, 1910.

Not all the sons of Satan, however, bear in their faces the mark of their diabolical descent. The "Mark of the Beast" in the children would defeat the aim of their father, who, in bringing these imps into the world, wished to promote through them in a more efficacious manner the work of hell on earth.

Many historical persons are believed to be of diabolical descent. The false prophet Bar-Jesus is called by St. Paul "child of the Devil" (Acts xiii. 10). Merlin the Wizard was, according to medieval legend, the son of a demon or an arch-*incubus* and a nun.[8] He was to undo on earth the work of Jesus, but instead turned from his father to Christ. It was Merlin, Satan's own son—for such is the irony of mythology—who helped Parsifal recover the largest of all diamonds, dropped from the crown of Satan as he fell from heaven, out of which, according to legend, the Holy Grail was fashioned.[9]

Robert the Devil, who also had Satan as his progenitor, did not follow in his father's footsteps, either.[10] On the other hand, Ezzelino, the tyrant of Padua (in Albert Mussato's *Eccelinus*), another son of Satan, lived as was befitting his procreation. Mohammed and Pope Sylvester II were also considered children of demons. Luther and Dr. Faustus were in the Roman Catholic eyes twin sons of the Devil. Voltaire was also held by his enemies to be of diabolical descent. It was even rumored that Satan (Eblis in the Koran) was the real father of Cain, whom Eve passed off on her unsuspecting husband. The medieval sect of the Cainites worshipped Cain as the son of Satan. The Catholics formerly believed that all Freemasons were the fruit of Eve's adultery with the Serpent.

Whole families, peoples and races were popularly believed to be

[8] According to the belief of the eighteenth-century occultists, as expressed in Anatole France's *la Rôtisserie de la Reine Pédauque,* Merlin was not the son of a demon but of a sylph, who had intercourse with his mother. On Merlin's diabolical descent, see also the chapter "The Devil-Compact in Tradition and Belief" of the present work, note 23.

[9] Geoffrey of Monmouth, in his adaptation of Nennius' *Historia britonum* (ninth century), brought the Marvelous Merlin into Arthurian romance and Robert de Boron, in a poem dating from the thirteenth century, connected the old Welsh enchanter with the legend of the Holy Grail. See F. Lot, "Etudes sur Merlin," *Annales de Bretagne,* XV (1900).

[10] A résumé of Balzac's lyrical analysis of Meyerbeer's opera, *Robert le Diable* (1831), will be found in the present writer's article, "Balzac and the Fantastic," *Sewanee Review,* XXXIII (1925), 2-24. On Robert the Devil's diabolic descent, see also the chapter "The Devil-Compact in Tradition and Belief" of the present work, note 27.

of diabolical descent. The Jews taught that all other races descended from the demons, while the other races believed that all Jews had horns. To the Greeks the Scythian race was of diabolical origin. According to Cæsarius of Heisterbach, the "fortissima gens Hunnorum" was descended from outcast Gothic women and *incubi dæmones*. All the kings of Britain down to the present day are alleged by Cæsarius to be the descendants of a *mater phantastica*. This credulous writer supports the belief expressed in English metrical romances that Richard Cœur de Lion had a demon mother, who flew off through the roof of the church when King Henry tried to detain her at the moment of the elevation of the host.[11]

*

* *

The *motif* of the demon lover plays a prominent part in the legends and literatures of all European countries. Many writers recall the fancy conceived by the fiends of hell for the fair daughters of this earth. The anatomically melancholy Burton tells of an evil spirit who was smitten with a mortal maiden. Walter Scott, in his *Minstrelsy of the Scottish Border* (1802), retells the old medieval legend of the dæmon lover.[12]

This legend of the dæmon lover has also been treated by Bürger in his "Lenore" (1774). In this ballad, the Devil appears on horseback at midnight beneath the window of Lenore in the form of her lover William, who fought at the side of King Frederick at the battle of Prague and died on that occasion, and calls her to ride with him to their bridal bed.

The French fantastic writer, Jacques Cazotte, in his romance, *le Diable amoureux* (1772), tells the story of Beelzebub, who, having taken the form of a fair young woman, conceived a passion for an earth-born man. This work is so important as the first specimen of French fantastic fiction that we offer a lengthy summary of its unusually interesting subject-matter.[13]

[11] See George L. Kittredge, *op. cit.,* pp. 116-7.

[12] Cf. Franz Hartmann: "The doctrine of the Demon-Lover," *Borderland,* III (1896), 353-8.

[13] The synopsis of this story has been written after the résumé given by Edward Yardley in his book: *The Supernatural in Romantic Fiction,* London, 1880. Cazotte's romance has been translated several times into English under the title *The Devil in Love.* The first English translation appeared in London in 1793, and the second translation followed seven years later. An English

In this work, a young Spanish gentleman named Alvarez is the speaker throughout the story, and relates the adventures as happening to himself. He is a captain in the guard of the King of Naples, and among his brother officers is one named Soberano who is a cabalist, or, in other words, a man versed in Hebrew necromancy. He is skilled in the science of transmuting metals and enslaving the elemental spirits. Alvarez burns with the desire to communicate with the spirits, and presses Soberano to give him at once the means of doing so. Soberano intimates that, to accomplish his desire without danger to himself, he should first pass through some long term of probation. But the impatience of Alvarez will not permit him to wait. He declares that nothing, however terrible, can shake his resolution, and that he would pull the ears of the biggest devil in hell. Seeing him thus resolved, Soberano lets him have his way. They dine together, in company with two friends of Soberano, who are also cabalists, and then set out to the ruins of Portici. Proceeding through the ruins, they arrive at a vault, in which Soberano inscribes a magic circle. He instructs Alvarez to enter the circle and pronounce certain words, calling out three times the name of Beelzebub. He then withdraws with his companions. Alvarez, left to himself, pronounces the words, and calls on the Devil, according to his instructions. Hardly has he done so, when a window opens opposite to him at the top of the vault, a torrent of light, more dazzling than that of day, bursts through the opening, the head of a camel huge and horrible, with ears of enormous size, shows itself at the window and cries out: *Che vuoi?* Alvarez sustains his courage and orders the phantom to appear under another form. Thereupon the camel vomits a white spaniel, with ears sweeping the ground, and vanishes. As Alvarez makes a movement to pull the spaniel's ears, it throws itself on its back, and he perceives that it is a female. The dog, or rather bitch, afterwards appears in the form of a beautiful woman, to whom Alvarez gives the name of Biondetta. She, submissive, and to all appearance passionately attached to her master, does all in her power to form with him the closest connection. Alvarez, although by no means insensible to her fascinations, is somewhat alarmed at the prospect

version also appeared in Boston in 1830. An illustrated edition of this romance was published again in Boston in 1925. It was also turned into an opera by Saint-Georges and Mazilliers and produced at the Theatre Royal, Drury Lane in 1843. A Spanish translation of Cazotte's work (*El Diablo enamorado*) appeared in Gibraltar in 1890.

of thus giving himself utterly to the Devil. She, however, deceitfully maintains that she is not the camel that appeared to him in the first instance, but that she is a sylphide, who, having fallen in love with him and assumed the form of a woman, is now doomed to continue this existence. As a compromise, he proposes marriage, but she naturally shrinks from anything so proper, and redoubles her efforts to seduce him. At last she is successful, and then the following conversation and scene take place:

"With a voice, to whose sweetness no music could be compared, she said:

" 'Have I made the happiness of my Alvarez, as he has made mine? But no; I am still the only happy one; he shall be so; I will intoxicate him with pleasure; I will fill him with knowledge; I will raise him to the summit of greatness. Wilt thou, beloved, be the most privileged of creatures, and rule with me over mankind, over the elements, over all nature?'

" 'Oh, dear Biondetta,' I said, 'thou art sufficient for me; thou fulfillest all the desires of my heart.'

" 'No! no!' she said quickly, 'Biondetta is not sufficient for thee; that is not my name; it flattered me; I bore it with pleasure; but it is necessary that thou shouldst know who I am. I am the Devil, my dear Alvarez, I am the Devil.'

"She pronounced this word with an accent of enchanting sweetness.

" 'Cease,' I said, 'my dear Biondetta, or whosoever thou mayst be, to pronounce that fatal name, and recall to me a mistake long since abjured.'

" 'No, my dear Alvarez, no, it was not a mistake; I was obliged to make thee believe so, my pet. It was necessary to deceive thee in order to make thee reasonable. Thou seest I am not so black as I am represented to be.'

"This badinage disconcerted me.

" 'But answer then,' she said.

" 'And what shall I answer?'

" 'Ingrate, place thy hand on the heart that adores thee; let a little of the delicious fire that burns in my veins be infused into thine; soften, if thou canst, the sound of that voice, so fit to inspire love, which thou usest only to terrify my timid soul; say to me, but with all the tenderness that I feel for thee, "My dear Beelzebub, I adore thee." '

"At this fatal name, though so tenderly pronounced, a mortal terror seized me; stupor and astonishment crushed my soul. She did not give me time to recover myself and reflect on my folly. Without perceptibly altering the tone of her voice, she continued:

" 'Thou camest to seek me; I have followed thee, served thee, assisted thee, and have fulfilled all thy wishes. I desired possession of thee, and, in order that I should obtain it, it was necessary that thou shouldst abandon thyself freely to me. Henceforth, Alvarez, our union is indissoluble, but it is important for us to know each other. As I already know thee by heart, in order to make the advantage reciprocal, I must show myself to thee as I really am.'

"I had no time to reflect on this singular harangue. I heard a sharp hissing at my side. . . . I turned my eyes, Instead of the ravishing figure, what did I see? Oh! Heaven! it was the frightful head of the camel. It articulated with a voice of thunder the gloomy *Che vuoi!* which had so terrified me before, burst into a fit of human laughter more dreadful still and put out a monstrous tongue."

In Vigny's poem, "Eloa" (1823), the Devil's Dulcinea is not an ordinary mortal, but an angel, for there are women among the angels, at least so the poets tell us. This woman angel, who abandons heaven in order to dwell with the Devil in hell, is no other than the daughter of Christ. Eloa has sprung from a tear shed by Jesus over the tomb of Lazarus and was transformed by the Lord into an angel of the beautiful sex. The mission of this woman angel is to console the disconsolate, to love the afflicted. She is the celestial original of those mortal women who devote themselves to suffering creatures, degraded and guilty, whom they endeavor to raise and redeem.

In heavenly conversation with her brother angels, Eloa happens to hear with horror the story of the fallen angels, and, far from feeling any antipathy toward her wayward brothers, she is stimulated to aid them in their affliction. Eloa is no longer happy in the perfumed groves, amid which the angels wander, but yearns to descend into the abyss to bring consolation to her condemned co-angels. She feels that the angels of heaven do not need her sympathy because they are all happy. Among the children of men there are indeed many unhappy, but among the fallen angels there are some who are still more unhappy; and the angel most in need of her sympathy is Satan himself. In her opinion, Satan as "the most culpable must also be the most unfortunate of all the unfortunates."

Eloa feels that, if she could but find this great culprit, she would comfort him and perhaps even lead him back to righteousness.

Tormented with this thought, Eloa vacates her celestial dwelling to go in search of the exiled archangel. One day, as she is winging her way in the solitudes of the sky, she encounters an angel of brilliant beauty and seductive melancholy. Without telling her who he is, the Devil ensnares the fair angel with his personal charms and eloquent speeches of sweet sensuality. The unsophisticated maiden from heaven listens to the bland words of the Arch-Deceiver, is won by his hypocritical tears and finally sinks into his arms. Not knowing who he is, she loves him. Angel as she is, she is also a woman. Her compassion is thus rewarded by falling passionately in love with the banished archangel and resigning herself to his fatal power. Mephitopheles awakened aversion in Margaret, Ada felt pity for Lucifer, in Eloa this pity changes into love. It is her pity for the poor Devil that brings about the undoing of this maiden angel. "The Catholic priests," remarked Anatole France apropos of this poem, in his essay on Alfred de Vigny (1868), "who have acquired such a sure knowledge of the human heart, are right in saying that pity is a dangerous sentiment." Born on this earth, Margaret contributes to the redemption of Faust, but the heavenly daughter of Christ, the angel Eloa, forfeiting forever the delights of heaven, falls into the arms of the king of darkness. Unsuccessful in her efforts to lift the Devil to heaven, she consents to be dragged down by him to hell. Wrapped in a flowing cloud, the two pass together down to hell; and a chorus of faithful seraphim, winging their way back to heaven, overhear this latest and fatal dialogue:

> "Où me conduisez-vous, bel ange?—Viens toujours.
> —Que votre voix est triste, et quel sombre discours!
> N'est-ce pas Éloa qui soulève ta chaîne?
> J'ai cru t'avoir sauvé.—Non, c'est moi qui t'entraîne.
> —Si nous sommes unis, peu m'importe en quel lieu!
> Nomme-moi donc encore ou ta Sœur ou ton Dieu!
> —J'enlève mon esclave et je tiens ma victime.
> —Tu paraissais si bon! Oh! qu'ai-je fait?—Un crime.
> —Seras-tu plus heureux? du moins, est-tu content?
> —Plus triste que jamais.—Qui donc es-tu?—Satan."

The Devil's greatest *passion de cœur*, however, was for a Georgian girl, who sought refuge from demoniac love in a convent and died there. Lermontov, in his poem, *The Demon* (written in

the years 1829-1841), depicts the Devil as suffering from boredom
and seeking happiness in a woman's love. He has broken with earth
and heaven and looks with contempt upon all who are moved by
petty passions. An exile from paradise and a hater of human
virtues, he has known these petty passions and despises them with
all his superiority. He flies over the earth and contemplates the
actions of men with contempt. He is weary of everything. Mankind has become corrupt and no longer offers any opposition when
he tempts them. Hatred is predominant in his heart, and he has
nothing but scorn for whatever he sees.

But Tamara, the daughter of Gudal, a Caucasian chief, is about
to be married to the Lord of Sinodal. She spends the evening
preceding her wedding, dancing and singing with her girl friends.
This girl is so pure and lovely that she would arouse noble thoughts
even in the Demon, and make him long for his lost paradise, if he
chanced to see her. The Demon does see her, and he loves her.
In order to prevent the marriage of Tamara to another, he tempts
the Lord of Sinodal, who is riding to the wedding at the head of a
gay cavalcade, to travel more swiftly through a dangerous mountain-
pass, where he is attacked by robbers and slain. The horse of the
groom arrives at Gudal's castle with the dead rider on its back.
The Demon appears to Tamara in her dreams, as she lies on the
bridal bed, after she has fallen asleep exhausted from the tears
shed over her dead lover, and urges her to grieve no more for one
who is now past help, but to open her heart to a love greater than
that of any mortal.

Tamara, seeking a way to protect herself against the visits of
the Demon and hoping to find consolation in religion for the loss of
her lover, begs her father to permit her to enter a convent. But
even in her sacred cell she can find no peace or safety. Her new
lover is but a phantom. She prays and weeps before her crucifix
but receives no comfort. In all her dreams the Demon appears and
begs for her love. The Demon, after long hesitation, finally ventures into the convent in person. He is confronted by a seraph,
Tamara's guardian angel, who, with a flaming sword in his hand,
wishes to bar the door for the Demon. Exulting in his great power,
however, the Demon tells the angel that the latter's efforts to protect
Tamara are all too late, for he is in love with her, and nothing can
now keep him from her. Angry words are exchanged, and the
seraph, believing Tamara to be hopelessly lost, leaves her. The

feeble light in Tamara's cell grows dim and finally is wholly ex-
tinguished, as the Demon enters. He makes known his identity to
Tamara and speaks words of passionate love. He tells her that he
has loved her from eternity, and that she will have his love to the
end of eternity. He begs her to love him and bring happiness to his
wounded heart. He will give her what she has never dreamed of,
though both must remain in hell. He offers her treasures untold and
declares that he will even make her queen of the world. So eager
is he to win her love that he expresses his desire for reform and
his wish to be allowed to believe again in the power of goodness.
He tells her that her love will redeem him to the heaven and happiness which he has forfeited. With all his powers of persuasion
he tries to win her love, only to be rebuked. In the end, however,
Tamara is overcome with pity and tells the Demon that if his words
are sincere, he must vow that from now on he will turn from all
thoughts of evil and lead a good life. So great is his love for the
mortal maiden that solemnly he finally swears to molest mankind
no longer and to ask pardon and mercy from his Maker.

Touched by his promise and his expressed desire for forgiveness, Tamara can no longer refuse the Demon, and permits him to
take her in his arms and impress a kiss on her virginal lips. The
Demon thus enjoys a brief moment of triumph. But Tamara, from
fear of him, loses her reason and dies in agony. The sentry on duty
hears a scream of pain and passes on. The Demon confronts the
angel who is bearing her to heaven and claims the soul of the woman
he loved. The angel, however, replies that God has already judged
her and forgiven her because she loved and suffered. The gates of
Paradise are open to Tamara, but the Demon remains alone as before, isolated and dissatisfied "without hope and without love."

The German poet, Friedrich Hebbel, in his poem, "Die Braut des
Teufels" (1836), treats an interesting old legend, which tries to
account for the name Die Jungfrau (The Virgin) given to one of
the Swiss Alps. According to this legend, there once lived in
Switzerland a beautiful and proud young maiden, who was in no
way inclined to yield to the gentle passion of love. Many youths
came from far and near to woo her, but all failed to awaken any
emotion in her heart. On a certain midnight, a young man in dark
clothes knocked on her window. So great was the potent charm
which the Devil exercised over her that tremblingly she admitted
him into her chamber, as if he were her husband. He clasped her

in his thin arms and stole kiss upon kiss. She wept, but, as if she were bound hand and foot, she could not resist. He proceeded to the last enjoyment, but still she did not utter the least sound of protest. When he had accomplished his evil deed, he said to her mockingly, "Good night, good night, thou art the Devil's bride." From shame, the young maiden climbed to the highest peak of the Alps, which has been named after her.[14]

Richard Garnett, in "Madam Lucifer" (1888), tells of a real infatuation on the part of the ruler of Gehenna for a slip of a girl. Lucifer falls head over heels in love with an earth-born maiden, named Adeliza. In order to win her, he dispatches her human lover to hell and assumes his form. The ruse, however, is discovered by the girl, and the discomfited Devil is forced to return to his Luciferetta in hell.

The belief in the wooing of mortal women by demons exists still today among the peasants of Ireland, as may be seen from the following anecdotes entitled "The Devil" (1892) by William Butler Yeats:

"My old Mayo woman told me one day that something very bad had come down the road and gone into the house opposite, and though she would not say what it was, I knew quite well. Another day she told me of two friends of hers who had been made love to by one whom they believed to be the Devil. One of them was standing by the road-side when he came by on horseback, and asked her to mount up behind him, and go riding. When she would not, he vanished. The other was out on the road late at night waiting for her young man, when something came flapping and rolling along the road up to her feet. It had the likeness of a newspaper, and presently it flapped up into her face, and she knew by the size of it that it was the *Irish Times*. All of a sudden it changed into a young man, who asked her to go walking with him. She would not, and he vanished.

"I know of an old man too, on the slopes of Ben Bulben, who found the Devil ringing a bell under his bed, and he went off and stole the chapel bell and rang him out. It may be that this, like the others, was not the Devil at all,

[14] On Hebbel's interest in the Devil, see the present writer's article, "Der Teufel bei Hebbel," *Modern Philology*, XV (1917), 109-22, and P. Sickel, "Hebbel und das Dämonische," *Zeitschrift für deutsche Bildung*, Bd. V, Heft II (1929).

but some poor wood spirit whose cloven feet had got him into trouble."[15]

*

*   *

European folk-lore records few instances in which the Devil sought a mortal maiden in marriage. In Fred B. Perkins' "Devil-Puzzlers" (1871), the demon Apollyon appears as a bachelor. "I have a mother, but no wife," he tells the charming Mrs. Hicok. "Permit me to say," this gallant demon, however, adds with a graceful bow, "that, if I could believe there was a duplicate of yourself in existence, I would be married as soon as possible." This was, however, a meaningless compliment. The Devil has never had any serious intention of getting married. It stands to reason that Satan, who can see sufficiently into future matrimonial complications, would not enter the bonds. Moreover, why should he encumber himself with a wife of his own, while so many husbands, as Fernán Caballero has so aptly said, are daily supplicating him to take theirs off their hands?

The French Romantic poet, Edouard d'Anglemont, however, represents Lucifer consenting to lead a poor young girl, whom he has seduced, to the altar in order to save her from shame. In the poem "Marie" (1829), based on a Breton legend, a young girl sees in her dreams a young man who is so wonderfully beautiful that, upon awakening, she still cannot get him out of her mind. Her dream soon turns into reality. The man of her dreams appears to her in flesh and blood. He is no other than the fallen angel in person. Marie, who finds no strength in her to resist his sweet words of seduction, offers herself to him body and soul. When she realizes that she is soon to become a mother, she implores her lover to marry her. The Devil consents out of pity for his victim. He approaches the altar, however, without making the sign of the cross. This omission deeply chagrins the pious young girl. When the priest, holding the consecrated wedding-ring, asks the groom for his name, the latter in lieu of an answer assumes his proper shape. Marie flees at this sight and goes mad from fright.

In most legends, however, it is the Devil, who, in his attempts to marry mortal maidens, is worsted in the deal. An Italian tradi-

[15] Among the latest novels relating the loves of the demons may be mentioned J. W. Brodie-Innes's *The Devil's Mistress.*

tion shows Satan, seized suddenly with a wish to know what it means to be married, successively leading three sisters to the altar. But he proves in the end to be no match for the cunning of his several spouses.[16]

The Spanish woman novelist, Fernán Caballero, in her adaptation of an old Andalusian legend entitled "The Devil's Mother-in-Law" (1859), tells how the Devil, with all his reputation for wisdom, meets a mother-in-law, who knows more than he does. He is just as helpless against this marital appendage as most married men. An old widow "uglier than the sergeant of Utrera" and nicknamed Mother Holofernes, curses her daughter. The latter, too much occupied with matrimonial plans to help her mother in her work, is consigned to marry the Devil himself. The Evil One, availing himself of the right given him by the anathema launched against the girl by her mother, presents himself as an aspirant for the maiden's hand and is accepted. But Mother Holofernes, in her shrewdness, discovers the identity of the red-haired and mild-mannered young man, and devises in her head a cruel plan of revenge. After the wedding has been duly performed and celebrated and the bridal pair is preparing to enter the nuptial chamber, the old lady presents her daughter with a consecrated olive branch, with which she is told to beat her husband as an indication of a woman's mastery over man. The Devil, at the sight of this holy object, wishes to make a hasty retreat. As the doors and windows are locked, he slips through the key-hole, only to find himself caught in a black bottle, which is held by his mother-in-law on the other side of the door. The Fiend is carried in the phial to a secluded spot on the summit of the highest mountain and remains imprisoned for ten years, when he is finally released by a soldier under conditions which he considers undignified and cruelly oppressive.[17]

Niccolò Machiavelli, the Italian statesman, pictures the demon Belphegor entering the bonds of matrimony as a sociological experiment. The story *Belfagor* opens in the infernal regions. Almost every man whom Charon ferries across complains that his wife was responsible for his downfall. The judges in hell are perplexed. They wish to be fair in pronouncing their sentences upon the sinful

[16] This tale "How the Devil Married Three Sisters" will be found in Thomas Frederick Crane's *Italian Popular Tales*, London, 1885.

[17] This story will be found in the present writer's anthology of *Devil Stories* (New York: Knopf, 1921).

men, and finally decide to send a demon to discover whether women really have the power to lead men to their ruin. Belphegor is delegated to go up to the earth, stay there ten years, and come back and report. The mission of the infernal deputy's terrestrial sojourn is to marry a mortal maiden and learn by personal experiences what are the respective conveniences and inconveniences of holy matrimony. But the demon's earthly career is cut short, and he abandons this earth before he has served the full term of his apprenticeship. He cannot support the asperities of the temper of the lady, who has made the earth a hotter hell for him than the place from which he came. He deserts her and runs back to hell as fast as he can.[18]

Machiavelli is said to have written several tales, but only his *Belfagor* has survived to our days. The Accademia della Crusca, which set no very great store by Machiavelli's productions, made an exception of *Belfagor* and placed it in the canon of Italian classics.

This story is of medieval origin, and is not based on the author's married life. The idea of the story is ingenious and contains many entertaining incidents. It was first printed by Giovanni Brevio in 1545, and appeared for the second time with the name of Machiavelli in 1549, twenty-two years after the death of the author of *The Prince*. The two writers did not borrow from each other, but had a common source in a medieval Latin manuscript which seems to have first fallen into the hands of the Italians, but was later brought to France where it has been lost. The tale of the marriage of the Devil appeared in several other Italian versions during the sixteenth century. Among the Italian novelists, who retold it for the benefit of their married friends, may be mentioned Giovan-Francesco Straparola, Francesco Sansovino, and Gabriel Chappuys.

In England, this story was no less popular. Barnabe Riche inserted it in 1581 in his collection of narratives. This version was the starting-point of a great number of dramatizations. We will but mention *Grim the Collier of Croydon or, The Devil and his Dame* by Haughton and Henslowe (1602) ; *Machiavel and the Devil* by Daborne and Henslowe (1613) ; *The Devil is an Ass* by Ben Jonson (1616) ; and *Belphagor or, The Marriage of the Devil* (1690). The story, *The Divell a Married Man* (1674), which is a

[18] This tale will also be found in the collection of *Devil Stories* mentioned in the preceding note.

skit upon marriage, has likewise Machiavelli's *novella* for its basis.

In France, this story was translated in 1664 and rendered into verse by LaFontaine in 1694, and in Germany it served the Nuremberg cobbler-poet Hans Sachs as the subject for his farce *How the Devil Took to Himself an Old Wife* (1557).[19]

[19] In Achim von Arnim's *Halle und Jerusalem* (1811), the sexton reveals himself as the Devil, and carries off Celinde's mother to be his bride.—The *Journal of American Folk-Lore*, XLV (1899), 128, contains an interesting Negro story of the Devil and his bride.—Mrs. Margaret Townsend published, in 1905, a very interesting play entitled *The Devil in Search of a Wife*, which is a satirical skit on the women of New York.

CHAPTER XIX

THE DEVIL, THE WORLD AND THE FLESH (I)

THE Devil, the world and *the flesh* are linked together in the phraseology of the baptismal formula. The world, as well as the flesh, is thus definitely associated with the Devil in the Christian religion. Although not explicitly stated in the creed of any sect, Protestants as well as Catholics consider the material world, in contrast with the spiritual realm, a diabolical work. The fact is that the Devil is commonly credited with the creation of the cosmos.

There is much significance in this often mentioned saying, which is well worth historical analysis. As a rule, popular phrases have a good deal of meaning for the investigator. Under the guise of a figure of speech there is psychological value, regardless of whether or not serious belief is given to such conceptions, inasmuch as this is a discussion in terminology rather than theology.

THE DEVIL AS MASTER OF MATTER

The belief in the world as a diabolical work can be traced back to Iranian-Persian teachings. In the Zend-Avesta we find that the Devil created the evil part of the world in contradistinction to the good part fashioned by the Deity. The Jews, who obtained their notion of the Devil from the Persians, rejected the theory of a dual creation. In the Old Testament the Lord is represented as the maker of the material as well as of the spiritual world, of darkness as well as of light. In the New Testament, however, the Devil's power over this world is strongly emphasized. He is not named the creator of this world, but is called "the prince of this world" (John xii. 31; xiv. 30; xvi. 11; cf. Eph. ii. 2; vi. 12) even "the god of this world" (2 Cor. iv. 4). The belief in the temporal world as the work of the Devil, however, soon took root in Christianity. First appeared the Gnostics with their teachings that the world was created and is ruled by the Devil. In the Valentinian Gnosis, this material world is the work of a fallen æon, and in the writings of the Gnostic Saturninus, dark matter as the domain of the Devil is placed in opposition to the light-realm of the Deity. The Manicheans, who drew the logical conclusions from the syncretic speculations of their Gnostic predecessors, taught that all matter, good as well as evil, had its origin in the kingdom of darkness. The creation of man, as of the material world in general, is, according to Manichean teachings, the work of the Devil, who wished to imprison and finally to destroy the souls emanating from the god of light in the diabolically created bodies, to which they must cling.

Although Manicheism was considered a heresy, the Church nevertheless could not wholly combat its concepts. Manicheism took deep root in Christianity and could not be extirpated.[1] Throughout the history of the Church, the belief in the creation of the world by the Devil appears again and again in various forms and in various parts of Christendom. This belief formed the essential element of the system of the heretical sects and is still held by the Yezidis, a sect of devil-worshippers in Asia Minor.[2] The Church itself adopted this belief, at least in part. If it did not consider the Devil the creator of the world, it regarded him as the master of all matter, and looked upon all nature as the domain of the Devil. This conception, prevalent in the Church, will account for the idea of the inherent wickedness of all matter and for the belief that evils of every kind spring from our material bodies. Our forebears held that all diseases were caused by demons and that relief from all ailments consisted in the exorcism of the demons—the diabolical ancestors of our modern germs—from the human body.

Many modern writers also share the belief in the creation of the world by the Devil. Gœthe, in his youth, looked upon Lucifer as the author of all creation. William Blake stated unequivocally: "Nature is the work of the Devil. The Devil is in us as far as we are Nature." Byron, in *Cain* (1821), represents Lucifer as co-creator of the world. In Immermann's *Merlin* (1832), Satan is

[1] See G. Messina's article, "la dottrina Manichea e le origini del Cristianesimo," *Biblica*, X (1930), No. 3.

[2] On the various sects who held the belief in the Devil as the creator of the world, see the present writer's essay, "Des Teufels Schöpferrolle bei Gœthe und Hebbel," *Neophilologus*, VI (1918-9), 319-22.

the demiurge, the creator of the earth in Gnostic and Platonic philosophy. The Spanish lyric poet, José de Espronceda, in his fragmentary *El Diablo Mundo* (1841), also identifies the Devil with the world. Leconte de Lisle expresses his belief that the world is the work of the Evil Spirit, and that it will exist only as long as Evil exists on earth. In his poem, "la Tristesse du Diable" (1866), this pessimistic poet affirms that the result of the six days' labor will be abolished on that day when, from the bottom of limitless spaces, the oppressed races of the earth hear a voice crying, "Satan is dead!" Anatole France, in his work, *le Jardin d'Épicure* (1895), speaking of the Devil, affirms that "he has created at least one half of the world . . ." In an earlier work, however, this latter-day diabolist expresses the belief that the Demon has created all the world (*la Rôtisserie de la Reine Pédauque*, 1893).

Alfred de Vigny also believed in the infernal essence of Nature. This "enigmatical divinity," with its inflexible and inexorable laws, was, in the opinion of this pessimistic poet, silent and indolent, cold and cruel, disdainful and unmerciful to the ephemeral creature, man. Nature, hymned by mortals as the beneficent mother of men, was to Vigny only their living tomb. In Baudelaire's eyes, Nature, though not created by the Devil, was nevertheless inherently defiled and, according to his own expression, Satanical. In the opinion of this Catholic and diabolic poet, original sin had indelibly stained all Nature.

Even if we do not hold the belief that the Devil created the cosmos, we may agree that it is he at least who makes the world go round. Satan is putatively a very potent power for evil on this planet. His kingdom is in the human mind, through which he directs the affairs of this earth. It is not without reason, therefore, that the Demon was popularly regarded in the Middle Ages, and even for many centuries afterwards, as the governor of this globe.

As for the creation of man, even if we do not favor the belief that man is the Devil's handiwork, orthodoxy contends that he was created through the instrumentality of Satan. For his existence on this earth, man is at least indirectly indebted to the Devil. It should be remembered that man was created solely as successor to Satan in the celestial choir-stalls. If the beautiful archangel had not rebelled, no vacancy would have occurred in heaven; and with no vacancy in heaven, there would have been no need for man's creation. It is thus proved, to the satisfaction of believers, that man's creation is at least indirectly the work of the Devil.[3]

THE DEVIL AS PRINCE OF THIS WORLD

Furthermore, it is to Diabolus that man is indebted for all human accomplishments and achievements. Inasmuch as the Spirit of Evil was in the eyes of the Church the master of all terrestrial matter, he was considered the incarnation of all human endeavor which was based on mundane interests. The Church was concerned with things spiritual and of the other world, consigning to the Devil the possessions and deeds of this world. This ecclesiastical antithesis between heavenliness and earthliness amounted in the end to this fact that whatever did not directly contribute to the glory of God, in other words, did not profit the Holy Roman Catholic and Apostolic Church, was denounced as diabolical. In fact, whatever was displeasing to Rome in any field of human thought or activity was regarded as the Devil's work.

SATAN AS SPONSOR OF REASON

It is a matter of historical record that the priests placed all mundane pursuits, professions and pleasures of man under the protection of the Powers of the Pit.[4] The learned pursuits in particular were believed to be under the inspiration of demons. The priests preached at all times, but especially in the Middle Ages, what André Gide calls "the evangelical depreciation of reason." Satan was regarded by the Church as the incarnation of human reason in contrast to the Saviour, who represented faith. The Spanish reactionary, Cortes Doñoso, less than a century ago, denounced reason as a gift of Gehenna. Heinrich Heine, in *Die Elementargeister* (1834), explains the Catholic condemnation of human reason in the following words:

> "The Devil is not only the representative of the supremacy of earthly interests, of sensual delights, and of the flesh; but he is also the exponent of human reason, simply because reason vindicates all the rights of matter. In this respect, Diabolus is the antithesis of Christ, who sets forth

[3] On the Devil's partnership with the Deity in the creation of the world, see also the chapter "Diabolus Simia Dei" in the present work.

[4] Baudelaire's dictum that commerce was in its essence Satanic should certainly meet with the hearty approval of the socialists.

not only the spirit, the ascetic abnegation of the senses, and heavenly salvation, but also faith. The Devil does not *believe*, he does not accept blindly the authority of other persons, he rather relies on independent thought; he uses reason. This method is of course dangerous and terrible; and the Roman Catholic Church has logically condemned independent individual thought as devilish, and declared that the Devil, as the representative of reason, is the Father of Lies."

It is for this reason that, in the eyes of the Church, thinking was equivalent to blaspheming, and that it imprisoned, tortured, hanged or burned every person who dared to think for himself.

*
* *

Modern writers, in conformity with Catholic teaching, regard Satan as a luminous genius of reason. Gœthe conceived the Evil Spirit not only as the subtlest of all the beasts of the field, but also as the subtlest of all the intellects of men. In the opinion of Anatole France, it was thought that led the beautiful archangel to revolt (*le Puits de Sainte-Claire*, 1895). Rapisardi's Lucifer is the exponent of Reason, which will finally conquer dogma and do away with superstition and unsupported tradition.

The Devil has a reputation for wisdom. He appears to possess a great amount of brains between the two horns on his head. Anton Chekhov, in "The Shoemaker and the Devil" (1883), maintains that Old Nick, notwithstanding his hoofs and tail, has more brains than many a (Russian) student. Max Beerbohm, in "Enoch Soames" (1916), affirms that the Devil is well informed in all things.

SATAN AS SCHOLAR

Satan, it is generally agreed among modern writers, is a learned scholar and a profound thinker. He has all philosophy and theology, ancient learning and modern science at the tip of his tongue. Anatole France, in his previously quoted work, *le Jardin d'Épicure*, calls the Devil "a great *savant*." This French writer credits Diabolus with a philosophical mind, and Friedrich Hebbel goes so far as to hail Satan as the first philosopher. Heinrich Heine, in the previously quoted *Elementargeister*, represents the Devil as a master in metaphysics, and Edgar Allan Poe, in "Bon-Bon" (1835), reveals the Devil as a practised metaphysician. Maxim Gorky, in "The Devil" (1899), maintains that Satan is a master ironist, who will, however, not apply "the scalpel of his irony" to the majestic fact of his own existence. Heinrich Heine, in the work just mentioned again, tells us that Satan is a logician. Anatole France says likewise, "The Devil claims that he is a logician" ("le Scepticisme," 1888). Paul Verlaine calls Satan "the old logician." Heinrich Heine assures us further that Diabolus possesses clear, luminous logic,—in fact the greatest ability in argument. According to this German poet, Satan is famed for sophistry and fine-spun syllogisms. Goethe, in *Faust,* has, to a great extent, availed himself of this characteristic of sophistry on the part of the Evil Spirit. Satan, it should be remembered, is a good dialectician, an incomparable casuist, and a controversialist. The Demon is very fond of disputing when driving a bargain with men for their souls. "The Devil," says Anatole France, in the essay just mentioned, "definitely remains the only doctor who has not yet been refuted." Huysmans warns us with regard to the Devil, "You must not discuss with him; however good a reasoner you may be, you will be worsted, for he is a most tricky dialectician" (*En route,* 1895). Mrs. Browning, in *A Drama of Exile* (1845), portrays Lucifer as an argumentative, introspective spirit, well read in modern poetry and well versed in modern thought. In Molnar's *The Devil* (1907), the protagonist is a masterful ironist and casuist, who demolishes all the stock arguments for goodness, which have been advanced by mortals throughout the ages.

The Devil is no less a theologian than a philosopher. Anatole France testified that the Tempter is a great theologian, and is thus necessarily well versed in the Sacred Scriptures. Martin Luther affirmed that the Devil can quote Holy Writ as fluently as any minister, and can twist and torture texts to any meaning that will suit his evil ends.

SATAN AS SYMBOL OF SCIENCE

By medieval man the Devil was believed to hold the key to all knowledge. This belief has scriptural sanction, inasmuch as mastery over the world through the intellect was one of the lures held out to Christ by the Tempter. The Serpent in the Garden of Eden also tempted our ancestors to eat of the forbidden fruit of the Tree of Knowledge. The reward which the Evil Spirit offered his victim for his soul in the Faust legend was likewise power through knowledge. For this reason, all worldly learning was taboo to the theologians.

To the dominion of the Devil the Church handed over philosophy, science and secular learning in general. Philosophy was regarded by the Church as the forbidden fruit of human reason. Ever since the day when the mob of Nitrian monks, in the month of March of the year 415, murdered Hypatia, the last of the Greek philosophers, Catholicism has considered philosophical speculation the work of Satan.

Especially was the study of science invested by the medieval Church with a diabolical taint. Satan has always been considered the symbol of science. In Flaubert's *la Tentation de saint Antoine* (1874), the father of the anchorites sees Satan as the personification of science. The Protestant clergy holds the Catholic view on this point. A speaker at an assembly of Lutheran pastors held at Berlin in the month of September, 1877, identified modern science and culture with Belial. All inquiry into the mysteries of nature was regarded by the Church as black magic. The practical investigation of natural laws was denounced as the work of the Evil One. A certain poet of a generation ago referred very seriously to the laboratory as Satan's smithy.

DIABOLICAL RESPONSIBILITY FOR SCIENTIFIC DISCOVERIES

Every discovery of science, every invention of material benefit to man, was believed, during the Middle Ages, and in Catholic countries for long centuries afterwards, to have been secured with the Devil's help. The Marquis de Mirville, author of the treatise, *Des esprits et de leurs manifestations fluidiques dans la science moderne* (1858), also refers all scientific discoveries to the demons of hell. Speaking from the Roman Catholic viewpoint, Jules Michelet exclaims: "Name me one science that has not been a rebel! Every new one," continues this French liberal thinker, "has been Satan." Accordingly, the Vicomte Louis de Bonald, a religious reactionary living in the beginning of the past century, long before our own fundamentalists, perceived the idea of evolution to be born of the Evil Spirit.

According to the contention of the theologians, it was Satan who in all ages inspired the philosophers and scientists. Every man who was distinguished from the masses by his learning was suspected of having signed the Satanic pact. Any extraordinary power of intellect was sufficient for our credulous forefathers to credit its possessor with a knowledge of the Black Arts or dealings with the Devil. The human mind was not considered capable of accomplishing anything outstanding without the aid of Satan. "In the popular belief," says Professor Ward, "pre-eminent success in any of the paths which human ambition follows, especially if achieved with extraordinary rapidity or in the teeth of unusual difficulties, was associated with the possession of supernatural powers."[5]

Scholars were especially regarded as servants of Satan. "You scholars carry on dealings with the Devil," says a character in Alexandre Dumas' la Tulipe noire (1850). It is common knowledge that men of great learning, like Albertus Magnus and Roger Bacon, figured in the eyes of our ancestors as magicians. Giordano Bruno, Servetus and Galileo, it was believed, owed their scientific theories to the inspiration of the demons below.

In all ages the Devil has received the laurels for the labors of the learned. The discovery of the art of printing—the right hand of our civilization—was ascribed to Diabolus. Heinrich Heine, writing of the invention of printing, also said that an art which gave science the victory over faith, an art, moreover, which plunged us into doubts and revolutions, finally delivered us into the hands of the Devil. Johannes Fust or Faust, a promoter of Gutenberg's invention of the art of printing, was considered by his contemporaries a servant of Satan and a magician. The black slave. whom Aldus Manutius, the great Venetian printer, employed in his printing shop toward the end of the fifteenth century, was popularly said to be an imp of hell. This belief accounts for the term "Printer's Devil." The invention of paper money was attributed to the Devil by Gérard de Nerval in l'Imagier de Harlem ou la Découverte de l'imprimerie (1851).

Among all scientific pursuits, chemistry was especially considered black magic and identified with alchemy. The chemist's crucible, and the fumes and vapors emanating therefrom, assumed the dimensions of the alchemist's cauldron. Sulphur and phosphorus, in particular, were regarded as articles of purely diabolical equipment. A character in Balzac's la Peau de chagrin (1831) also calls

[5] Cf. A. W. Ward: Old English Drama. 4th ed., Oxford, 1901.

chemistry "that science of a devil." This idea survived so long that, in the eighteenth century, Friedrich Hoffmann, a professor at the University of Halle, and a prolific writer on chemical and medical subjects, was believed to have discovered carbonic acid gas with the aid of the Devil.

The German Franciscan monk, Berthold Schwarz, who invented gunpowder about 1350, was believed to be a servant of Satan. A plate in Johannes Brantzius' *les Artifices de feu* (1604) shows the Devil instructing Schwarz in the art of making gunpowder. Chapelain, in *la Pucelle* (1656), represents the Devil as the inventor of gunpowder and owner of a cannon factory. Milton, in *Paradise Lost* (1667-74), also credits the Devil with the invention of the cannon. Tammuz, the Syrian god of vegetation, who, together with all other pagan gods, was converted into a demon by Christianity, is said to be a rival inventor of artillery. P. J. Stahl, in *le Diable à Paris* (1842), similarly attributes the invention of fire-arms to Satan. This writer also terms the silkworm the Devil's worker.

The clergy also counted steam-power among the illusions of the Devil. Pope Gregory XVI called steam an invention of Satan. The priests found no difficulty in spreading this distrust in scientific discoveries among the masses of poor and ignorant country-folk. The peasants of Provence also considered steam an emanation of hell (Alphonse Daudet: "le Secret de Maître Cornille," 1869). The construction of the first steamboat was attributed to the Devil. "Fulton," said one of the characters in Victor Hugo's *les Travailleurs de la Mer* (1866), "was a variation of Lucifer." The locomotive passed originally for Satan's chariot. The school board of the town of Lancaster, Ohio, in 1828, declared the railroad a device of the Devil. In the eyes of the Old Order branch of the Church of the Brethren in America, the automobile is a "devil-machine." The Polish peasants call the radio the "devil-box." The possessor of a radio was recently murdered by Polish peasants in his vicinity, who, in justification, asserted that it killed their crops. Even sanitary appliances were attributed to the Devil. Peter the Venerable, abbot of Cluny, living in the twelfth century, beheld Lucifer lurking in lavatories. The Russians, down to the seventeenth century, regarded purgings and clysters as infernal inventions.[6]

---

[6] The telephone is considered by many Europeans, on grounds other than religious, as a diabolic invention, inasmuch as it implies a negation of per-

But more than anything else, it was art that Catholicism counted among the works of Satan. The Church has at all times affirmed the diabolical origin of all artistic beauty. "Inasmuch as the Evil Spirit," says M. André Thérive, "was the most beautiful of angels, it stands to reason that he will tempt mortals, not by denying art, but through art and under the mask of beauty."[7] According to the Church fathers, the Devil lurks behind all beauty. St. Cyprian saw the Fiend in a flower. The Protestants were not behind the Catholics in their anathema against all art. The Church of England believed the Muses to be daughters of the Devil. The English poet and preacher, John Donne, in a sermon delivered before Oliver Cromwell at Whitehall, affirmed that the Muses were damned spirits of demons. By the Puritans the seven arts were counted among the works of Satan. Thomas Carlisle reported that his pious friend wished that "the Devil would fly away with the fine arts."

Strangely enough, this belief in the diabolical origin of art is sincerely shared by many moderns. André Gide, the contemporary French diabolist, affirms, "There is no true work of art without the collaboration of the Devil." James Huneker says similarly, "Without the Devil there would be no art." If art has always been diabolical in its essence, it has assuredly become increasingly so in modern times. Charles Baudelaire, a profound and penetrating thinker as well as poet, saw correctly when he said, "Modern art, in particular, has an essentially devilish tendency." This trend results from the fact that, more keenly than their predecessors, the moderns are interested in the demoniac element of human nature.

THE DEVIL AS ARTIST

The popular belief, which credits the Devil with a mastery of all arts, is also shared by many modern thinkers. Anatole France ap-

sonal liberty by forcing man's attention at all hours of the day and the night. Read the editorial printed on the occasion of the death of Graham Bell, the inventor of the telephone, in the Paris daily, le Temps, of August 3, 1922. The reader who is interested in the war between the monastery and laboratory is referred to Andrew D. White's classical work on the subject, A History of the Warfare of Science with Theology. 2 vols., New York, 1898.

[7] André Thérive: "M. André Gide et le Diable," l'Opinion, August 17, 1923.

plies to Diabolus the singular epithets of "great artist" (*le Jardin d'Épicure,* 1895) and "wonderful artist" (*Thais,* 1890).

The Devil is credited in the popular mind with great skill in the technical arts; skill which he inherited, be it parenthetically remarked, from the giants of the old North. The Fiend, in fact, is famed as an architect. The many devil-bridges in Germany and other countries speak for his talents, and the cathedrals even show some of his handiwork as a great builder.

The Devil was always ready to aid artisans who found that they could not complete the work they had undertaken. For, in earthly pursuits, the Devil is man's best friend, ready to lend a hand whenever man is at the end of his natural capacities. "I am one," says Old Nick to Steenie Steenson in Walter Scott's "Wandering Willie's Tale" (1824), "that, though I have been sair misca'd in the world, am the only hand for helping my freends." The Devil never shrank from performing the most arduous tasks, and never even recoiled from carving intricate church-pillars for architects who found that unaided they could not carry out their plans. Solomon found no difficulty in recruiting demons to help him build his temple at Jerusalem. They quarried and cut stones for that edifice, which was erected to the glory of their Great Enemy.

*

* *

In Jewish mythology it was the fallen angels who instructed men in all the arts and sciences. Samsaweel taught men the signs of the sun, Seriel, the signs of the moon, and Arakiel, the signs of the earth. Kawkabel was, according to Jewish belief, the demon who taught men astrology, just as Set or Seth, in Egyptian mythology, is the originator of astronomy and many other arts, especially agriculture.[8] Barakel instructed men in the art of divination from the stars, and Ezekeel taught them augury from the clouds. Armaros showed men how to break spells, and Shemhazai taught them exorcism and how to cut roots. The inventor of the finery and ornaments with which women attract men is Azazel. This demon showed the daughters of Eve "armlets and all sorts of

[8] *Cf.* Moncure Daniel Conway: *Demonology and Devil-Lore* (London, 1879; 3rd ed., New York, 1889), II, 279.

trinkets, taught them the use of rouge, and showed them how to beautify their eyelids and how to ornament themselves with the rarest and most precious jewels and with all sorts of paint."[9]   This demon also showed the different metals to men and taught them "how to make slaughtering knives, arms and shields and coats of mail."[10] In European folklore, Bel, a prince of fire, is said to have made possible those technical arts of man which cannot be produced without the aid of fire.

[9]*Cf.* Louis Ginzberg: *The Legends of the Jews* (4 vols., Philadelphia, 1909-25), I, 125.
[10] *Ibid.*

CHAPTER XX

THE DEVIL, THE WORLD AND THE FLESH (II)

MUSIC, DANCE AND DRAMA OF INFERNAL ORIGIN

THE Devil has been popularly credited with the invention of music. Victor Hugo repeatedly refers in his works to the popular belief in the diabolical origin of music. Asmodeus himself, in LeSage's novel, *le Diable boiteux* (1707), asserts that he is the inventor of music. This popular belief is based on Church tradition, which ascribed the origin of music, not without good reason, to the Devil. Catholic asceticism denounced all instrumental music as the Devil's work. Even some Protestant sects not many decades ago condemned music during religious services as a Satanic artifice to lure men's thoughts away from God. The popular English preacher, Rowland Hill, long ago admitted the fact that the Devil had all the good melodies, and a popular hymn-writer of this country likewise thought it unfortunate that Diabolus should have all the good tunes.

This view is shared by many modern writers who can hardly be said to believe in Beelzebub. James Huneker, in his already quoted *Bedouins,* speaking of the Devil, affirms, "Without him . . . there would be . . . no music . . . He created the chromatic scale—that is why Richard Wagner admired the Devil in music—what is *Parsifal,*" the great American art critic concludes his pæan of praise of the Prince of Pleasure, "but a version of the Black Mass?" Dr. Henry van Dyke, in a statement dated February 27, 1921, credits the Demon with the invention at least of jazz-music. The songs of a musical comedy are considered by our high-brow critics "the Devil's own ditties."

The Devil always has given sufficient proof of his musical talent. Again James Huneker, in his *Bedouins* just quoted again, goes so far as to call Satan "the greatest of all musicians." The vocal ability of the demons of hell was early discovered by the medieval monks. Thomas de Cantimpré, writing in the thirteenth century, tells how a demon composed a famous song about St. Martin and circulated it abroad all over France and Germany. In the second, more sketchy, part of Novalis' *Heinrich von Ofterdingen* (1802), the Principle of Good and the Principle of Evil appear in open competition, singing antiphonies. The French composer, Boieldieu, believed that he had composed the "Valse infernale" for his comic opera *Faust* (1828) with the help of the Devil in person.

But Satan's greatest musical work is perhaps the *Sonata del Diavolo* (1713) nominally composed by Giuseppe Tartini, an Italian musician. According to Tartini's own testimony, the Devil appeared to him in his dream and played on his violin an air of such great beauty that the composer, upon awakening, seized his own instrument and played "The Devil's Trill."

Diabolus is also credited with a sonata by Gérard de Nerval in *la Sonate du Diable* (1830). This story tells how a musician, chagrined that his daughter understood nothing of music, offered her hand to the man who could write and execute the best sonata, "be it the Devil in person." The Evil Spirit, who is never slow to appear when called, arrived with two accompanists at the musical tournament, which the master had arranged. The Devil, it transpired, had written the best sonata of all the aspirants to the hand of the maiden. But an angel, wishing to checkmate the Devil, on the evening preceding the day fixed for the tournament, handed a sonata to the young man who was in love with the musician's daughter. But even the angelic sonata was inferior to that of the infernal composer. However, when the Devil's players approached the end of their superb composition, convinced of their final victory, the young man surreptitiously substituted his own parchment for theirs and thus won out in the end.[11]

While the Devil plays all instruments equally well, he seems to prefer the violin. He was said in the Middle Ages to own a violin with which he could set whole cities, grandparents and grandchildren, men and women, girls and boys, to dancing, dancing until they fell dead from sheer exhaustion. The Devil appears in this rôle in the medieval legend of the Pied Piper, which is well known to English readers through Robert Browning's poem, "The Pied Piper of Hamelin" (1843), Robert Buchanan's opera, *The Piper of*

[11] Mr. W. H. Snyder has written, in 1911, a drama in three acts entitled *The Devil's Sonata.*

Hamelin (1893), and Miss Josephine Peabody's play, *The Piper* (1909). The miraculous musician in this legend carried off one hundred and fifty children when the inhabitants of Hameln in Saxony refused to pay him for ridding them of the rats, which had infested their town. This Pied Piper was, according to Johannes Wierus and Robert Burton, none other than the Devil in person. The rats were the human souls, which the Devil charmed by his music into following him. In the Middle Ages, the soul was often represented leaving the body in the form of a mouse. The soul of a good person, it was believed, comes out of the mouth as a white mouse, while, at the death of a sinner, the soul escapes as a black mouse, which the Devil catches and carries off in his sack to hell. Mephistopheles, it will be remembered, calls himself, in Goethe's *Faust*, "the Lord of rats and mice" (i. 1516). Death, the Devil's first cousin, if not his *alter ego*, similarly is represented, in the Dance of Death, marching off the souls to hell to the accompaniment of a merry tune on his violin.

Satan appears as a fiddler in the poem *"Der Teufel mit der Geige,"* which has been attributed to the Swiss anti-Papist, Pamphilus Gengenbach, of the sixteenth century. Klemens Brentano, in the fragmentary *Romanzen vom Rosenkranz* (written in 1909 and published posthumously in 1852), represents the Devil playing the violin, sending forth from this instrument shockingly shrill tunes. In Lenau's *Faust* (1836), Mephistopheles takes the violin out of the hands of one of the musicians at a peasant-wedding and plays on it a diabolical *czardas,* which fills with voluptuousness the hearts of all who hear it. An opera *Un Violon du Diable* was played in Paris in 1849, and Benjamin Webster's extravaganza in verse, *The Devil's Violin,* was performed the same year in London. The Devil also appears as a limping fiddler in a California legend, which appeared, in 1855, in the *Pioneer,* a Californian magazine, under the title "The Devil's Fiddle." In his story "les Tentations ou Éros, Plutus et la Gloire" (1863), Charles Baudelaire presents the Demon of Love holding in his left hand a violin, "which, without doubt, served to sing his pleasures and pains." We also meet the diabolical musician in "The Devil in a Nunnery," a medieval legend modernized by Francis Oskar Mann (1914). In this story, the Devil, disguised as a pilgrim, enters a convent, and plays on his "cithern" for the entertainment of the nuns. Slyly he

drifts into the most voluptuous music, until the nuns are overcome
with old memories that should be dead. The effect is so disastrous
to their serenity that in expiation a fast is ordered for the next
day.[12]

*

* *

Naturally the Devil is also the originator of the dance, particularly the rapid and fantastic variety. Asmodeus, in Le Sage's
previously mentioned novel, assumes credit for the invention of
the dance.[13]

The demons inherited their dancing ability from the ærial spirits, who were too etheral in nature to walk prosaically on earth.
For this reason, dancing is their distinguishing characteristic. In
many legends, the Devil becomes the dancing partner of the girls
who show too great a fondness for dancing, and who, therefore,
must dance with their diabolical partner without rest or repose till
they fall dead. Friedrich Hebbel has used this legend in his poem
"Der Tanz" (1832). In this romance, based on an Eiderstedt
legend, a young girl is seized by such transports of joy in dancing
at a ball that she keeps whirling about after all the others have
left the hall. When her mother warns her that she is fatiguing
herself and asks her to stop dancing and go home, the girl boastfully replies that even if the Devil himself were present, he could
not tire her out. But no sooner has she uttered these words when
a young man in dark clothes approaches her and invites her to
dance with him. The girl accepts the invitation, and the pair
swing around in the empty hall. But now the girl finds no joy in
her dancing; she feels rather as if she stood on the edge of her
grave. The mother enters the hall and again asks her daughter to
stop dancing. But the young girl cannot break away from the
grasp of the weird looking youth, who holds her so firmly in his

[12] In this connection it may be interesting to refer to the following Irish
tale mentioned by Leland in a footnote to his translation of Heine's *Elementargeister:* Pat O'Flanagan, the tailor, was dancing in mad joy with the Devil,
who was fiddling, while both took alternate sups from Satan's whisky-bottle.
"Whin, och what a pity! all at wanst this foine parrety was broken up by
the appairence of Judy, Pat's wife." In the end, the Devil goes off with
Mrs. O'Flanagan.

[13] It is believed that our waltz originated in a dance called *la Volta* performed at the medieval Witches' Sabbath. See Margaret Alice Murray's
The Witch-Cult in Western Europe (Oxford, 1921), pp. 134-5.

arms. Suddenly blood spurts out of her mouth; and as she sinks dead to the ground, the diabolical young man disappears in the fog and the night.

*

* *

In addition to his sponsorship of the dance, the Devil is likewise regarded as the inventor of the drama. Asmodeus, who figures in the novel by LeSage, contends that he is the creator of comedy. Certainly the Church condemned all secular . dramatic performances as *"pompæ diaboli."* The Church fathers declared that all dramatic arts emanated from the Devil (Pseudo-Cyprian: *De Spectaculis,* iv; Tatian: *Oratio ad Græcos,* xxii). St. John Chrysostom also denounced the "Satanic corruptions of the stage." Indeed, the actors were regarded by the Catholic Church in the Middle Ages, and even for many centuries afterwards, as servants of Satan and denied the holy sacraments and burial in consecrated ground. It is a matter of common knowledge that Molière, the creator of the French comedy, who died in 1673, was considered unfit for Christian burial. In revenge, the condemned comedians starred Satan in their plays. Protestants were likewise opposed to play-production. During the sixteenth century, the faithful were forbidden by the Church of England to attend plays of any kind, and any person connected with the stage was denied the offices of the church.

The Puritans considered the play-house the Devil's own place. Stephen Gosson, in his *School of Abuse* (1579), affirmed seriously of theatrical productions: "There is more in them than we perceive; the Devil stands at our elbow when we see not, speaks when we hear not, strikes when we feel not, and wounds sore when he raises no skein, nor rents the flesh." Archbishop John Sharp of London (1645-1714) said that going to the theater was equivalent to looking at the Devil. Our own George Jean Nathan, who certainly cannot be suspected of orthodoxy, fancifully terms the theater "the house of Satan" in his book by that title (1926). A story is told of the demon who entered a woman in the theater and, when exorcised, excused himself by saying that he had found her in his own "demesne."[14]

[14] See Thornton S. Graves, "The Devil in the Playhouse," *South Atlantic Quraterly,* XIX (1920), 131-40.

LUCIFER AS LITTÉRATEUR

The Devil was also regarded by our ancestors as the patron of publications. The assertion that his Satanic Majesty hates nothing so much as writing or printer's ink is surely a calumny. In Samuel Crothers' essay, "The Merry Devil of Education" (1910), Diabolus declares, "Ink is my native element." The German mystic, Jacob Bœhme, relates that when Satan was asked the cause of God's enmity toward the Adversary and of the latter's subsequent downfall, he replied, "I wished to be an author."[15] The punishment meted out to Satan for his diabolical genius has evidently not cured him of his literary aspirations.

The Devil is recognized as a great writer, although he may never have received any royalties on work published over his own signature.[16] Having been denied copyright privileges on earth, and probably also lacking asbestos paper, Diabolus must perforce publish over human signatures. He finds it, moreover, to his advantage to dictate his ideas through the pens of mortals in order to carry on his work better on earth.

It may be said without exaggeration that all writers, consciously or unconsciously, owe their inspiration to the Devil. Gœthe remarked jokingly on the tenth of January, 1789, that he would have to sell his soul to Satan in order to write his *Faust*. But it is not necessary to enter formally a bond with Beelzebub in order to obtain his aid in writing a book. The Devil is always near to them who are engaged in the profession of letters. It is not without good reason, therefore, that the priests maintain that "the writers are all more or less demons" (Victor Hugo: *les Quatre vents de l'esprit*, 1882, and *Toute la lyre*, 1888-93).

It is a well-known fact that books have in all times been considered tools of hell. For the things that men write have their influence in formulating the ideas and ideals of the reader, and to this extent authors stand in the service of Satan. Thomas Carlyle also believed that he served Satan, but his only regret was that he received no reward for his services. "Sad fate!" he exclaimed, "to serve the Devil and yet get no wages even from him."

15 The word "author" is used in this connection in its current meaning.

16 In this connection it is interesting to note that Diabolus has been credited with the authorship of the biggest Bible in the world—the *gigas librorum*—which is found in the Royal Library at Stockholm and which is therefore called the Devil's Bible.

It is especially the imaginaive works of literature which are generally considered to be of infernal inspiration. When Asmodeus, in LeSage's noteworthy novel, maintains that he is the inventor of all things that make for beauty in this world, he might just as well have said that he was also the creator of literature. If, from modesty, he did not personally make this assertion, others affirmed it for him. It stands to reason that whatever we read for our enjoyment is in the eyes of Catholic asceticism of infernal origin.

But apart from its joy-giving quality, what we call *belles lettres* is decidedly diabolical in its essence. The writers themselves admit the infernal origin of their work. "I have heard all the men of lettres say that their profession was diabolical," asserts Eugene Delacroix. The demonic element is most essential for the success of great creative literary works other than treatises of a scientific or historic nature. The fire and originality in many a masterpiece is due to that power which Timoleon calls *Automatia* and Gœthe, in his conversation with Eckermann in 1828, *das Dämonische*—the dæmonic—"that which cannot be explained by reason or understanding, which is not in our nature, but to which we are subject."[17] Voltaire believed that, to be a successful author, it was necessary to have *le diable au corps*. In full agreement with the dictum of the patriarch of Ferney, Gottfried Keller, the Swiss novelist, has this to say in regard to literary success:

> "He who has had no bitter experiences knows no malice; and he who has known no malice has not the Devil in him; and he who has not the Devil in him cannot write anything that will have force and vigor."

Fiction figures in the eyes of many men as a fabrication of the Fiend. Many indictments may indeed be drawn up against all forms of fiction. On account of its frequently immoral matter, the novel has received the condemnation of many a moralist. "The personages of fiction," the great Tolstoy declares, "have souls; and it is but truth to say that their malignant authors send them forth among us like demons to tempt us and to ruin us." According to the famous Russian author, Balzac, the Titan of the French novel, is the Lucifer of literature. But the creator of the *Comédie hu-*

---

[17] Gœthe undoubtedly used the word "demonic" as a synonym for "supernatural" with a complimentary connotation. But a writer may be inspired by a good or an evil spirit according as to whether the gravitation of his imagination is toward heaven or hell.

maine is not the only French novelist who has been under anathema. It has been said that all French novelists are of the Devil's party. Nor, for that matter, will the romancers of other countries take their places among the elect of heaven.

Many a well-known noveltist, in other countries as well as in France, has produced his work *cooperante Diabolo*. The Fiend has always shown partiality in aiding fictionists. The German fantastic writer, E. T. A. Hoffmann, held the opinion that the Devil was "an ever helpful aid-de-camp of story-tellers in need of help." Tradition has it that the demons of hell guided the pen of many a fiction writer. Asmodeus, for example, wishing to take vengeance on the monks, his sworn enemies, whispered the *Decameron* (c. 1350) into the ears of Boccaccio, while Beelzebub avenged himself on the devil-fighting knights of the Middle Ages by inspring Cervantes with *Don Quixote* (1605-16).

As for poetry, no argument is needed to show that this emotional art is an expression of the powers of darkness. The poetry of passion in particular is poison. All lyricists are the Levites of Lucifer. Moreover, poetry is often used to sing the praises of the Prince of this world. Byron, the poet of doubt and despair, is not the only "chanter of hell," as Lamartine called him. Even Milton, the great Puritan poet, showed himself as a partisan of the powers of darkness. "The reason," said William Blake, "Milton wrote in fetters when he wrote of angels and God, and at liberty when of devils and hell, is because he was a true poet, and of the Devil's party without knowing it." It cannot be denied that the personality of the Devil was the chief preoccupation of the poet. Addison and Dryden, among many other English and foreign authorities, regarded Milton's fallen archangel as the focal point of attention or the real hero of the poem. "The finest thing in connection with this [Milton's] *Paradise*," says Taine, in his *Histoire de la littérature française* (1863), "is Hell; and in this history of God the chief part is taken by the Devil." What fascinated also Chateaubriand in Milton's poem was the character of Satan, whom he considered the finest conception of all poetic personifications of Evil.[17a]

Criticism, as all creative writers will agree, is without any doubt whatsoever the work of the Devil. "Literary criticism," says Sainte-Beuve, "the kind that I am writing, is alas! hardly com-

[17a] On this question, see Emily Hickey's article, "Is Satan the Hero of *Paradise Lost?" Catholic World*, XCVI (1912), 58-71.

patible with Christian practice . . ." The literary critic may wish to be fair, but not infrequently the animus of professional rivalry or scorn seizes him, and he plays the rôle of the Spirit of negation and destruction. The critic of books and their authors, considered in this light, is nothing if not a Devil's advocate. On the other hand, the writers with whom the critic differs are identified by him, in one way or another, with the person of the Devil.

But not only literary works enjoyed the distinction of being considered of diabolical inspiration. In Catholic eyes, the majority of books produced by men owed their origin to the unholy devices and corruptions of Satan. It is a well-known fact that, in the good old days, every book printed without the approval of the Church was associated with the demons of hell.[18]

THE DEVIL AS RADICAL AND REFORMER

The Devil was popularly regarded as a pioneer of progress. He was hailed as the standard-bearer of the great reformers and innovators of all ages. Satan was credited with all aspirations for improvement in every field of human activity. The Church contended that it was Satan who inspired the opposition against priest-craft and kingcraft, and that it was the Devil who filled man with the love of liberty, equality and fraternity. Diabolus represented discontent with existing conditions in matters social, political, and ecclesiastical. He was identified with the spirit of progress so disturbing to those who are satisfied with the existing order of things. Every democratic institution, every social reform, was attributed by the reactionaries to the machinations of the spirits of hell.[19]

The French Revolution was regarded by the Catholic Church as a creation of the Evil Spirit.[20] It was asserted by Catholicism that France was possessed of the Devil during the revolutionary period. According to Victor Hugo, the Catholics believed that the members of the Convention were carried off at their death by the Devil (les Misérables I. i. 10). This great French poet himself,

[18] In this connection it may be well to refer the reader to the story, "The Printer's Devil," published anonymously in 1836 and reprinted in the present writer's anthology of Devil Stories (New York: A. A. Knopf, 1921).

[19] Soviet Russia, on account of her experimentation in social and political reforms, is envisaged at the present day by two writers as the "Devil's work-shop."

[20] The Catholic view of the French Revolution down to the present day may be seen in le Diable et la Révolution (1895), a work written by the impostor Leo Taxil and dedicated to Pope Leo XIII.

in his royalist days, described the Convention as a Pandemonium (*Odes et poésies diverses,* 1822). Marmontel had already previously said that the members of the Convention were "living bronze figures of demons."

The priests taught the French peasants that the civil Constitution promulgated by the Convention, which transferred the property of the Church from the Catholic hierarchy to the French government, was the diabolical masterpiece of this infernal Revolution. Count Joseph de Maistre, the theoretical proponent of absolutism in church and government, also considered the French Revolution the work of Satan (*Considérations sur la France,* 1796). His yoke-fellow, the Viscount Louis de Bonald, saw in Jacobinism "the reign of demons." Chateaubriand, the partisan of pontiffs and potentates, shared this Catholic view with regard to the French Revolution. In *les Martyrs* (1809), he went so far as to put the revolutionary hymn of his country into the mouth of the Devil.

The revolutionaries, no less than the reactionaries, regarded the French Revolution as the work of Satan. The difference in the conception of this great historical event by the two parties is that the monarchists considered the revolt against the God-ordained powers as a sin, whereas the republicans saw it in a different light.

Either party was absolutely correct in regarding Satan as the moving spirit of the French Revolution. For the emperean rebel is the incarnation of the spirit of revolt in men and the instigator of all social and political upheavals on earth. The Devil, waging on earth the war he started in heaven, will always be found as a partisan of those who seek to throw off the yoke of their heavenly ordained oppressors. Satan is the grandest symbol of protest against tyranny, celestial or terrestrial, that the world can conceive. "The Devil," says Anatole France, "is the father of all anarchy." Was not Satan the first of all rebels against constituted authority? Did he not first utter the words, *"Non serviam,"* which burn on the lips of all revolutionaries? Satan was the symbol of the movement for the liberation of the human spirit from the bonds of absolutism,—a movement which started with the French Revolution. He was the embodiment of the revolutionary movement, which was sweeping Europe a century ago. He was the leader of the great army of Human Freedom, as Heine called the lovers of liberty of his day. It was under the standard of Satan that the oppressed masses in all European countries fought in 1830 against the princes and potentates, who assumed to rule them by divine right. Satan stood at the head of all the agitators and conspirators against political oppression of the past century, and as predicted by the Italian poet, Rapisardi, Lucifer will also accomplish the social revolution which is now preparing in all European countries and bring a new era for mankind, in which social equity as well as political equality will be effected.

*

* *

The Devil was represented by the theologians as the Arch-Fiend, the bitter enemy of the good and holy men. The champions of the common folk, on the other hand, saw in Satan the defender of the downtrodden, and the protector of the poor and helpless against the high and mighty of the land. The Devil, who has always been a democrat, is said to have interfered in favor of the peasants or serfs against the feudal lords. The Fiend appears in the folk-lore of all European countries as the defender of accused innocence, and as an exemplar of honesty and fidelity. Diabolus exerted his powers of retribution on misers, on men who brought no good to themselves or to others despite all their hoarded wealth. He was also represented as a chastiser of the Pecksniffs, the moral pretenders. Satan was universally regarded as the Nemesis of the publicans and ale-wives who adulterated the beer they poured out, or who gave short measure to their customers. Gratitude is the crowning quality with which man has invested the Devil of his dreams. Many medieval legends report the Devil's gratitude whenever he is treated with justice. With regard to this trait, Satan can certainly be cited in marked contrast to the sons of Adam.

THE DEVIL AS HEDONIST

Satan has always been portrayed as the Prince of Pleasure. The joys and delights of life were considered by Catholic ascetics as emanations from hell. "Laughter and gaiety," said St. John Chrysostom, "come not from God, but from the Devil (*Opera* vii. 97; x. 590). The modern diabolist, Charles Baudelaire, similarly detected the Devil in human laughter. The excitable poisons, such as tobacco, alcohol, opium, hashish, were for this French poet "Satanic suggestions," the most terrible means employed by the Evil One to enslave humanity. They all represented for him "artificial paradises."[21] Liquor is to our own teetotalers the Devil's invention. "King Alcohol is the Devil's worst emissary on earth," recently said a certain Methodist preacher.[22]

The Church looked upon Lucifer as the lord of earthly love. The affection of one sex for another was believed, from the earliest period of the Christian era, to be under the special control of the powers of hell. Carnal love was regarded by the Christian monks and missionaries as nothing short of demoniac possession, and its enjoyment was believed to lead man to certain and eternal perdition.

The Church considered celibacy to be the only perfect state, and hesitated for a long time to give its sanction to marriage, which it regarded as unworthy of the "spiritual man." St. Paul denounced marriage in strong terms. "Celibacy must be chosen," said St. Tertullian, "even though the human race should perish." Origen denounced marriage in the following terms: "Matrimony is impure and unholy; a means of sensual passion." When, at the Council of Trent, marriage was finally included among the sacraments of the Church, it was regarded as a *remedium amoris* conceded by the kindness of God to the turpitude of the "natural man."[23]

WOMAN AS INSTRUMENTUM DIABOLI

The Church fathers believed that Satan brought about the downfall of men through the allurements of women. All women were regarded as the daughters of the Devil, and all men as bewitched by these sorceresses of Satan.[24] St. Paul expressed his horror of women's charms. He confessed that it was only by the strongest practice of faith that he could stay in their society and remain sinless. As Satan is the eternal tempter, so is woman in

[21] See Wilhelm Michel's essay, "Baudelaire und die Gifte," *Masken.* Bd. XXIII. Heft 21 (1930).
[22] The reader will recall in this connection Captain John Silver's song— "Drink and the Devil had done for the rest."
[23] On the final inclusion of marriage among the sacraments, see G. Serrier: *le Mariage contrat-sacrement.* Paris, 1928.
[24] Mr. H. M. Tichenor, former editor of the *Melting Pot,* in his clever booklet, *Satan and the Saints* (1918), has described the manner in which the saints escaped the sorceries of Satan incorporated in the daughters of the earth.

the eyes of the Church the eternal instrument of temptation—
instrumentum Diaboli, the most efficient of stalking-horses, behind
which the Devil goes hunting for the immortal souls of men. St.
Cyprian said, "Woman is the instrument which the Evil One employs to possess our souls," and St. Tertullian addressed the beautiful sex with the following words: "Woman, thou ought to go
about clad in mourning and ashes, thine eyes filled with tears of
remorse, to make us forget that thou hast been man's destruction.
Woman, thou art the gate to hell." This feminine-diabolical kinship is expressed by the rabbis in their belief that both the Devil
and woman entered the world simultaneously.

Many thinkers and writers seem to concur with the fathers of
the Church with regard to women. The belief in woman as Satan's instrument in his work of temptation is almost universal
among moderns. The German poet and playwright, Lessing, back
in the eighteenth century, asserts, "The hand of a woman is often
the glove in which Satan conceals his claw." Prosper Mérimée
speaks fully in the spirit of the Church fathers when he says,
"Woman is the surest instrument of damnation which the Evil
One can employ." Woman is especially used by the Devil as a
tool to lead man to ruin. This belief explains the French proverb
which says, "Man is tow, woman is fire, and the Devil blows on it."
Anatole France also affirms, "It is through woman that the Devil
takes great advantage of man." Barbey d'Aurevilly believes that
women possess greater powers of temptation even than the Devil
himself. "Women," this writer says, "are all temptresses, ready to
tempt God or the Devil."

Woman's natural inclination to evil is expressed by Gœthe in
the following lines:
"When towards the Devil's house we tread,
    Woman's a thousand steps ahead." (*Faust* i. 3980-81.)
Other writers think that woman is a match for the Devil in
wickedness. Schopenhauer's contempt for woman is too well
known to need further comment. "Where the Devil gets through,
a woman will get through, too," says Mérimée. "The Devil," this
writer also expresses through the mouth of one of his characters,
"has nothing left to teach women who overdress themselves and
coil their hair fantastically." (We post-Victorians might say,
"who underdress themselves and bob their hair fantastically.")

Kornel Makuszynski believes that woman is even more wicked than the Devil. In his *Another Paradise Lost and Regained* (1926), this Polish writer affirms that "Satan himself would not do the things a woman will do and lay to his charge."

Thus woman is believed by modern writers to be possessed of the Evil One. "Every woman," Barbey assures us, "has a devil somewhere who would always be her master, were it not for the fact that she has two others also in her—Cowardice and Shame —to interfere with the first one." This saying is fully in keeping with the proverb which affirms that "The heart of a beautiful woman is the most beloved hiding-place of at least seven devils."

Many writers go so far as to express their belief that woman is partly or wholly the Devil in person. Woman is for Diderot a combination of angel and Devil. Heine does not consider woman wholly diabolical, but he does not know at what point in her the angel ends and the Devil begins. Molière considers woman as the very Devil, and for Balzac woman is a perfected Devil.

Baudelaire regarded woman as wholly diabolical in body and spirit. As a dandy he despised woman, as a Catholic he considered her "one of the most seductive forms of the Devil" and wondered why she was admitted into churches. "Woman," again says this French poet, "is the feminine form of the Other, the most dangerous incarnation of the Evil One." Commenting on the romance *le Diable amoureux* (1772), he remarks, "The camel of Cazotte, camel, Devil, and woman." It should be remembered that Baudelaire was less attached to the form of woman as to her spirit, which he regarded as diabolical. Verlaine, following the lead of the poet Baudelaire, his master in Satanism, likewise believed in woman's identity with the Devil ("Femme et chatte," 1866). Strindberg saw in woman a living Gehenna adorned with all the allures of Satan.[25]

For the etcher Rops, who was also a disciple of the diabolist Baudelaire, woman is the demonic incarnation of lust, the daughter of darkness, the servant of Satan, the partner of hell, the vampire who sucks the blood of the cosmos. In Barbey's tales as in Rops' etchings, we behold woman engaged in her worship of the Devil. She is described by these diabolist and decadent artists as an adept

[25] On the woman as an impersonation of the Devil, see also the end of the chapter "The Form of the Fiend" in the present work.

in all black arts and an expert in all forms of sexual perversion. She is portrayed wallowing in the wildest orgies of lewdness and licentiousness, continually invoking, extolling and worshipping Lucifer, the lord of lust.

Concerning love, too, the Church fathers find support among many poets and philosophers of modern times. Voltaire regarded the Devil and love as synonymous. Love, for Alfred de Vigny, was the art of the Devil and not of the Deity. This pessimistic poet, considering love as idle and mendacious, did not deny to it, however, a narcotizing value in the hands of Satan. Baudelaire always saw the Satanic side in love, and proved his thesis by the animal names we give to the woman we love. "Have not the devils the forms of beasts?" he asks. "The one and supreme bliss of love," this poet again says, "rests in the certainty of doing evil; and man and woman know from birth that in evil is found all pleasure." "Love," this diabolist again affirms, "is the most terrible of all incarnations at the service of Satan." Schopenhauer, in his essay, "Metaphysik der Geschlechtsliebe" (1859), arrived at the same conclusion, arguing that love does not exist to make us happy, but to deceive us under the cover of happiness, and to compel us to perform actions profitable to the human race, but suicidal to the individual. The conception of love as a demonic factor prevails throughout all modern literature; Ibsen, Tolstoy, Ola Hansson, Przybyzewski, Prus, Hardy, and Shaw, all perceiving in eroticism not an ideal which should be pursued, but a cosmic power which makes the human being a puppet moving to some incomprehensible goal.

CONCLUSION

Thus the Devil is the representative of terrestrial interests and enjoyments, in contrast to those of the spiritual realm. As a skillful reasoner and logician, he plays havoc with those who dispute his clever materialistic philosophy, for he excels in dialectic. He stands for the glorification of the flesh in painting and sculpture, in the dance and drama, in fiction and romantic adveture, depicting forbidden pleasures in vivid colors, luring on the amorous and the yearning to supposed happiness only to dash this expectation into an empty sense of unreality and frustration. It is his restless impulse in men which provokes them to unsettle the old order of things and become reformers in the hope of promoting greater happiness. His efforts are inspired by a lusty, democratic hedonism. The protean character of this supermalevolent Personality is attested by a mixture of beneficent traits, such as his ambition, his spirit of good fellowship and democracy, and a progressive desire to unsettle things too long established. Besides which, what would life be without the gratification of the senses? Drabness itself is a mockery of life. But to submit this important Personage to close cross-questioning by Kantian or Huxleyan dialectic is taking an unfair advantage over this mysterious mythological entity, this superhuman presence in our midst.

CHAPTER XXI

THE DEVIL IN LITERATURE

OF all the myths that have come down to us from the East, and of all the creations of Western fancy and belief, the Devil has exercised the strongest attraction upon the human mind. The imagination of man has from earliest times persistently played with the Personality of Evil. The Fiend has never failed in fascination. He is an everlasting fountain of pathos and poetry, a perennial power for interest, inspiration and achievement. So large a place has Diabolus taken in our imaginations, and we might also say in our hearts, that his expulsion therefrom, no matter what philosophy may teach us, must forever remain an impossibility. Whether or not we favor the belief in the Devil's spiritual entity apart from man's, we always show a deep interest in his literary incarnations. All intelligent men and women, believers and unbelievers, may be assumed to hold a unanimous opinion with regard to the Fiend's fitness as a fictional character.

It is generally admitted that, as a poetic person, the Devil has not his equal in heaven above or on the earth beneath. In contrast to the idea of Good, which is the more exalted in proportion to its freedom from anthropomorphism, the idea of Evil owes to the very presence of this element its chief value as a literary theme. Lucifer may have been inferior to St. Michael in military tactics, but he certainly is his superior in literary æsthetics. The fair angels—perfect in their virtues—are beyond our ken, but the fallen angels, with all their faults and foibles, are of our kin.

Of all Christian supernatural beings, it is the Devil who, as a poetic figure, is superior to the pagan divinities. In poetic possibilities no mythical personage can be compared with the Christian Devil. "The fallen archangel," said Father Duchesne, "is not only superior to the old Pluto, but is perhaps the richest dramatic type, on account of his stormy passions." In Chateaubriand's opinion there is no poetic character, ancient or modern, to equal the Devil in grandeur. Contrasting Milton with Homer, this French writer finds nothing in the *Odyssey* comparable with Satan's address to the sun in *Paradise Lost.* What is Juno," Chateaubriand asks in his *Génie du Christianisme* (1799-1802), "repairing to the limits of the earth in Ethiopia, compared to Satan, speeding his course from the depths of chaos up to the frontiers of nature?" "What is Ajax," he exclaims, "compared to Satan?" "What is Pluto," echoes Victor Hugo, "compared to the Christian Devil?"

The poetry of the Christian religion is mainly manifested in the Prince of Demons. Paradoxically enough, the beauty of Christianity is finally reduced, in its poetic aspect, to the Adversary. Of all Christian characters, Satan has appealed most strongly to the poets of all ages and languages. It may be said picturesquely but not inaccurately that the Devil has dominated most literary forms to the present day. To call the roll of the writers who celebrated Satan in verse and prose is to marshal the names of almost all great men of letters.

While most writers content themselves with recording the Devil's activities on this planet, there never have been lacking men of sufficient courage to call upon the Prince of Darkness in his own proper dominions in order to bring back to us, for our instruction and edification, a report of his work there. The most distinguished poet his Infernal Highness has ever entertained at his court, it will be recalled, was Dante. The mark, which the scorching fires of hell left on the face of the Florentine poet, was to his contemporaries a sufficient proof of the truth of his story.

*
*   *

Lucifer looms large in literature. The "Morning Star," hurled from heaven, shines brilliantly in the firmament of fiction. The discrowned archangel has waxed truly formidable in literary stature. Beelzebub bears on his shoulders the burden of *belles-letters.* It is a significant fact that Diabolus has been the principal *motif* of inspiration for the world's greatest masterpieces. Strike the Devil out of the reckoning, and you strike out the pith and marrow of Dante, Calderon, Milton, Goethe and Byron. Sorry, indeed, would the plight of literature be without the Devil. Lacking the Devil, there would simply be no literature. With the Devil eliminated, there would be no plot, no complication, and consequently no story. Syllogistically stated, the idea may perhaps be expressed as follows: All real stories depend upon plots; all plots depend upon the intervention of the Devil; consequently, all real stories depend upon the Devil.

Thus, figuratively speaking, the Fiend is the fountain-head of all fiction. The novel, that wanton fable, may, without straining at the figure, be considered the work of a special demon who has the function of agitating the quill. Mr. H. G. Wells, in *The Undying Fire* (1919), affirms, "Satan is a celestial *raconteur*. He alone makes stories." Barbey d'Aurevilly, the French diabolist, prefaces his story "Happiness in Crime" (in *les Diaboliques,* 1874) with the following statement: "In these pleasant days, when a man relates a true story, it is supposed that the Devil has dictated it." Jules de Gaultier, the great French paradoxist, is of the opinion that Evil came into the world to promote and perpetuate the art of story-telling.

The literary and artistic value of Evil cannot be overestimated. There is a fascination in Evil which allures men to the edge of the pit to gaze at all the writhing horrors within, execrable as these misshapen things may be to the stern moralist. The existence of duplicity, sensuality, knavery, and malice prepense, is not to be denied by the Realist or Romanticist—who portrays these moral abominations without greatly exaggerating their sway. These imaginative writers know that goodness and mercy are but partial ingredients in the composition of human nature, where the struggle is going on between the higher and the lower natures. It is generally admitted that a happy nation has no history. Nor can a wholly virtuous person be used as the protagonist of a novel. It is thus proved that the Diabolical is essential to all forms of fiction.

If Diabolus is essential to the novel, he is even of greater validity and necessity in the drama. There could certainly be no drama without the Diabolical. "True dramatic action," says the German dramatist, Friedrich Hebbel, "arises only when the Devil ranges himself as antagonist." As for poetry, no proof is needed that the Prince of the Pit is a patent and potent power in verse. "Poetry," recently said the French poet, Raymond de la Tailhède, "is nothing but revolution"; and it is obvious that the Devil, by his very nature, is the spirit of revolt and rebellion.

*

*   *

The Devil has never been absent from the world of letters, just as he has never been missing from the realm of politics. Though the subjct-matter of literature may always be in a state of flux, the Demon has been present in all the stages of literary evolution. All schools of literature in various times and tongues have set themselves, whether consciously or unconsciously, to represent and interpret the Devil; and each school has treated him in its own characteristic manner. We must remember that there are fashions in devils as in dresses; and what is a devil in one century or one country may not pass muster as such in another. Each generation and each nation has a special and distinct devil related to its own temperament. The Fiend reflects the faith and philosophy of each period, each people, and each personality. Different lands each have a distinct fauna of imps, as of animals. The German devil is as different from the French devil as the racial complexion of the German is different from that of the Frenchman. Each mind, moreover, stamps the Devil with its own individuality. Thus there are as many kinds of devils as there are men and women writing of them. The literary historian will find devils fascinating and fearful, devils powerful and picturesque, devils serious and humorous, devils pathetic and comic, devils fantastic and satiric, devils gruesome and grotesque.

The Devil is an old character in literature. Perhaps he is as old as literature itself. He is encountered in the story of the paradisiacal sojourn of our first ancestors; and from that day on, he has appeared unfailingly, in various forms and with various functions, in all the literatures of the world. From his minor place in the Holy Scriptures, the Devil grew to a position of paramount importance in the works of the Christian poets of all lands and languages. It is an interesting fact that the first literary document distinctly English and Christian (we refer to Cædmon) contains a personification and deification of the Power of Evil. The medieval writings simply swarmed with the spirits of hell. The illuminations of medieval manuscripts were full of ferocious demons. On the medieval stage, the Fiend even frisked in the flesh. Diabolus was undoubtedly the most popular actor in the mystery-plays, calling forth half-terrified interest and half-enthusiastic respect. Although the Devil was hailed by our medieval ancestors with such laughter as still rings across the ages, it need not be inferred from this fact that his audience did not stand in awe and trembling of him. It is a well-known psychological fact that we strive to laugh ourselves out of our fears and to grin away our apprehensions.

The Reformation left the Devil's position intact. Indeed, it rather increased his power by withdrawing from the saints the right of intercession on behalf of the sinners. In Protestant poetry, the Devil was both the abstraction of Evil and the personal tempter of man. He was at once the great fallen archangel of heaven and the painted clown of the country-fair; the unconquered adversary of the Almighty and the buffoon baffled by book and bell.

The Renaissance, on the other hand, meant a serious setback for Satan. In its reaction against medieval thought, it disdainfully turned away from the Devil. The classical school, particularly in France, dealt Diabolus a still deadlier blow. As a member of the Christian hierarchy of supernatural personages, he could not but be affected by the ban under which Boileau, who dictated the classical creed, placed all Christian Supernaturalism. The writers of that period treated the Devil at best allegorically or satirically.

In the eighteenth century, the belief in the Devil was fast disappearing. In fact, all faith in good as well as evil was at a low ebb. This *sæculum rationalisticum,* which was such a bitter enemy of the Supernatural, showed itself particularly loath to employ Lucifer in literature. The writers of that period even scorned to mock at Moloch. Voltaire, who, though believing in nothing, believed in ghosts for tragedy (*Sémiramis,* 1748), opposed the introduction of the Devil into poetry as violently as did Boileau.[1] But even this devil-despising generation produced two master-devils in fiction, LeSage's Asmodeus and Cazotte's Beelzebub—both worthy members of the august company of literary devils. The novel, considered a frivolous diversion by the French Classicists in imitation of the ancients, escaped the observation of the lawmakers of French Classicism and was, happily enough, not bound by the rules and regulations of a criticism not even deigning to pay it attention. A distinct reaction in the Fiend's favor was, however, brought about at the beginning of the nineteenth century.

---

[1] Henry Fielding likewise gave preference to the ghost in literature. He states in *Tom Jones* (1749): "The only supernatural agents, which can in any manner be allowed to us moderns, are ghosts."

*
* *

Satanism, and Supernaturalism in general, in nineteenth-century literature sprang from such varied roots, developed according to such various methods, and served such a variety of purposes that it is very difficult to enter into a detailed investigation of its different aspects. Supernaturalism was an important element in the Romantic movement of all European countries. It was an essential part of the Romantic recoil from the rationalism of the previous period. In their revulsion against the *salons* of the eighteenth century, the men of the nascent nineteenth sought refuge in the nursery. Thus the revival of a belief in the Supernatural was fated to come as the predestined swing of the pendulum. But this belief received a great impetus, particularly in France, from the revolutionary wars. For war spells atavism, a re-emergence of the primitive in man. In moments of danger, we always return to the faith begotten of the deep feelings and fears of childhood. When the dread of death is upon us, all thoughts which hitherto have lain hidden in some remote chamber in the back of our brain forge their way to the fore. In hours of calamity, nations as well as individuals show a tendency to return to the pious beliefs of the past.

Moreover, in times of war, the mystic notion is generally revived that the war waged upon earth is but a part of the great cosmic conflict between the powers of Good and of Evil, with each belligerent claiming the Deity, of course, for himself and assigning the Devil to his enemy. Our recent war has furnished abundant illustrations of these propositions.

The Devil, furthermore, comes into vogue during a revolution. In fact, each of the great poetic personifications of Evil appeared during a critical moment in the world's history, when the old order was disappearing to make way for the new. Periodical upheavals in the social and political world give men a renewed realization of the fact that a power of evil is always at work in their midst. This new realization of the Devil as the controlling power in the world's affairs takes form in the imagination of a Dante, a Luther, a Vondel, a Milton, a Goethe, a Chateaubriand, a Soumet, a Victor Hugo, an Anatole France, and a Bernanos.

It may also be noted in passing that most of the re-creators of the Devil were exiled from their country or ostracized from the community of their class. We need but refer to Dante, Luther,

Vondel, Milton, Byron, Heine, Lermontov, Quinet, and Victor Hugo. These men, suffering imprisonment or banishment from their country for their opposition to a tyrannical government, were naturally attracted to the archangel banished from heaven for having, in the words of Milton's Satan, "opposed the tyranny of Heaven" (*Par. Lost* i. 124).

Satan was the great inspiration of the Romantic generation. The Fiend was the very fount and foundation of the Romantic movement. He was at first dimly seen as if behind a veil. The veil was soon lifted, and he appeared in all his fiendishly fascinating beauty. Satan's shadow was cast over all the works of the Romantic period. Romanticism is thoroughly suffused with the spirit of Satan. Satanism is not a part of Romanticism. It is Romanticism. It may well be said without any levity that Satan was the patron saint of the Romantic School. He impressed it with his personality to such an extent that it was soon named after him. The expression "Satanic School" applied by Southey to the Byronic group in England was accepted by Victor Hugo as an epithet of honor for the corresponding movement in France.[2]

Of all European countries, France showed herself particularly eager to make amends for her long lack of appreciation of the Devil's poetic possibilities. Whether or not the Devil was indigenous or an importation in France, it is certain that he enjoyed a greater vogue there than elsewhere. The rebel of the empyrean was actually the rage of the revolting Romantics in France. The interest which the French Romantics showed in the Devil, moreover, passed beyond the boundaries of France and the limits of the nineteenth century. The Parnassians prostrated themselves at the altar of Satan in the form of Prometheus. The Symbolists, for whom the mysteries of Erebus had a potent attraction, were particularly obsessed by Diabolus. Even the Naturalists, who certainly were not haunted by phantoms, often succumbed to Satan's seduction. Foreign writers, turning for inspiration to France, where the literature of the past century perhaps reached its highest development, were also caught up in the French enthusiasm for the Devil. In fact, the prevalence and persistence of the personality of Evil in the literature of the past century constitutes one of its chief and characteristic charms.

The Devil, to be sure, did not again assume the prominent posi-

[2] *Cf.* S. Osgood: "The Satanic School in Literature," *Christian Examiner*, XXVII (1839), 145-61, and the present writer's essay: "Satanism in French Romanticism," *The Open Court*, XXXVII (1923), 129-42.

tion he occupied in medieval literature; but if he is a less important, he is a more imposing character in the literature of modern times. In our days, the Devil is not an object of contempt, but of consideration. He is treated not comically but seriously, nay sympathetically. We have come to realize that there is so much of us in the Devil and so much of the Devil in us that it would not be fair to treat him harshly.

*

*   *

It is related that, after the glory of Greece had departed, a mariner, voyaging along her coast by night, heard from the woods the cry, "Great Pan is dead!" But Pan was not dead; he had fallen asleep to waken again as Satan. In like manner, when the eighteenth century believed the Devil to be dead, he was, as a matter of fact, only recuperating his energies for a fresh start in a new and nobler form.

The modern Devil is a great improvement on his prototype of medieval days. He differs from his older brother as a cultivated flower differs from a wild blossom. Diabolus has lost the awe which he exercised in the Middle Ages. He is no longer the old monster with horns, hoofs and tail, as described and illuminated in the medieval monastic missals and legends, and as he is still seen today on the capitals of the medieval cathedrals. Satan has nowadays added to that dignity of person, already conferred upon him by Milton, a corresponding nobility of character. The Devil as a human projection is bound to partake in the progress of human thought. Says Mephistopheles in Goethe's *Faust:*

> "Culture, which the whole world licks,
> Also unto the Devil sticks" (i. 2495-6).

The Devil advances with the progress of civilization, because he is what men make him. He has benefited in characterization by the modern leveling tendency. Nowadays supernatural personages, like their human creators, are no longer painted either as wholly white or wholly black, but in various shades of gray. The Devil, as Renan has aptly remarked, has chiefly profited from the relativist point of view which now prevails in ethical judgments, and which no longer permits any rigid interpretation of good and evil, or any strict division of men into saints and sinners. The Spirit of Evil is better than he was, because evil is no longer so bad as it was. The Devil is no longer a villain of the deepest dye. At his worst he is the general mischief-maker of the universe, who loves to stir up the earth with his pitchfork.

We no longer look upon Lucifer as the opponent of the Lord, who seeks to frustrate His providential plans for the human race. We regard the Devil, on the contrary, as one of the instruments in the government of the world and the education of the human race. Willingly or not, Beelzebub is the benefactor of mankind. The Devil declares himself in Goethe's *Faust* as part of that power which, though it always wills the bad, is always working for the good. Diabolus is the necessary, though unwilling, instrument of man's betterment. He supplies the motive power, without which man would soon reach the stage of stagnation. We must know the spirit that denies if we are to learn the truth. The Spirit of Negation is not man's enemy, but his companion on the path of perfection, rousing him out of his lethargy and thus prompting him onward and upward. In Nietzsche's words, the Eternal Malcontent is "man's best force," inasmuch as he represents our progressive, inquisitive nature, which will not permit us to remain satisfied with lesser achievement, but urges us on to higher and nobler aims.

In modern literature, the Devil's chief function is that of a satirist. This clever critic directs the shafts of his sarcasm against all the faults and foibles of men. He spares no human institution. In religion, art, society, marriage—everywhere his searching eye detects the weak spots. Among the recent demonstrations of the Devil's ability as a satirist of manners and morals, we may mention Mark Twain's posthumous romance *The Mysterious Stranger* (1916) and Leonid Andreev's equally posthumous work *Satan's Diary* (1920).

CHAPTER XXII

THE SALVATION OF SATAN IN MODERN POETRY

THE reversal of poetic judgment with regard to the Devil is among the most striking characteristics of the modern period. The popular medieval conception degraded Diabolus from the former high potentate of paradise to a powerless and ludicrous personage, who served our ancestors as the butt of such laughter as still rings across the ages. The modern period, on the other hand, has clothed the Devil with the pathos of a defeated hero. The Devil of today forms a complete contrast to his *confrère* of former times. The modern devil is as fascinating as the medieval devil was frightful; he is as bright and beautiful as his predecessor was dismal and dreadful. The new devil enlists as much of our sympathy and admiration as the old devil inspired horror and terror in medieval man.

This change of attitude toward the Devil during the past century has been well expressed by Renan, who, in an anonymous article, writes as follows:[1]

> "Of all the formerly accursed beings that the tolerance of our century has raised from their anathema, Satan is, without contradiction, the one who has chiefly profited from the progress of the lights [of reason] and of universal civilization. The Middle Ages, which understood nothing of tolerance, found pleasure in representing him as wicked, ugly and distorted. . . . A century as fruitful as our own in rehabilitations of all kinds could lack no reasons for excusing an unfortunate revolutionary, whom the need of action threw into hazardous enterprises. If we have become indulgent toward Satan, it is because Satan has thrown off a part of his wickedness and is no longer that

[1] *Journal des Débats,* April 25, 1855.

baneful spirit, the object of much hatred and horror. Evil is evidently nowadays less strong than it was in former times."

As so aptly stated by Renan in the foregoing passage, the century which demanded the rehabilitation of all outcasts of terrestrial society, the bastard and the bandit, the courtesan and the criminal, also claimed the restoration and return to heaven of the celestial outlaw.

From the philosophical point of view, the conception of Satan's conversion and re-admission to heaven is the corollary of faith in the perfectibility of man, and belief in the consequent end of evil on earth. This utopian hope for the final triumph of universal good, which was aroused in the minds of men during the eighteenth century, was still strengthened by the French Revolution. The enthusiasts of this great historical event believed that the revolutionary revelation would put an end to the reign of the Powers of Evil, and usher in the universal reign of the Powers of Good. Furthermore, many metaphysicians developed the theory of the Devil's repentance and return to heaven as part of their explanation of the origin and function of evil in the cosmic order. They believed in the essential unity and fundamental identity of good and evil. The poets of the past century followed the path paved by the philosophers of the preceding century and envisaged the salvation of Satan as a symbol of their belief in the messianic era approaching for all mankind. They desired to bring about a reconciliation of the Deity with the Devil, or, as it would seem, aspired to marry hell to heaven.

From the æsthetic point of view, the idea of Satan's salvation is the natural outgrowth of the literary conception of Satan. Byron and Shelley created in the Devil a personage whom a superficial reader might well call Promethean. What then was left to their French followers? Nothing but a step further in the attempt to lead the fallen archangel back to heaven.

It must be admitted, however, that this original and spiritual idea of the salvation of Satan, beautiful as it may be philosophically, is neither æsthetically nor theologically acceptable. Such a conception of Satan is inconsistent with the grandeur of the Personality of Evil. The sentimental devil, who repents his past wrongs and is willing to creep to the Cross, is certainly inferior to Byron's impenitent Empyrean, who scorns all ideas of reconciliation with his ancient Adversary, and who prefers torment to "the smooth agonies

of adulation, in hymns and harpings, and self-seeking prayers."
The idea of Satan's return to his former paradisaical position is also
in flat contradiction to the traditional belief in the irreversibility of
the Devil's doom. All successful treatment of the Devil in literature
and art, however, must be made to conform to the norm of popular
belief and Catholic dogma. In art we are all othodox, whatever our
views may be in religion.

Orthodoxy has always taught that Satan is doomed for all
eternity. The Devil, it is maintained by the theologians, is damned
beyond redemption, and cannot repent and win pardon like Adam.
The fall of Satan, according to Catholic creed, is greater than that
of our first ancestor. The original sin, by which mankind fell a
prey to the powers of hell, will be wiped out, at least for a part of
mankind, but Satan's sin can never be expiated. This Catholic conviction is based on the biblical text that "the Devil will be destroyed
utterly" (Hebr. ii. 14; cf. also Ez. xxviii. 18-19). St. Michael,
who appears in Jude 9 as the enemy of Satan, will in the end of
days, according to the Revelation of St. John (xii. 7 ff.), vanquish
the diabolical dragon. The Adversary will be chained eternally in
hell, the portals of which will never again open to permit him to
molest mankind.

The dogma of the eternal damnation of the Devil was, however,
not universal in the Church. Basing their belief on the biblical
passage: "Even the devils are subject unto us through thy name"
(Luke x. 17), several fathers and doctors of the Church entertained
hopes for the Devil's reform and restoration to heaven. Origen,
who was among the leading authorities in deciding what was and
what was not to be included in the New Testament, predicted the
Devil's purification and pardon. This belief in the salvability of
Satan was apparently shared by Justin, Clemens Alexandrinus and
afterwards by Didymus and Gregory of Nyssa. In the eighth century, St. John Damascene taught that the Lord gave Satan some
time to reform after the sin of the fall, but that the Tempter used
it instead to lead Adam astray. In the following century, the famous
Irish philosopher and theologian, John Scotus Erigena, professed
the belief that, inasmuch as all beings came from God, they must
all return to him, including the evil spirits. A religious poem of
the thirteenth century, *A Moral Ode,* contains the assertion that the
Devil himself might have had mercy if he had sought for it.[2]

[2] *Old English Miscellany (Early English Text Society),* I, 214ff.

Father Sinistrary, the famous *consulteur* of the Inquisition, in the seventeenth century, argued that the atonement wrought by Christ included the demons, who might attain final beatitude. He even intimated, though more timidly, that even their father, Satan himself, as a participator in the sin of Adam and sharer of his curse, might be included in the general provision of the Deity for the entire and absolute elimination of the curse throughout nature.[3]

The belief in the final unity of Good and Evil, and the reconciliation of the Deity and the Devil, was taught by the magi and Gnostics and shared by many medieval sects. The modern George Sand, who expressed through the mouth of Lélia her belief that "the spirit of evil and the spirit of good are but one spirit, *i.e.* God," later put this idea in the mouth of a heretical sect. We read in her novel *Consuelo* (1842-3) the following report concerning the supposed followers of John Huss in Bohemia:

> "A mysterious and singular sect dreamed . . . of uniting these two arbitrarily divided principles into one single principle. . . . It tried to raise the supposed principle of evil from its low estate and make it, on the contrary, the servant and agent of the good."

Many pietists, deviating from orthodox teaching, also believed in the possibility of the repentance and restoration of the Devil. Madame de Krüdener (1764-1824), the Swedenborgian mystic, who converted many handsome but wicked men even at the cost of her own virtue, had the utmost confidence in her ability to bring about even Satan's conversion. This lady from Courland turned to religion after a rather dissipated youth, which she prolonged as much as she could.[4] Having arrived at the conclusion that all was not well with the world, she decided to reform humanity, and was seized with a great ardor of proselytism. During her apostolic mission, she traveled all over Europe and preached her gospel to everyone she could reach; princes, kings, emperors, dwellers in huts, all listened with rapture to her inspired words. Her holy zeal to recall to the mercy of the Lord the inhabitants of this earth extended even to the hosts of hell. Again and again the idea of converting the very denizens of darkness,—nay the Devil himself, occurs in her writings. "What can I say to Thee, O my Beloved?" she addresses

[3] Anatole France, in *les Opinions de Jérôme Coignard* (1893), quotes the liberal abbé, contrary to Catholic dogma, expressing his hope for the redemption of Satan.

[4] The most pathetic episode of her first period, her *liaison* with Alexandre de Skatieff, Mme de Krüdener described in her novel *Valérie* (1803).

the Lord. "Would that I could shout over the whole earth, and through all the heavens, how much I love Thee! Would that I could lead not only all men, but all the rebel spirits back to Thee!" In another connection she writes: "I cannot help wishing that hell might come to this God who is so good."

But the Church has always condemned the belief in the redemption of Satan. Protestants and Catholics alike hold out no hope for the deliverance of the Devil from his deserved damnation. In our own country, the Reverend Mr. Tillotson, a minister of the Universalist Church, which believes in the salvation of all men, was unfrocked by his church for wishing to extend its doctrine of universal salvation to Satan.

Christianity showed itself less tolerant with regard to the Evil Spirit than the ancient religions. The Hindus thought that, inasmuch as evil is but a passing form of the realization of existence, it cannot last eternally and must some day disappear by merging with the Absolute. Buddha believed in the universal redemption of every creature throughout the worlds. In Persian eschatology, Evil will in the latter days disappear from the face of this earth, and the Spirit of Evil, having been wholly regenerated, will be the last to arrive saved and sanctified in Paradise. The Yezidis, a sect of devil-worshippers living in ancient Assyria, still hold the belief that the rebel will in the end of days celebrate his return to heaven.[5]

*
*   *

When the beautiful Balder, god of light, was slain by Loki and descended to the land of the dead, Hel, the queen of the lower world, promised that he would be raised from the dead if one day there would be found on earth someone who would weep for him. In like manner, Satan, the successor to Balder and all other pagan gods, should long ago have been redeemed from hell and returned to heaven by virtue of the tears which the French Romantic poets of the past century have shed over him.

The Devil has not been denied pity in earlier ages. He has had apologists even among the saints, particularly among the saints of the weaker sex. St. Theresa desired that men should not speak ill of the Devil, and pitied him for not being able to love. St.

[5] See I. Joseph, "Yesidi Texts: The Devil Worshippers; their Sacred Books and Traditions." *American Journal of Semitic Languages and Literatures,* XXV (1909), nos. 2-3.

Thomas Aquinas could hardly be happy, it is said, from thinking of the doom of the Devil and went so far in his pity for the prisoner of the pit as to spend a night in prayer for the pardon and restoration of the dethroned archangel. "O God," he prayed, "have mercy upon Thy servant the Devil."[6]

It was, however, particularly in the peasant's mind and in the peasant's heart that there slowly grew up a flower of pity for the doomed Devil, who could never hope to be at peace. Robert Burns, the Scotch poet, who was first and last a peasant, expressed his sympathy for the sufferings of Satan in his "Address to the Deil" (1785). This very human poem is full of fellow-feeling for the Fiend. It reaches its climax in the unexpectedly pathetic stanza at the end, in which the poet credits the Devil with something akin to compunction, and ventures a faltering hope on his behalf. The Scotch bard salutes Satan in the following words, which suggest Carducci's *Hymn to Satan* (1865):

> But fare-you-weel, auld Nickie-Ben!
> O wad ye tak a thought an' men'!
> Ye aiblins might—I dinna ken—
>   Still hae a stake:
> I'm wae to think upo' yon den,
>   Ev'n for your sake!

Satan secured his strongest sympathy, however, from the French poets of the Romantic period. This sympathy among the French Romantics for Satan is a part of their humanitarianism, which a misanthropic humorist has named "redemptorism"; that is, the desire to redeem all sinners by means of love. Emotionalism, which, as we know, was an essential part of the Romantic temperament, manifested itself, among other characteristics, in a feeling of boundless sympathy for suffering humanity. Compassion was a master passion with the Romantics. In their eyes the greatest of all virtues was pity—pity for the forsaken and forlorn, pity for the dispossessed and disinherited of this earth, pity even for sin and sinners. This sympathy, which the Romantics felt for all the erring, was also extended to the Sinner from the Beginning. As a matter of fact, it was precisely on account of his sin, as will be shown later, that Satan inspired the Romantics with their singular sympathy.

Satan's suffering puts a halo around his sin. Supreme suffering, hence supreme sympathy. Indeed, what agonies can be compared

---

[6] The English poet, Wathen Mark Wilks Call, has treated the prayer of the Angelical Doctor on behalf of the Devil in a beautiful poem on the subject, which will be found in his *Reverberations* (1849).

to those of Satan? Just think! For thousands of years he has been dragging himself through this world of sorrows, the most wearied and the most restless of all afflicted spirits. As his ordeal seemed endless, he was particularly an object of pity to the Romantics. We know what a resistless attraction hopeless woe had for Romantic imagination. As Satan was, moreover, staggering beneath the unjust condemnation of a superior power, he was the worthiest object of Romantic devotion. He figured among the "lost causes, and forsaken beliefs, and impossible loyalties," in support of which the Romantics threw their weight. It is a psychological fact that an individual who is an artist, or peculiar in some other way, naturally has great sympathy with unpopular causes or individuals for the reason that he himself is unpopular.

Moreover, the Romantics felt a deep admiration for solitary grandeur. This "knight of the doleful countenance," laden with a curse and drawing misfortune in his train, was the ideal Romantic hero. As the original *beau ténébreux*, Satan was the typical figure of the Romantic period and its poetry. It has been well remarked that if Satan had not existed, the Romanticists would have invented him.

The sympathy of the Romantics for Satan was far greater by reason of the bond of kinship which they felt with the celestial rebel. We must bear in mind that the spirit of revolution is at the very root of Romanticism. This movement was a revolt against all authority, in heaven as well as on earth. Romanticism was the logical reflex of the political revolution which preceded it. All French Romantics were members of the Opposition. The Romantic School, we may say without any derogatory intent, was a human Pandemonium. They all were "of the Devil's party," to employ the term applied to Milton by William Blake. George Sand might just as well have called her contemporaries sons of Satan as "sons of Prometheus." The most characteristic trait of all the Romantics was a proud and rebellious spirit. Even the sweetest and serenest of the great Romantics, Lamartine, also revealed a Satanic streak. He, too, shouted to heaven his "Désespoir" (1818); and the echo of his cry of despair uttered in this poem is prolonged through most of his later works.

The Romantic generation saw its own spirit best personified in Satan. He was the symbol of all its aspirations and afflictions, the incarnation of all its longing and yearning. In himself Satan

THE SALVATION OF SATAN IN MODERN POETRY

personified the daring and self-sufficiency, the mystery and gloom, the love of liberty and hatred of authority; all held as the highest ideal of every Romanticist. The Devil is the very embodiment of the malady of the century, which is the most characteristic trait of Romanticism. This malady—the *Weltschmerz*—has been made flesh in the celestial outlaw.

The Romantics painted themselves and recognized themselves in Satan more fully and more perfectly than in any other historical or mythological character. They found in his career much of their own unhappy lot, of their own thwarted ambitions. In their eyes he represented all that they loved and cherished. They felt they had so much in common with him that they looked up to Satan as to a blood brother.

The man in opposition to a society which refused to accept his claims had a fellow feeling for Satan, who is the father of all unappreciated geniuses. The Devil has always complained that he is misunderstood on earth. "Le démon souriant dit: Je suis méconnu," says Victor Hugo. The Devil, in Sir Walter Scott's "Wandering Willie's Tale" (1824), also complains that he is "sair misca'd in the world." The Shavian demon, in *Man and Superman* (1905), likewise bemoans the fact that he is so little appreciated on earth. He who shook off the trammels of tradition had a spirit kindred to that of the fallen angel, who was the first to combat conformity. The man who craved personal dignity and political freedom was attracted by the Demon, who was the first to proclaim the sovereignty of the individual spirit. The rebels against conventions, creeds and critics on earth felt drawn to him who demanded freedom of thought and independence of action in heaven.

The Romantics could never speak of Satan without tears of sympathy. The fighters for political, social, intellectual and emotional liberty on earth could not withhold their admiration from the angel who raised the standard of rebellion in heaven. "Cher Satan" was always on their lips. They pitied the fallen angel as an outlaw; they applauded him as a rebel. "A noble heart will always love the rebel," declared a Romantic poet in 1846. The rebel of the Emperean was hailed as the first martyr in the cause of liberty—"the first dreamer, the oldest victim," as Leconte de Lisle terms the Devil. The word Satan on the lips of the French poets offered the hint of a hard-won salvation. The rebellious Romantics were bold enough

to demand a revision of the judgment pronounced against the
celestial hero and endeavored, each in his own mannner, to rewrite
Milton's *Paradise Regained*.   They even predicted the day when the
Devil should return to heaven and occupy his former seat at the
right hand of the Lord.

*

*   *

It must be admitted, however, that the idea of the rehabilitation
of the Devil was not wholly original with the French Romantics.
The theme was touched upon by writers in other countries as far
back as the eighteenth century.[7]   Klopstock, in his *Messias* (1748-
73), depicts the fallen angel, Abbadona, of lower rank to be sure,
re-entering heaven.   Goethe intimated that he had written a passage
in his *Faust* "where the Devil himself receives grace and mercy
from God."   It was, however, in France during the Romantic period
that the idea of the Devil's redemption and restoration to celestial
favor found frequent expression in the different forms of various
poetical works.   The sympathy extended by that country, considered
the center of the revolutionary spirit of Europe, to all victims of
oppression and to all rebels, whether individuals or classes or nations, could not well be denied to the expatriate from Paradise.

The happy change in the character of the Devil, which Origen
anticipated, for which St. Thomas Aquinas prayed, to which Robert
Burns looked forward, which Goethe contemplated, and which Mme.
de Krüdener wished to bring about, was eloquently preached by the
French Romantics.   First, they believed in this conversion from a
feeling of sympathy, and secondly, as a part of their conviction that
the end of the reign of Evil on earth was imminent.   Byron, from
across the Channel, also shared the belief of his French *confrères*
in a new earth and a new hell.   In his *Heaven and Earth* (1822),
the English poet predicted a time

"When man no more can fall as once he fell,
And even the very demons shall do well!"

The only discordant note in this general clamor for clemency
toward the celestial outlaw was sounded by Balzac.   The creator of
the *Comédie humaine* was prevented by his Catholic convictions

[7] William Blake's *Marriage of Heaven and Hell* (1790) has nothing to
do with the idea of a reconciliation between the powers of Good and Evil.
This allegory is a mystical work full of diabolical humor, in which hells and
heavens change names and alternate through mutual annihilations.

from sharing the dream of his day for the final salvation of Satan. Balzac thought, however, that if Satan should ever make his peace with God, unless the Fiend were a greater scoundrel than popularly depicted, he ought to bargain for the pardon of his adherents (*l'Élixir de longue vie*, 1830).

Alfred de Vigny is the first French poet to approach the problem of the Devil's purification and pardon. The beautiful poem *Eloa* (1823), already discussed in a previous chapter, may be considered the turning point in the literary treatment of the relations between hell and heaven. Vigny's work was the prologue to a long series of compositions, the authors of which, rejecting all tradition, endeavored (without especial success, however) to lead the legend of the Devil into new channels.

Eloa expresses in its highest form the sympathy for suffering which is at the root of Vigny's best work. This pessimistic poet had a passion for pity, which he wished to see manifested without limits. His sympathetic heart was always touched by the sorrows of his fellow men. He loved, as he said, the grandeur of human sufferings, and poured out all his treasures of tenderness and devotion on his "companions in misery." He was a great champion of lost causes in his period. He pleaded for the aristocrat, the soldier and the poet. But, though the aristocratic bent of his mind led him to dwell on exceptional natures, he was equally touched by the boundless misery in the lot of the common man.

His *Eloa* is inspired by his feeling of pity—pity for all suffering, pity for all that lives but a moment, pity even for sin and Satan. Supreme guilt, therefore, supreme misfortune! This poem is the glorification of compassion, of tenderness and sacrifice, of vain self-immolation and of pity without hands to help. It is the story of a bright being, a woman-angel, born from a tear of the Redeemer. Tempted by pity, she falls a victim to the Spirit of Darkness. This "sister of the angels," having heard in heaven the tale of the misfortune of the brightest archangel, leaves her dwelling of delights and descends to the bottom of the pit in order to search for her unfortunate brother and bring him back to bliss. But, unsuccessful in her efforts, she prefers to remain with him in hell rather than return to heaven.

In a sequel poem, which was to bear the title *Satan sauvé*, the author, however, intended to bring this woman-angel out of hell, to save this pathetic damned spirit, the least criminal and certainly the most lovable that hell has ever received. And the poet conceived the notion of saving Satan himself by the grace of Eloa, and, at the same time, of abolishing hell by the all-powerful virtue of love and pity. The following are the poet's notes on his proposed sequel to *Eloa:*

"Eloa had not spoken since her fall. She sat immovable in the eternal shade, like a precious stone which casts its ray of light. The night was less profound since she came into the nether darkness. The spirits of the damned passed and repassed near her, to see themselves by the light of her beauty, and their despair was calmed. A mysterious restraint prevented Satan from approaching her. He walked around her like a wolf round a sheep. From time to time, he rejoiced over the misfortunes of men. . . . Every time that more souls arrived in hell Eloa wept. And one day, while her tears were flowing, Satan looked at her. He had ceased to take pleasure in evil. She saw his change of heart and spoke to him. He wept. Eloa smiled and raised her finger to heaven, a gesture which one dares not make in that place.
'Listen!' she cried. 'It is the crash of worlds which fall in dust. Time is no more.—Thou art saved.' "

Vigny never carried out his project of portraying the redemption of Satan through the pity of this woman-angel who descended into hell to bring cheer and comfort to her fallen brother. It is, therefore, fair to say that Théophile Gautier is the first of all French Romantics to treat the beautiful subject of Satan's salvation.

This dramatic poem, *la Larme du Diable* (1839), is one of Gautier's most original fantasies. In its consistent levity, it is most characteristic of his art. It is a clever *pasticcio* of the medieval miracle-plays, and nothing illustrates better the way in which Gautier conceived the most exalted ideas as subject-matter for pictorial purposes. The play is full of humor and irony. The scene is placed alternately in heaven and on earth. Satan is the hero, and "le Bon Dieu" and Christus, comically assembled with Othello and Desdemona, are among the minor characters. The poem is less indecent, but more impudent and irreverent than *Albertus* (1832). Satan offers the impression that he is a good fellow, pleasing and amusing, mischievous rather than malicious. He bears no ill-will toward God or man. He jokes with the Lord about the denizens of heaven and maintains that any man of good judgment and independent spirit would prefer going to hell. Satan wins the sympathy of the women among the elect in heaven, and they plead with the great God in his behalf.

The principal *motif* of the poem involves a wager between the Lord and the Devil in regard to two mortal maidens. God believes them to be proof against all temptation, but Satan insists that he could cause their fall. A bet is arranged between the Deity and the Devil. If Satan wins, he is to obtain pardon for Eloa, the beautiful woman-angel, who (in Vigny's poem) forsook heaven to seek Satan in his misery. But this angel makes her voice heard in heaven. From the depths of hell she proclaims that she still loves the rebel spirit, and that she prefers hell with him to heaven without him. Satan then requests a glass of cold water to cool his parched lips as a reward in the event he accomplishes his aim.

Satan sets his wiles to work and is about to win the wager, but touched by the purity and delicacy of the feelings of the young girls he is about to lead astray, he sheds a tear. The angels gather up the tear and lay it at the feet of the Lord. This exhibition of pity on the part of Satan so stirs the hearts of the blessed women among the hosts of heaven that they plead with the Lord in behalf of the fallen archangel. The magnanimous God is willing enough to pardon his old enemy, but he cannot reverse the judgment he previously pronounced, and so prefers to drag the matter out at great length. "I cannot perjure myself like an earthly king," he informs the angelic delegation." It is not, however, a flat refusal, for he adds, "In two thousand years we shall see!"

Vigny considered setting free the damned spirits through the daughter of Christ, but Alexandre Soumet, in his *Divine Épopée* (1840), makes Christ himself redeem the dwellers in hell. Soumet supposes that the Saviour returns to earth to offer himself a second time, and on this occasion his mission is not to redeem the inhabitants of this earth, but the damned spirits of hell. Christ suffers a second Calvary. Lucifer is given again his place among the archangels of heaven, a general hosannah is sung to the Highest; and the poem ends with the following words written across the heavens in letters as bright as the sun:

"*Salut Éternel.*"

The popular French song-writer, Jean Pierre de Béranger, also treated the subject of Satan's salvation. His poem, "la Fille du

Diable" (1841-43), inspired by a touching philosophy, contains notes of deep and universal tenderness for all sufferers, including the Devil.

Satan, traveling in Rome in the form of a young man, seduces a virgin, who presents him with a daughter. The Devil, moved by the smile of this child, wishes to preserve her from the evils of earth so that after her death she will go to heaven. He has his child baptized, intentionally choosing the name "Marie," puts her into virtuous hands, and leaves hell every day, assuming a human form, to visit her on earth. At the age of fifteen, this saintly child, who has consecrated herself from her earliest youth to almsgiving and prayer, is admitted to her first communion. Her father trembles at the idea that God might repudiate her. But this fear is without foundation. So Satan conceals himself in the organ of the church, which under his hands sends forth torrents of such celestial harmonies that, in order to hear them the better, the angels descend from heaven. After the ceremony, Marie totters and drops dead in the arms of her heartbroken father. Satan falls into despair, just like an ordinary mortal, but does not blaspheme against the Lord, for the soul of his daughter is perceived rising up to heaven. Broken-hearted, the Devil returns to hell, where he abandons himself entirely to his sorrows and to thoughts of repentance. He reviews all the wrongs of his past and is tortured by remorse. Satan implores his daughter to intervene on her father's behalf with the Lord. Christ is so touched by the repentance and the sorrow of Satan that he begins to weep. One of the tears which Christ sheds over the misfortune of the banished angel penetrates into hell and falls on the heart of Satan. In an instant, the infernal spirit is trasformed into the dazzling Lucifer and goes to join his daughter in the celestial choir-stalls.

Edgar Quinet, in his *Merlin l'enchanteur* (1869), a vast prose dramatic epic, containing twenty-four books and nine hundred pages, depicts the son of Satan redeeming his father. Merlin, as the legend goes, was born of the morganatic marriage of the Devil with a nun. Prodigies—such as a great storm—occurred on the night of his birth. As often happens with young men of good family, Merlin in his youth evidences traits more characteristic of his mother, the daughter of heaven, than of his father, the ruler of hell. Instead of carrying out his father's mission among men, he helps to establish the Kingdom of Heaven on earth. When Satan sees that he no longer wields the power of sowing evil in a world which has been transformed under the influence of his own son, he repents and turns in prayer to his old Adversary. After having received pardon and mercy from the Lord, the Devil with his own hands destroys the pillars which support the vaults of hell. The souls of the damned receive liberty and perfect happiness in the world, and the Devil is restored to his ancient estate in heaven.

Victor Hugo has perhaps carried the new evangel of universal sympathy further than the other Romantics. This writer is the most illustrious representative of the Romantic ideal of cordial compassion for all beings, even for those who have fallen into the very depths of the abyss. The greatest French poet of modern times had that general unlimited sympathy for the unfortunate which is finally extended to the wicked as well as to the luckless. In his "la Prière pour tous" (1830), the Christian poet asks his daughter to pray for all the sorrowful, including Satan. How, indeed, could he deny the Devil that pity which in his heart was not limited to humanity but comprehended all creation, including animals, plants, and even inanimate objects? What does it matter if Satan is guilty or not? Victor Hugo with his doctrine of universal indulgence and forbearance does not judge; he forgives. He refuses to recognize a single being on earth or under the earth whom one could hold responsible for his crimes.

Thus Victor Hugo is primarily the poet of pity. He felt a deep and ardent compassion for all who suffer through the fault of others. His sympathy went out to the sufferings of all the downtrodden, of all the oppressed, whether peoples or individuals. He gave pity an important place in his poetry, and to this sentiment he finally consecrated his work *la Pitié suprême* (1879), in which he asked pity for hatred, pity for evil, pity for the Devil. A few passages from this new gospel of evangelical pity, referring to his compassion for the denizens of hell, follow:

"Oh! je me sens parfois des pitiés insondables,
Je gémis. . .
Sur les démons grondants."

(la Pitié suprême, V.)

"Pardonnons. Jetons même aux démons l'indulgence."

(ibid., XIII.)

Victor Hugo's pity for the demons of hell may also be noted in his
other works:

"Bénir le ciel est bien; bénir l'enfer est mieux."
(le Pape, IV.)

"Ma pente est de bénir dans l'enfer les maudits."
(les Quatre vents de l'esprit, I, xxxiii.)

Victor Hugo's pity for the Devil is so great that he declares,

"Si Jésus. . .
. . . venait à son tour crucifier Satan,
Je dirais à Jésus: tu n'est pas Dieu. Va-t'en."
(ibid., I. xx.)

The great exile of Guernsey had a fraternal feeling for the
archangel banished from heaven. Exile alone in the eyes of the
expatriate poet was sufficient to put the aureole of martyrdom on
the Devil's brow.
"C'est une chose
Inexprimable, affreuse et sainte que l'exil," said Victor
Hugo in June, 1870.
(l'Année terrible.)

The fighter for freedom on earth, who lived for twenty years
as a martyr to his ideal, was deeply affected by the fate of the
fighter for liberty in the skies. The champion of the sacred right
and the holy duty of opposition to tyranny on earth must perforce
extend his hand to him who, in the words of Milton, "opposed the
tyranny of heaven" (Par. Lost i. 124). The champion of all outlaws
could not refuse his protection to the first outlaw. The warm defender of the fugitives of all nations, who turned toward him as
toward a lodestar, declared himself ready to protect even Satan if
the latter should seek asylum with him.

His Messianism—his belief in the final extinction of all evil in
this world—led him also to predict the end of Satan. His beautiful
epic poem, la Fin de Satan (begun in 1854 and published posthumously as a fragment in 1886), describes the end of the reign of
the Spirit of Evil on this earth. Satan's fate, however, for Victor
Hugo does not consist in the exiled archangel's final punishment and
eternal perdition, but, contrary to Church dogma and tradition, in
his pardon and peace. The salvation of Satan, which the poet of
pity predicts, will come about through the mediation of a being
engendered jointly by the Devil and the Deity. A feather, detached
from the wings of the archangel when he was hurled from heaven,
remains lying on the edge of the abyss. The Lord takes pity on it.

A ray from the eternal eye of Him, who created the world, is fixed on it and puts life into it. Under this animating glance, the feather comes to life and grows into a woman-angel. In answer to an inquiry from the angels, the Lord gives the name Liberty to this "daughter of hell and heaven." The spirit who thus owes her birth to the Devil and the Deity will, when the proper occasion presents itself, deliver from sin and suffering the Devil along with humanity. In order to conquer death and redeem the individual, the Son of God was made man. In order to break the shackles of the masses and deliver the nations from bondage, the daughter of the Devil was made a woman. This woman-saviour will on a certain day lead the masses in their rebellion against their oppressors. We may detect in this detail Victor Hugo's political views. Liberty is created by the Lord from Lucifer's feather. Liberty is born only from rebellion. Revolution is necessary to set the nations free from political oppression.

When Satan's heart softens and he turns to the Lord, beseeching mercy, his prayers ascend to heaven and touch the heart of his daughter. She asks the Deity's permission to descend into the dismal darkness and bring deliverance to the Devil. This supplication granted, the angel Liberty, after much wandering, finally alights at the feet of Satan, and bends over her father, who has fallen asleep from exhaustion. Pitying him, consoling him, bathing him with her tears, the angel of pity and mercy falls on her knees before the unhappy accursed archangel. She extends her supplicating arms towards him, enveloping him with a mysterious incantation. All the infernal pride, all the hatred in the Demon's soul melt in the warmth of the humanly humble and divinely tender words of his daughter. The angel Liberty begs her father to pity the misery of mankind and end his own sufferings. "Father," she implores him, "permit me to save the good, the pure, the innocent. Look! I weep over them and over you. Oh, hear my prayers. *Dieu me fit Liberté, toi, fais-moi Délivrance.*"

The struggle between good and evil in Satan's heart is reflected on his face. Suddenly on his forehead appears a light similar to that which formerly shone on his countenance, and from his lips escapes the word for which the angel has been waiting. It is the signal for her to break the chains that bind humanity. Liberty makes her appearance on earth to carry out the mission of delivering humanity from the fetters of oppression. Immediately the angel starts for Paris to break the bolts of the symbolical prison, the Bastille, which is to disgorge its captives. By the fall of the prison-fortress of Paris Victor Hugo intended to represent the symbolical liberation of humanity. The work of evil was for him incarnated in this famous prison for political offenders. According to Victor Hugo's symbolism, Cain, in order to murder his brother, Abel, used a nail, a stick and a stone. The nail later became the sword of Nimrod. The Lord broke it, and war was eventually to disappear. The stick became the cross of Calvary. Religion, alas! crucified Christ. The Church founded by Christ, placing itself at the service of the State, oppressed the masses and blessed mass-murder, war.[8] The stone served as a foundation for the Bastille. The French nation will tear it down and carry out the work left uncompleted by Christ. France will again take up the interrupted work of Jesus and guide it to fruition. Human liberty will bring about what the Nazarene himself could not accomplish. Through the destruction of political tyranny, progress will be advanced to such an extent that misery, misfortune, and perhaps even death, will be no more. For in the eyes of the great French poet, the French Revolution is the most important event in the history of humanity. The real Messiah is no other than the Revolution.

The deliverance of man will be followed by the deliverance of the fallen angel. The harmony between the inhabitants of this earth, particularly between the oppressors and oppressed, will also bring about a reconciliation between the Deity and the Devil. Good, having conquered Evil, will now reign forever over all creation.

The merits of the angel Liberty are counted to her demon-father for righteousness. The Lord applies to the Devil the Catholic dogma of the reversibility of punishments and rewards. As the poem ends, Satan is offered amnesty. The Devil is dead; the archangel is reborn.[9]

Leconte de Lisle, in his poem "la Tristesse du Diable" (1866), which shows echoes of Victor Hugo's la Fin de Satan, predicts another fate for the Devil. Satan, sitting silently on a mountain peak covered with eternal snow, and thence surveying the sufferings of

[8] During the Great World War an eminent bishop of the Episcopal Church justified war on the ground that there was already war in heaven. In Stephen Phillips' play Armageddon (1915), on the other hand, war is represented as being planned in hell.

[9] A longer analysis of Victor Hugo's la Fin de Satan will be found in the present writer's study, Satan et le Satanisme dans l'œuvre de Victor Hugo (Paris: Les Belles Lettres, 1926), pp. 88-103.

humanity on this Sorrowful Star, is willing to put an end to himself and to the world in order to do away once and for all with sin and suffering on this earth.

Paul Verlaine, the leader of the decadent poets of France and the most distinguished disciple of Baudelaire, also envisioned the end of the old antagonism of the Deity and the Devil. Verlaine, however, was not interested in the cosmic conflict carried on between Good and Evil so much as in the war waged in his own heart between his guardian angel and his evil demon, as he has described this conflict in his collection of poems entitled *Sagesse* (1881). What Verlaine attempted was the reconciliation of the seven deadly sins and the three cardinal virtues, or a harmonizing of the pagan idea of self-affirmation and the ascetic theory of self-abnegation. What he desired was the reconciliation within him of St. Francis of Assisi and the Marquis de Sade, as Vance Thompson (*French Portraits*, 1899) puts it.

Verlaine kept the affairs of his soul in two separate compartments. The effects of his conversion in the prison of Mons did not last long. The old Adam within him soon reasserted himself. He continued to proclaim himself a Catholic, but he practised few of the tenets of that religion. "Verlaine believes in the Roman Catholic Church," said Jules Lemaître, "as earnestly as the Pope himself, but in Verlaine there is only belief; practice is wholly wanting in him."

The work of Verlaine shows a twofold aspect. His poetry offers alternations of fervency and flippancy, spirituality and sensuality, mysticism and eroticism, piety and perversity. This satyr-songster introduced an infinitely more religious mood into his poetry than did any of the other Symbolist poets. "Verlaine wrote the most Christian verses we have in France," says Jules Lemaître. "Certain strophes in *Sagesse* recall in their accent the *Imitation of Christ*" (*les Contemporains*, 4e série, 1886). But, we might add, he has also written some of the lewdest lines in modern French poetry.

Verlaine's interest in diabolism derived in a direct line from Baudelaire, that superb singer of sin and Satan. The poet of the *Fleurs du Mal* (1857) was a deity in the youthful eyes of Verlaine. The latter's *Poèmes saturniens*, published in 1866 but written for the most part during his later school-days, reveal many traces of his master's Satanism. But *Jadis et Naguère* (1884) is the Bible of the young decadent and diabolist poets. And in this perfection of their methods and aims, we find Verlaine's most important diabolical poem. It is in this poem, "Crimen Amoris," written in the prison of Petits-Carmes, Belgium, in 1873, that Verlaine treats the subject so dear to the Romantic generation, the salvation of Satan. Mr. Arthur Symons puts this poem at the head of all of Verlaine's work "for a certain diabolical beauty, for an effect of absolute sublimity" (*The Symbolist Movement in Literature,* 1919). The words have a marvelously musical rhythm, "full of the sound of gongs and trumpets," to employ Symons' expression.

The poem takes for its subject-matter the wish on the part of Hell to sacrifice itself of its own accord to Universal Love. In a palace blazing with silk and gold, at Ecbatane in Asia, to the sound of Mohammedan melodies, a band of juvenile demons "font litière aux sept péchés de leurs cinq sens." Finally, satiated with their sensual pleasures, the demons vainly attempt to break away from the evil to which they are attached, but which at heart they abhor. And one, the youngest and brightest of them all, despairingly exclaims:

"Nous avons tous trop souffert, anges et hommes,
    De ce conflit entre le Père et le Mieux!"

He proposes with his fellow-demons to suppress hell, in order to do away with sin and suffering in the world. They set the infernal palace on fire. The flames rise to heaven. Singing hymns, the demons perish in the flames. Everything crumbles down. At that moment, a thunderbolt descends from heaven as an indication that the sacrifice has not been accepted. As a good Catholic, Verlaine realized that no reconciliation could be effected between Good and Evil, and that the Devil was damned for all eternity.

The last French evangelist who assumed to convert the Devil was Jules Bois, who wrote a curious "esoteric drama," to which he gave the name of *Noces de Satan* (1890).

*
*   *

The subject of the Devil's absolution and redemption has also been appropriated by a few English and German poets of the past century. Philip James Bailey treated it in his *Festus* (1839), a philosophical poem, which at the time of its publication was favorably compared with Goethe's *Faust* and enjoyed a greater popularity than it deserved. The idea of Satan's final return to his former glory in heaven also served as subject for Kurt von Rohrscheidt's *Satans Erlösung* (1894) and Wilfrid Scawen Blunt's *Satan Absolved: a Victorian Mystery* (1899), a dramatic poem of political content, also suggested by the Prologue to Goethe's *Faust*.

The American writer, Henry Mills Alden, has expressed his belief in the final redemption of the Devil as follows:

"Lucifer is the light-bearer, the morning-star, and whatever disguises he may take in falling, there can be no new dawn that shall not witness his rising in his original brightness."

The most important treatment of the subject of Satan's salvation by a poet other than the French is found in Lermontov's *The Demon* (1829-41), already discussed at length in a previous chapter of this work.

The woman in this Russian poem, who finally, out of pity for the fallen angel, consents to return his love, is no longer the symbolic virgin, who held Vigny's enamoured fancy. She is not like that being born from a tear dropped by Christ over the tomb of Lazarus, but a living, passionate woman—a Jewess of the Babylonian captivity in the first sketch of the work, then a Spanish nun, and finally a Georgian princess. It must be admitted, however, that Lermontov's version, though written in the main under the inspiration of Vigny's poem, is based on a Caucasian legend, according to which the Evil Spirit will reform and become regenerate when he is redeemed by the love of an innocent young woman.

It may be recalled that, the moment the Demon sees the beautiful Georgian maiden, Tamara, he becomes more and more freely human in his feelings and actions. The first awakening of passion brings to him the long forgotten thought of redemption. But Tamara is too weak a woman to bring about a reform in the heart of her demon-lover. At his first kiss, she dies from terror. Only Vigny's angel, not Lermontov's woman, would have conceivably succeeded in converting her demon-lover to repentance and reconciliation with God.

*
* *

Other French Romantics, not satisfied with leading the Devil back to celestial glory, wished him to carry out after his restoration the project which he had failed to accomplish before he was hurled from heaven. They expected him again to start the revolution he

THE DOWNFALL OF THE REBEL ANGELS
ILLUSTRATION BY BLAKE IN PARADISE LOST SERIES.
(Museum of Fine Arts, Boston)

had headed in the beginning of time, and supplant the King of Heaven in the government of this earth. This champion of celestial combat, in the Romantic version of the war in heaven, was not actuated by hatred and envy of man, as Christianity was thought to teach us, but by love and pity for mankind. The eternal war waged between the Lord and Lucifer, in the opinion of the Romantics, was not for glory but for humanity.

It is needless to say that the Devil, as conceived by the writers of the past century, is the very antithesis of the dogmatic demon. He has been divested of his traditionally diabolical character. He is an altogether new species of the *genus diabolus*. Instead of a demon of darkness, he is a god of grace. He continues to be the enemy of the Lord, but he is no longer the enemy of man (Tasso's *"gran nemico dell' umane genti"*). Far from being the tormentor, he is regarded as the benefactor of mankind. In Byron's *Cain* (1821) Lucifer takes men under his protection as his natural allies and his brothers in misfortune in his war against the Ruler of the Heavens. Strindberg's Lucifer also is full of compassion for men. He enters into combat with Jehovah not to wrest the power from Him, but to prevent Him from torturing mankind. Marie Corelli, in *The Sorrows of Satan* (1895), describes the Devil as a generous spirit, who wanders up and down the earth, lamenting the fact that the Christians will not suffer to aid them. As Mr. George Arliss portrayed the Devil in Molnar's well-known play, Satan is seemingly the friend to all mankind.

This commendation of Satan implied the condemnation of God, and, as a corollary, the belief that the accomplishment of the salvation of humanity must be taken out of the hands of the Ruler of the Heavens. The Romantics, from their pessimistic point of view, thought ill of the world and consequently also of its Creator. Of all French Romantics, Alfred de Vigny perhaps held the most pessimistic attitude toward this earth. He considered the world an evil creation and compared it with a prison. In 1824 he jotted down in his diary the following remark:

"We have been thrown into the world, and as in a prison we are forced to do our sentence of penal servitude for life, yet we know not what wrong we have done."

This French poet had so poor an opinion of the world, into which mankind had been tossed, that he wished to see it destroyed.

"If there were a God," he said again in his dairy, "we

would provoke Him to shatter this earth into a thousand fragments; and so, by our suffering a speedy annihilation, at least the generations of the future would be spared existence."

Romanticism is the consciousness of a disorder in the individual and in the world in general. The Romantic generation of 1830 thought the world out of joint more than ever. To Hamlet, Denmark seemed gloomy; to the Romantic, the whole world appeared dark. In this world composed of good and evil, the Romantics believed that the evil far outbalances the good; in fact, to paraphrase Leibnitz, that all is for the worst in this worst of all possible worlds. They did not believe that there was any balm either in Gilead or Golgotha. And if we wish to be truthful with ourselves we must admit that the world is not actually well run; rather, that it is very badly run; and no Huxley is needed to point out this obvious fact.

Now if the Romantics did not think well of the world, how could they think well of its Creator and Ruler? The author of an evil world must necessarily himself be evil. There is no escaping from this inference. The French, with their logical minds, were more consistent in their disillusionment than the men of other nations. If we abandon the Christian teaching of purification through suffering—and that is just what the Romantics did—what answer, indeed, can we find to the eternal question: "Why is the world so full of difficulties and dismays, of deceptions and disappointments, of defeat and despair, of sin and suffering, of misery and malady, of decay and death?" It is necessary to reach the conclusion that God is either not omnipotent or not benevolent.[10] As we cannot very well doubt the omnipotence of God (for otherwise He would not be God) we must reach the conclusion that He is not benevolent This is just what the Romantics finally deduced from the existence of evil in the world. Stendhal, speaking of the reality of evil, remarked, "God's only excuse is that He does not exist." Proudhon, author of the famous dictum, "Property is theft," said, "God is evil."

Mme. Louise Ackermann was deeply indignant against what she called "la caprice divine" and its disarrangement of human affairs. In her poem, "les Malheureux" (1871), she depicts the dead at the Last Judgment refusing to rise at the summons of the archangel, and

[10] The present writer was told a few years ago by a Hindu that he had seen the following inscription on the portal of a secret Gnostic church in Paris: "Si Dieu existe, il n'y a pas de mal. Si mal existe, où est Dieu?"

rejecting even happiness, since it is God, the author of evil, who brings it to them.

It must be counted to the Romantics for righteousness that they deeply concerned themselves with the problem of human destiny. The question of the presence of evil in a God-governed world obsessed their minds. Their eyes were open to the sorrows, the sufferings and the struggles of humanity. They made moan over the miseries and maladies of mankind. They were touched by the boundless wretchedness of the common lot of humanity. They were puzzled about man's painful powerlessness over life. Their souls were filled with righteous indignation concerning the reign of injustice all about them. They were always "complaining and sighing and wailing" over the woes of this world.

The Romantics were faced by a world whose inhabitants were sick and weary, yet battled on with a courage which would make a pagan god relent, but which had no power to move the Christian God What other conclusion could they reach except the alternative that either God did not concern himself with the affairs of men or that he even delighted in human struggling and suffering? Theirs was the revolt of the human reason crying out in despair, "He who is almighty has willed that pain should be!"

Alfred de Vigny considered the Creator cold, capricious and cruel, standing aloof from his creation in eternal unconcern, or even actually finding joy in the sufferings of mankind. This French poet could not suppress a cry of anger against the Author of all Evil, who is deaf to man's cries of anguish and who refused even to lend an ear to the prayers of His Son who, sad unto death on the Mount of Olives, implored his Father in Heaven to permit him to remain on earth in order to help humanity. In a postscript to his poem "le Mont des Oliviers," which he entitled "le Silence" (1862), he exclaims:

> "If it be true that, in the Sacred Garden of Scriptures,
> The Son of Man said that which is reported;
> Mute, blind, and deaf to the cry of his creatures,
> If Heaven abandoned us like an abortive world,
> The just man will meet absence with disdain,
> And a cold silence will evermore be the reply
> To the eternal silence of the Deity."

Vigny even went so far as to depict the Deity as a God of blood, intoxicated by the fumes of the sacrifices offered on His altar, causing the just and unjust to perish together in the Flood, delivering up a daughter to her father's ax.

In our indignation over the bold blasphemies of Vigny, we should not forget that the God of the Hebrew Dispensation is actually represented in the Old Testament as unjust and cruel, and that the official creeds of many churches of Christianity even today contain conceptions of God's nature and of His actions toward the human race which are intolerable in the light of the ethical standards and ideals of the nineteenth and twentieth centuries.

In one of his projected poems, Vigny depicts a young man committing suicide and appearing before God in order to ask the creator of the world:

"And why hast Thou created the evil of the soul—sin, and the evil of the body—suffering? Was it necessary to offer Thee still longer the sight of our sufferings?"

The sketch entitled "le Jugement dernier," found among the poet's papers at his death, contains a scathing arraignment of God, an indictment unprecedented in Christendom. The poet represents God himself on the last day standing before the bar of justice, with Man sitting in judgment over his Creator.[11]

Small wonder that God saw the great Rebels rising up against Him: Still less need we wonder to discover that man harbors a secret admiration for these Contemners of the Creator! Says Alfred de Vigny:

"The world revolts at the injustices entailed by the creation; dread of the Eternal prevents it from speaking openly; but its heart is full of hatred against the God who created evil and death. When a defier of the gods, like Ajax, the son of Oileus, appears, the world approves of him and loves him. Such another is Satan, such is Orestes, such is Don Juan. All who have combated the injustices of heaven have been admired and secretly loved by men."[12]

We now can understand why Satan was such an object of admiration to the Romantics, and why he was selected to express their dissatisfaction with the celestial government of terrestrial affairs.

[11] Alfred de Vigny would furnish an interesting subject for a psychoanalytic study. In a recent number of *Psyche and Eros* (III, 68), Dr. Wm. Stekel, of Vienna writes: "Those who suffer from nervous depression hate God just as they hate everybody else. The malady is often ushered in with some blasphemy or revolt against God."

[12] Émile Montégut (*Revue des deux Mondes*, LXVIII, 231) thinks that Vigny might have shown better judgment in his selection of the contemners of the gods. Satan will do, but not Orestes, still less Don Juan.

It was out of the mouth of the Great Malcontent that the Romantics expressed the darkness and doubt, the disenchantment and despair of their souls. Satan was the interpreter of their sorrows and heart-searchings. He voiced their rebellious and blasphemous words. He was the patron of their poetry of complaints. The genius of the hapless and hopeless generation of a century ago uttered its protest against the world and its Ruler through the mouth of the Great Accuser. From his lips was heard man's despairing cry of anguish against the accumulated miseries of many thousands of years, and against the ever-increasing sufferings of thousands of generations.

Even when the Romantics portrayed Prometheus, they had Satan in mind. The railing of the fettered Titan against Jupiter in the numerous Prometheus-poems of the Romantic School was but a thin veil for the blasphemies of Beelzebub. Louise Ackermann, in her "Prométhée" (1866), pictures her protagonist rebelling against the Creator—the Being who fashioned man and caused his misery. "Why are there evils in the world?" Prometheus asks, and concludes that the God who could prevent it willed that suffering should exist. The Titan blasphemes against the Creator and predicts for Him judgment, vengeance, and ultimate rejection by man, who shall be "delivered from faith as from an evil dream." Again, in Rapisardi's epic *Lucifero* (1877), the two Titans join forces to dispel the darkness from the earth. Lucifer departs for Hell to tell Prometheus of his plan to hurl God from Heaven and reign in His stead.

Cain, another favorite character with the Romantics, was a kind of Satan clad in human flesh. In his Promethean anger, this afflicted and heavily laden primal son of man, becomes the avenger of mankind by insisting on the eternal *why*. It is significant that the story of Cain has inspired three of the greatest poets of the past century—Byron, Victor Hugo, and Leconte de Lisle. Victor Hugo, as might be expected, treated the subject from a less heterodox point of view than the other two. Byron in his *Cain* (1821) brings together two titanic spirits, Lucifer and Cain, drawn to each other by mutual sympathy. The first was exiled from the celestial paradise, the latter from the terrestrial paradise. Leconte de Lisle personifies in the hero of his poem *Quain* (1869) suffering humanity in revolt against the injustices of a jealous God. He uses the accursed son of Adam as a mouthpiece to rail against the God of the Catholic Church, the monks, the Inquisition, and the smoking *auto da fé*.[13]

*
*   *

Just as pessimism leads to anti-theism, anti-theism leads to Satanism. If what has been considered good is found to be evil, what opposes it must necessarily be good. Thus the denunciation of the Deity led to the sanctification of Satan. If the ruler of an evil world is bad, his adversary must necessarily be good. This paradox accounts for the belief held by many Romantics that Satan was wronged and that there was, as Vigny asserted, a great historical case to be judged anew before the court of our conscience. Baudelaire, who addressed prayers to Satan, also argued from this assumption when he termed the Devil *"Dieu trahi par le sort"*—"a Deity betrayed by Destiny." Thus was born among the Romantics the wish for Satan's return to heaven, with the aim of delivering man from the cruelty of his Creator. In the modern Anatole France's *la Révolte des Anges* (1914), however, Satan declines an opportunity to head a second revolution against his adversary. He decides in the end that it is not worth the effort to supplant the King of Heaven, as a successful revolt with a new ruler will make so little difference on earth that he really prefers to remain in the Opposition. Power makes for tyranny; rebellion is the essence of nobility.

It must not be denied, however, that among the Romantics many might be named who were led to their adoration of Satan through their love of evil. Instead of exchanging, they accepted the traditional conceptions of the Deity and the Devil, nevertheless substituting Satan for the Saviour in their adoration. "Naturally," says Max Nordau in his *Entartung* (1893), "the love of evil can only take the form of devil-worship or diabolism, if the subject is a believer, that is if the supernatural is held to be a real thing. Only he who is rooted with all his feelings in religious faith will, if he suffers from moral aberration, seek bliss in the adoration of Satan, and in impassioned blasphemy of God and the Saviour."

We know of at least two groups in Paris who, in the first half of the last century, organized a Satanic cult and created a class of poetry expressing their worship of Satan and predicting his usur-

[13] *Cf.* Henri Bernes: "le *Quain* de Leconte de Lisle et ses origines littéraires." *Revue d'histoire littéraire de la France*, XVIII (1911), 485-502.

pation of the power of heaven.[14]   Just as the Christians gathered on
Sunday morning to sing glory to God, these diabolists congregated
on Sunday evening to honor Satan with hymns and harpings, and to
address prayers to the powers of Evil for alliance and aid.   Each
member of the group officiated in turn; in other words, recited the
verses he had written for the occasion.   These extravagants, in their
eagerness to show their opposition to all orthodoxy, proclaimed that
"fair is foul and foul is fair."   "Evil," they declared, "be thou my
good, and good my evil."   Thus the son of poor Pierre Huet declares
in Eugène Sue's *Salamandre* (1832): "Vice, crime, infamie, voilà
les seules choses qui ne trompent jamais."   These diabolists expressed delight over the works of the Devil and disgust for the acts of
the Deity.   They even argued the merits of the seven deadly sins.
Eugène Sue sang the praises of the seven sins in his *Sept péchés
capitaux* (1847-9).   In all likelihood a few among them went even
so far as to put their teachings into practice, and "romanticized"
their lives, as they called such perversions in those Romantic days.
The Romantic search for new sensations led to all sorts of sexual
aberrations.   In this manner, the Romantic rant about self-expres-
sion and self-fulfillment was reduced to the ridiculous.   These devotees of the Devil wished and prayed for a universal reign of evil,
and predicted the day when the Devil should regain heaven, wrest
the reins of government from the hands of God, and clutch the world
completely in his claws.

This movement, however, may have been of a very harmless
character.   It probably was but another manifestation of that search
for singularity which was the besetting sin of all Romantics.   The
Bohemian must, perforce, hold beliefs diametrically opposed to those
of the bourgeois.

Furthermore, any affirmation of the Devil in modern times must
necessarily follow the rehabilitation of the world and the emanci-
pation of the flesh, both of which Catholicism associated with the
Spirit of Evil.   In discarding the ascetic dogmas of Christianity and
refusing any longer to reject the world and the flesh, the youthful
generation of a century ago also declined to deny the Devil.

In the last analysis let us not forget that, at a period in which
monarchism and Catholicism were joined in holy wedlock, the crown
and the cross could not be separated.   Neither of the two could be
rejected without the other.   If the monarchists claimed the Deity for

[14]*Cf.* Louis Maigron: *le Romantisme et les mœurs* (1910), p. 187.

themselves, the republicans could not help declaring for the Devil.[15]

*

*   *

We can offer no better end for our chapter on the idea of Satan's salvation in contemporary thought than by quoting the following paragraph of the penetrating study of the Polish critic, Ignace Matuszewski:

"The poetic type of Satan has to a certain degree ended the cycle of his individual existence. He has passed from one form into another, until he has gone through the various forms and existences of all life. He has passed through all the rungs of the double ladder on which, according to the theory of the Hindu thinkers as well as of certain European pantheists, every nomad of the eternal existence must descend and remount. In the beginning Satan descended from the absolute to matter, from heaven to earth (the fall), where he was lowered to the rank of the inferior animals and was even forced, according to the New Testament, to enter into the bodies of the unclean animals. Then rising endlessly from a lower form to a higher form, he finally dematerialized himself in the works of our contemporary poets. He has reconquered his attributes of an archangel and has entered again into the Infinite (the redemption)."[16]

[15] This idea has been developed at greater length toward the end of the present writer's monograph: *Romantisme et Satanisme* (Paris: Les Belles Lettres, 1927).

[16] *Cf.* Ignace Matuszewski: *Dyabel w Poezyi.* 2nd edition. Warsaw, 1899.

ADDITIONAL NOTES

I. THE LEGEND OF LUCIFER

Page 2. On the belief in an independent power of evil as an integral or essential element in all organized religions, see the present writer's article "Diabolism" in the *Encyclopædia of the Social Sciences.*

Page 8. According to Dante's interpretation of the fall of the angels, Satan's sin was treachery. The bright and beautiful archangel was banished from heaven for committing high treason against his Creator by conspiring to wrest the crown of heaven from Him. The Florentine poet, who saw his country torn asunder by its own jealousies and rivalries, considered treason the greatest of all evils (*Inf.* xxxii. 106). According to Chateaubriand, in his *Martyrs* (1809), the sin of Satan consisted of nothing more than essaying to establish a different order of precedence in the court of heaven.—Remy de Gourmont, who follows the Jewish tradition in his *Lilith* (1892), has Satan revolt after the creation of man out of envy of the appointed king of the earth, whose position he desired for himself. According to this version of the war in heaven, Satan's sin consists in refusing to join the general angelic acclamation of Jehovah's crowning work of creation. When man was fashioned from clay, the seraphs burst out in a hymn to honor the master of the earth. But in the midst of the courtesan complacency of the seraphic choirs Satan struck a discordant note by remarking apropos of man, "This creature is not displeasing, but methinks the smell of earth lingers." Such a sneering remark with regard to man filled Jehovah with wrath, and He banished Satan from His sight together with his *nephilim*. The exiled angel, however, did not withdraw until he had announced to the Lord his intention henceforth to exercise his sinister power in endeavoring to frustrate the designs of the Deity. The orthodox teaching of the Church, however, is that the creation of man, far from causing the rebellion of the angels, was its consequence and not planned until after the expulsion of the angels from heaven. Satan needed no pretext for his ambitions and evil designs upon the throne of the Deity.

Page 12. An expression of Satan's yearning for the heaven he has lost will also be found in the German puppet-plays of Faust. "Tell me," says Faust to Mephistopheles, "what would you do if you could attain to everlasting salvation?" And the Devil answers: "Hear and despair! Were I able to attain everlasting salvation, I would mount to heaven on a ladder, though every rung were a razor edge."

Page 15. In *The Devil's Opera*, played by Wieland in 1838, the Devil is the ally of love and virtue, against blind tyranny and silly superstition.—The play *Lucifer or God* was written by Strindberg prior to his conversion, on which occasion he returned to the religion of his childhood, abandoning the free-thinking ideas that he had entertained during his most troubled years. However, the old Adam remained in the Swedish playwright even after his conversion, at least so far as his interest in the Devil is concerned, as may be seen from the following remark noted in his autobiographical works: "From childhood I have sought for God and found the Devil." An interesting biography of August Strindberg by V. J. McGill has just appeared in England. —Satan has also gained vindication from the American Unitarian minister, poet and painter, Christopher Pearse Cranch, who, in his libretto *Satan* (1874), glorifies the celestial rebel. This work was revised and reprinted in 1886 under the new title *Ormuzd and Ahriman.*—On the subject treated in this chpater, consult also P. E. Dustoor's article, "Legends of Lucifer in early English and in Milton," *Anglia*, XIL, 213-68, November, 1930.

II. THE NUMBER OF THE DEVILS

Page 18, n. 5. In his amusing book, *Zywoty Djablow Polskich* (Lives of the Polish Devils), the Polish writer, Witold Bunikiewicz, tells us that every class has its own devils. Thus there are devils of noble birth as well as devils of peasant stock. The noble devils, among whom Boruta in the Leszycki regions was the most notable, have chivalric pretensions, and do not shun the sword and the cup. The peasant devils are coarse, vulgar, and, with all their cunning, stupid, so that a clever peasant will often bring a devil into a field, harness him to work on the soil and in the stable, and in the end escape his snares. And there always have been and still are many devils in Poland. Nor were there lacking she-devils, who, it appears, had to display infernal charms as soon as any one of them had married a nobleman. But were they the only ones?

Page 24. A critical edition of the *Theatrum diabolorum* was published by Max Osborn in 1895 as a Berlin disseration. Among the other curious works of Protestant demonology of the sixteenth century may be mentioned Andreas Musculus' *Von des Teuffells Tyranney* (Frankfurt, 1556), and Jodocum Hocker's *Der Teuffel selbst....* (Frankfurt, 1568) later finished by Hermann Hamelmann. Among the eighteenth century Protestant works on demonology may be mentioned the *Gallerie der Teuffel* (1776-7), signed Cranz, pseudonym of Peter Gassner der Jüngere, which is a description of a diabolical family composed of personified sins who gather at a meeting on the Blocksberg.

Page 25. A German translation of the first part of Wierus' *De præstigiis dæmonum* appeared in Frankfort three years after the Latin original.—Another infernal statistician is John Bohomolec, a Polish doctor of liberal arts and theology, who, in his work *The Devil in his Shape,* in answer to the question whether or not there are spirits manifested on earth, undertook the enumeration of the devils and arrived at the conclusion that their number was fifteen thousand millions. It is comforting, however, to find him add that "their number, however, in many respects, is uncertain."

IV. THE FORM OF THE FIEND

Page 35. The Devil can take whatever form he will, inanimate as well as animate. We find in J. W. Horst's *Zauberbibliothek,* a work in six volumes (1820-25), which has been called a perfect encyclopædia of the doctrine and methods of magic, that the Devil can even turn himself into a salad. Heinrich Heine, in his *Elementargeister* (1834), also tells the story of a devil who transformed himself into a salad in order to be eaten by a nun.

Page 38. Among the other animal forms under which the Devil showed himself to the medieval witches may be mentioned the horse, the cow, the cock, the hen, the frog, the calf, the lamb, the sheep, the deer, and the stag. See Miss Margaret Alice Murray's *The Witch-Cult in Western Europe* (Oxford, 1921).

Page 40. Mercury also had a tricephalic form and was, therefore, given the epithet *Tricephalos, "three-headed."*

Page 42. When we speak of the cat as a diabolical incarnation we have in mind rather the wildcat or the lynx.—Note 14. The original title of Champfleury's book is *Les Chats. Histoire. Mœurs. Observations. Anecdotes* (Paris, 1869). A scholarly work on the cat is M. Oldfield Howey's *The Cat in the Mysteries of Religion and Magic* (London, 1930). We may also refer to the following two works on the cat: H. W. Winslow: *Concerning Cats* (Boston, 1900), and Agnes Repplier: *The Cat. Anthology of Prose and Verse* (New York, 1913)—Note 15. Other works dealing with the dragon are the following: F. B. Stacy: *The Dragon* (London, 1860), and J. E. Anderson: *Der Drache und die fremden Teufel* (Leipzig, 1927). Some Devon witches, however, did speak of the devil in the form of a lion.

Page 44. The serpent, as Professor A. H. Godbey has pointed out to the present writer, was worshipped among all primitive peoples as the friend or the reincarnated kinsman of the family. Serpent-worship was the most obstinate cult which the old Hebrew reformers had to combat. The serpent with a woman's head simply meant the reincarnation of a woman. It may also be found on the old Sumerian seals, antedating the medieval period by several thousand years.

Page 45. The Hindu god, Ganésa or Ganéca, considered the god of science and literature, son of Shiva and Pārvati, was also represented with the head of an elephant.—With regard to the Devil's cock's foot it should be remembered that the cock was sacred to Ahura-Mazda or Mithra, the sun-god, and consequently obnoxious to the Jews, who therefore, assigned the foot of this animal to the Devil. The custom of the cock-sacrifice at Yom Kippur, which, as has been pointed out to the present writer by Professor A. H. Godbey, was practiced by the Judaized Persians, was steadily repudiated by Babylonian rabbinism for more than a thousand years. It was only about 850 A. D. that the Gaonim or academy heads in Babylonia officially accepted this custom.—As far as the Devil's black color is concerned, the chimney-sweep in the new medieval cities gave this idea valuable support.

Page 49. The Devil appeared to an excited hat-maker at Spandau in 1594 in the form of a gloomy man wearing a wolf-skin. But he generally manifested himself to the witches in the garb of a courtier with a red feather on his hat or with a blue hat flaunting a white plume of nobility.

Page 50. It will be recalled that the poet Donne, in one of his songs, wants to know "who cleft the Devil's foot." But the notion that a transformed or disguised spirit always has a certain physical defect is an idea common to the folk-lore of all races. In Tertullian's *Ad nationes* I-XIV, the transformed ass-numen still has one hoof. It will be recalled that the witch in *Macbeth* would appear as a "rat without a tail."—Coleridge's Devil is also a gentleman, as may be seen from the following lines taken from his poem, "The Devil's Thoughts" (1799):
"And backward and forward he switched his long tail
As a gentleman switches his cane."
Southey claimed this poem as his own and included it in his collected works under the title "The Devil's Walk." Some maintain that the two have written it together, while others prefer to believe that neither Southey nor Coleridge wrote it but that it was the work of Professor Porson. In Max Beerbohm's story, *Enoch Soames* (1916), the Devil also insists that he is a gentleman.

Page 52. Satan appeared to St. Pachonius in the form of a voluptuous Ethiopian maiden in order to entice this pious monk to sensual pleasures.

VI. JOURNEYS TO HELL

Page 74. Heinrich Heine also paid a visit to the ruler of the netherworld, which he described in his *Unterwelt* (1840). On the visit of this German poet to hell, read Haller von Königswinter's *Höllenfahrt von Heinrich Heine* (1856), which was republished, in 1904, by S. Aschner.

VIII. THE ORGANIZATION OF PANDEMONIUM

Page 76. note 3. A French pamphlet on Wierus appeared as volume 3 of the *Bibliothèque diabolique* under the title *Jean Wier* (Bureau du Progrès médical).

Page 77, note 5. Another book of magic ascribed to Faust is *Doctoris Johannis Fausti sogenannter Manual-Höllenzwang* (Wittenberg, 1524).

Page 81, note 10. An account of the conclave in hell will also be found in Paolino Pieri's *Storia di Merlino* and *Vita di Merlino*.

Page 85. Cæsarius of Heisterbach, in his *Dialogus miraculorum* (thirteenth century), tells a legend about a demon who was fond of the ringing of church bells. This story was retold, in 1870, by the French Catholic and mystic writer, Villiers de l'Isle-Adam and published in the *Hebdomadaire*.

X. BELIEF IN THE DEVIL

Page 105. The belief in the Devil has now gone out of fashion. It is the custom nowadays for many persons who plume themselves on their scientific view of things to treat the Devil as an enigma or even as a myth. Men no longer cross themselves at the mention of the Devil's name. They smile instead or flippantly use his portrait to advertise potted ham or Pluto water. Baudelaire has, however, rightly remarked over the lack of logic which modern men show in their disbelief in the Devil. They feel the presence of the Devil in the world more than the presence of the Deity, yet still pretend to believe in the Lord and not to believe in Lucifer. Indeed, one of the last tricks that the Evil One has played upon us is to persuade us that he himself does not exist. "This neglect of the Devil," says André Thérive in his essay on André Gide, "must form his most beautiful conquest over men. Sublime subtlety of Satan!"

Page 107. "The Middle Ages," says Anatole France, "frightened us with a lugubrious phantasmagoria of devils snapping at a sinner's soul as it passed."

Page 110. The French monk, Raoul Glaber, also describes, in his *Chronique* (11th cent.), the Great Enemy, who appeared to him in his cell.

Page 112. Anatole France's mother herself, who was a devout but not a bigoted Catholic, refused to believe in hell.

XII. DIABOLUS SIMIA DEI

Pages 121. On the contrast between the marvelous acts of the Deity and of the Devil, consult Bern. Maréchaux' work, *le Merveilleux Divin et le Merveilleux Démoniaque* (Paris, 1902).

Page 122. The French poet, Sully Prudhomme, in his poem *les Filles du Diable* (1866), represents the brunettes with their burning black eyes as the creation of the Devil in contrast to the blondes who are the handiwork of the Deity—Note 3. Perhaps the greatest charm the Devil can give a woman is red hair. "When the Devil wishes to make a woman seductive beyond the ordinary," says Michael Monahan in his book, *Heinrich Heine* (1924), "he adds red hair as his culminating effect."

Page 127. The legend of Pope Joan will be found in S. Baring-Gould's *Curious Myths of the Middle Ages* (London, 1874).—Alphonse Karr has written a story on the Black Madonna, an English translation of which will be found in James Hain Friswell's *Ghost Stories and Phantom Fancies* (London, 1858).

XIII. THE WAR FOR THE WORLD

Page 132. A critical study of the dogma of Christ's descent to hell is J. A. McCulloch's *The Harrowing of Hell* (Edinburgh and New York, 1930).

Page 138, note 13. A chapter on the Devils of Loudun will also be found in H. A. B. Bruce's *Historic Ghosts and Ghost Hunters* (New York, 1908).

Page 140. The Reverend Mr. W. S. Harris published in Philadelphia in 1903 a book of *Sermons by the Devil* and had it illustrated by Paul Krafft and others. Sermons by the Devil and his grandmother at the Witches' Sabbaths of the years 1903 and 1904 were published under the following titles: Heinrich Heinemann: *Teufelspredigt zur Walpurgisfeier am 30. iv. /1. v. 1903;* Anna Weisser: *Standesrede von des Teufels Grossmutter zur Walpurgisfeier am 30. iv. /1. v. 1904; Teufelspredigt zur Walpurgisfeier am 30. iv. /1. v. 1904* von einem Braunschweiger. Richard Taylor's *The Devil's Pulpit* (1830) is a book on religious origins which caused a great stir in England.

Page 142. Heinrich Heine in his *Elementargeister* (1834) tells a curious story of the temptation of a nun by the Devil. This pious sister, who was virtuous enough but who did not strictly observe all the rules of her order and make the sign of the Cross as often as she should, once ate a salad. And as soon as this was consumed, she experienced sensations which were new to her and not at all in accordance with her profession. Of evenings she began to feel strangely when she sat in the light of the moon, and the flowers gave out their perfume, and the nightingales sang so softly and sighingly. Soon afterward she became acquainted with a delightful young man. And after they had become intimate, he said to her, "Do you know who I am?" "No," replied the nun, startled. "I am the Devil," he answered. "Dost thou not remember that salad? That salad was I."—Byron in his *Vision of Judgment* (1822), which is a burlesque on Southey's poem with the same title, presents the case of Satan vs. St. Michael over the body of George the Third. Satan appears as accuser, and he and St. Michael dispute the possession of the royal body. Angels and devils alike take flight when Southey begins to read his own works aloud to testify for the king.

XIV. THE SYNAGOGUE OF SATAN

Page 150. On the Yezidis, consult also the following works: Austen H. Logard: *Nineveh and its Remains; with an Account of a Visit to....the Yezidis or Devil-Worshippers,* 2 vols., New York, 1840; Jean Spiro: *les Yezidi ou les adorateurs du Diable,* Neuchatel, 1900 (Miscellanea-Stade, vol. 55, no. 2), and J. Ménant: *Les Yezidiz; épisodes de l'histoire des adorateurs du Diable,* Paris, 1892.—Reverend Samuel Mateer, in his book, *The Land of Charity; an Account of Travancore and its Devil-Worship* (New York, 1870), tells of a devil-worshiping sect in southern India.

Page 156, note 13. An earlier translation of Michelet's book by L. J. Trotter appeared in London in 1863 under the title *The Witch of the Middle Ages.*

Page 158. Often the witches would transform a man into a horse, while he was asleep in his bed, by throwing a magic halter over his head. Then they would lead him from the house, mount him, and ride away to their Sabbath.

Page 161. On the musical program of the Witches' Sabbath read Harvey R. Gaul's article, "Music and Devil-Worship," *The Musical Quarterly,* XI (1925), 192-5.

Page 163. On the belief in the evil eye, read S. Seligmann: *Der böse Blick und Verwandtes* (Berlin, 1910).

Page 164, note 20. Read also Dr. Georges Surbled's article, "le Diable et les sorciers," *Science catholique,* of August 1898.—The English translation of Huysmans' novel, *Là-Bas,* prepared by Keene Wallis, appeared in New York in 1924 and in Paris in 1928.—A few interesting recent works on vampirism are the following: St. Hock: *Die Vampyrsagen und ihre Verwertung in der deutschen Literatur* (Berlin, 1900), Dudley Wright: *Vampires and Vampirism* (London, 1924), and Pierre Bataille: "Quelques sources du vampirisme [dans la littérature allemande et francaise]," *la Nouvelle Revue critique,* Jan. 1930.

Page 165. Joséphin Péladan, an occultist and magian, organized in Paris the Order of the *Rose et Croix,* a society in imitation of the order of the sixteenth century, whose members devoted themselves to the study of the problems of supernatural life.

XV. THE DEVIL-COMPACT IN TRADITION AND BELIEF

Page 169. Mr. J. V. S. Wilkinson has just published a critical edition of Firdausi's *Shah-Nahmah* (Oxford University Press).

Page 174. In Charles Nodier's "la Combe de l'homme mort" (1833), the term of the devil-compact is thirty years. On the other hand, the term has been reduced to twenty years in F. B. Perkins' "Devil-Puzzlers" (1871) and in John Masefield's "The Devil and the Old Man" (1905).—Salatin, in Rutebeuf's *Miracle de Théophile,* is probably a variant of Saladin, who stands without doubt for an Arabic Jew or simply a Turk, a Saracen, an unbeliever "who spoke to the Devil whenever he wished."—Dante Gabriel Rossetti, in "Jan Van Hunks," a long poem of forty-four stanzas, tells about a Dutchman who sold his body to the Devil.

Page 178. Paul Perdrizet, in his article, "Satan und Jungfrau," *Zeitschrift für Religionspsychologie,* IV (1910), 161-8, represents the Devil and the Virgin as the two poles of Catholic Christianity.

XVI.-XVII. THE DEVIL-COMPACT IN LEGEND AND LITERATURE

Page 184, note 4. On the legend of Theophilus in Christian art, consult Ernest Faligan: "Des formes iconographiques de la légende de Théophile," *Revue des traditions populaires,* V (1890), 1-14.

Page 186, note 8. On the legend of Twardowski, consult the scholarly essay by Ian Kuchta, "les Motifs locaux dans les légendes concernant Maître Twardowski," *Lud,* 2nd series, VIII (1929). This article is written in Polish and followed by a résumé in French. Waclaw Sieroszewski's recent two-volume novel *Pan Twardowski* is built around the Polish Faust. The German novelist, Franz von Gaudy, published in the thirties of the last century the Novel *Frau Twardowska,* which is based on Mickiewicz' poem.

Page 187. Wierus tells how Pope Benedict the Ninth (1033-48), who had arranged a compact with the Devil, was strangled by the Devil in a forest and after death appeared in the likeness of a bear with the head of an ass.

Page 189. It has been aptly remarked that only a transcendental German devil would ever think of inveigling a soul by any such thing as learning.

Page 191, note 13. On the Faust-legend in Russian literature, consult K. Bittner's recent article, "Die Faustage im russischen Schrifttum," *Zeitschrift für deutsche Philologie,* LV (1930).—Goethe's relation to Marlowe is studied by Otto Heller in his *Faust and Faustus* (St. Louis, 1931).

Page 196, note 21. The past year marked the three hundredth anniversary of the publication of *El Burlador de Sevilla.* On this occasion ,the career of the great lover throughout the ages has been summarized and interpreted by Angel Valbuena in the *Gacetta litteraria* for November 1st, 1930, and by Wilhelm Michel, in his article, "Die Don-Juan Gestalt," *Theaterwelt,* VI (1930). Don Juan also found a biographer in the French novelist, Joseph Delteil.—Don José Zorilla's play, *Don Juan Tenorio,* was first performed in 1844.—An interesting treatment of the Don Juan legend is Baudelaire's poem, "Don Juan aux enfers" (1846). On the relation between the Faust-saga and the Don Juan legend, see the recent article by Maximilian Harwich, "Faust, Don Juan und Ahasver," *Der getreue Eckart,* VIII, 3 (Wien, 1930).

Page 198, note 23. K. Jahn's *Immermanns "Merlin"* (1899) is the best study on the origin and literary position of this play.—Note 24. On Goethe's influence in France, consult also *Was die Bücherei erzählt* (Leipzig, 1889).

Page 199. Lammennais also considered Mephistopheles the real hero of Goethe's poem.

Page 210. A critical edition of Horace Walpole's *The Castle of Otranto* was issued in London in 1929 .

Page 211, note 45. On the novelists of the English School of Terror, read also Edith Walter's *The Tale of Terror; a Study of the Gothic Romance* (London, 1921).

Page 212. Baudelaire likewise had a great admiration for the English novelists of the School of Terror, particularly for Lewis and Maturin. He speaks of Melmoth and his devil-compact in the *Paradis artificiels* (1860) and in his diary calls Melmoth "the great Satanical creation of the Reverend Maturin." But Baudelaire would have invented his Satanism even without the Melmoths of Maturin and Balzac. On this subject, consult the recent article by G. T. Clapton, "Balzac, Baudelaire and Maturin," *The French Quarterly,* June and September, 1930.

Page 215. A critical study of Hauff's *Memoiren des Satan* was published last year by Edwin Sommermeyer as a Berlin dissertation. Friedrich Hebbel also intended to bring out a "Devil's Diary."—There appeared in London in 1834 a curious work ascribed to the Devil under the following title: *Six Letters from a High Personage; the first four on the nature of his character and government; and the last two addressed to Miss Martineau and Dr. Malthus on the subject of the new poor laws.*—Aloysius Bertrand, one of the *poetæ minores* of the French Romantic School, a dreamer and a visionary, composed in 1842, a collection of prose poems under the title *Gaspard de la Nuit,* to which he gave as sub-title, *Fantaisies à la manière de Rembrandt et de Callot* in imitation of Hoffmann's *Phantasiestücke in Callots Manier* (1814). The author pretends to be only the publisher of the fantasies of a certain Gaspard de la Muit, an old man whom he encountered in the Jardin de l'Arquebuse of Dijon, and who turned out to be the Devil in person. In the preface to this curious work, Bertrand describes the supposed author of these beautiful prose poems in the following words:

"A poor devil whose exterior announced nothing but poverty and suffering. I had already noticed in the garden his frayed overcoat, buttoned to the chin, his shapeless hat that never brush had brushed, his hair long as a weeping-willow, combed like a thicket, his fleshless hands like ossuaries, his mocking, wretched and sickly face; and by conjectures had charitably placed him among those itinerant artists, violin-players and portrait-painters, whom an insatiable hunger and an unquenchable thirst condemn to travel the world in the footsteps of the Wandering Jew...."

A few passages of this work have been translated into English by Stuart Merrill in his *Pastels in Prose* (New York, 1890). A full translation of these prose poems has been given to us by Mr. Arthur Ransome (London, 1925).

Page 217, note 50. The career and crimes of the brilliant French nobleman, companion-in-arms of Joan of Arc, who was burned at the stake in

1440 for the lust-murder of two hundred children, has attracted many writers. S. Baring-Gould devoted a chapter to him in his *Book of Were-Wolves* (London, 1865), and Joris-Karl Huysmans wrote the biography of this devil-worshipper in *la Sorcellerie en Poitou. Gilles de Rais* (Paris, 1897). Edgar Saltus has a chapter on Gilles de Rais in his ambrosial essays published under the title *Pomps of Satan* (1904). Among recent biographies of this fifteenth-century fiend, the following may be mentioned: A. L. Vincent and Clare Binns: *Gilles de Rais; the Original Bluebeard* (London, 1926), Aleister Crowley: *Gilles de Rais; a Banned Lecture Which was to have been Delivered before the Oxford Society* (London, 1930), Mr. Gabory: *The Life and Death of Gilles de Rais; the Original Bluebeard* (New York, 1930), and Tennille Dix: *The Black Baron* (Indianapolis, 1930). The German writer, Franz Blei, has also devoted a chapter to Gilles de Rais in his book, *Ungewöhnliche Menschen und Schicksale* (Berlin, 1929).

The reader will probably be interested in the following comment on the last two chapters by Professor F. Piquet, of the University of Lille:

Nombreux sont les hallucinés, les simples et les malins qui ont cru ou dit avoir fait un pacte avec le diable. Bien connus sont les termes de ce contrat: l'humain promet son âme à Satan: en revanche il obtient dans sa vie terrestre l'accomplissement de ses désirs, soit des jouissances matérielles, soit la révélation de mystères qui tourmentent sa raison, soit l'un et l'autre. M. Maximilian Rudwin est un de ceux qui ont conjuré Satan. A vrai dire il n'espère rien du maître des enfers. Ce à quoi il prétend c'est nous informer des modes d'intervention de l'esprit du mal dans la littérature. La matière est riche. On en trouve les premiers éléments dans la légende de Théophile, qui aurait vécu vers l'an 600. Le XIXe siècle est fécond en récits où apparaît l'ange déchu. M. Rudwin a passé en revue les textes anciens et récents qui mentionnent un pacte conclu avec lui (The Devil compact in Legend and Literature, dans la revue *The Open Court*, Chicago, juin et juillet 1930). Il est remarquable que Béelzébub ait été évoqué si fréquemment à l'époque moderne, où l'histoire de Faust a hanté plusieurs grands esprits et où, plus près de nous, la sombre figure du damné illustre les pages de prose ou de vers d'un Gérard de Nerval, d'un Balzac, d'un Hauff, d'une Radcliffe et de bien d'autres auteurs nommés par M. Rudwin. C'est chose curieuse, constate M. Rudwin, que le pacte ait été si souvent violé au detriment du diable. Satan tient généralement ses promesses, mais est facilement dupé par son partenaire. Si l'âme de M. Rudwin est un jour menacée de choir dans l'abime infernal nul doute que le maître du logis ne lui tienne compte de l'avoir ainsi réhabilité et aussi d'avoir accru sa popularité dans le monde des vivants.

—Revue germanique, Janvier-Mars 1931.

XVIII. THE LOVES OF THE DEMONS

Page 230, note 10. On Robert the Devil, consult Thierry-Sandre's l'Histoire merveilleuse de Robert le Diable (Paris, 1925).

XIX.—XX. THE DEVIL, THE WORLD AND THE FLESH

Page 244. Josephus, in his *Wars of the Jews* (VII. vi. 3) also states that sickness is produced by demons.

Page 259. Ch. Urbain and E. Levesque, in their recently published work, *l'Église et le Théâtre* (1930), describe the war against the theater carried on by the Gallican Church in the seventeenth century.

Page 263. Hugh Kingsmill has collected a good number of uncomplimentary words which writers have been in the habit of saying about one another in his two volumes *An Anthology of Invectives and Abuse* and *More Invective* (New Yerk, 1931).

XXII. THE SALVATION OF SATAN IN MODERN POETRY

Page 280. Ernest Renan's article on the Devil appeared in the form of an article on Ary Scheffer's painting, *la Tentation du Christ*.

Page 284, note 5. A more critical work on the Yezidi texts is M. Bittner's study, *die heiligen Bücher der Jeziden oder Teufelsanbeter*. Wien, 1913. (Denkschrift der Kaiserlichen Akademie der Wissenschaften zu Wien.)

Page 296. An English translation of Leconte de Lisle's poem, "la Tristesse du Diable," will be found in Irving Brown's study, *Leconte de Lisle* (2nd ed., New York, 1929), pp. 223 and 225.

Page 306. An analysis of Leconte de Lisle's poem "Quain" will also be found in Brown's book just mentioned, pp. 114-21.

INDEX

INDEX

Forrest, William, 184
Fortunatus, purse of, 174
Fouchardière, G. de la, 135, n. 10
Fouqué, Karl Friedrich de la Motte, 139, 222
Fox, Charles James, 211
fox, Devil as a, 39
France, Anatole (pseud. of François-Anatole Thibault), 8, 16, 36, n. 1, 37 and n. 5, 38, n. 6, 41, 43, 45, 52, 63, 86, 88-9, 93, 96, 103, 112, 117-9, 122, n. 3, 134, 139, 177, n. 13, 222, 224, 227-8, 230, n. 8, 245, 247-8 252-3, 264, 267, 276, 283, n. 3, 306, 312
France, x, 40, 89-90, 154, 163-5, 166, n. 28, 167, 177, n. 13, 187, 195, 198, 208, n. 42, 211, 225, 241-2, 256, 263, 276-8, 296-7; adaptations and imitations of Goethe's *Faust* in, 198-209, 315; adaptations and imitations of Klinger's *Faust* in, 203-6; influence of English School of Terror in, 211-7 (*see also* Avignon, Bordeaux, Brittany, Cluny, Dijon, Jura, Loudun, Lyons, Metz, Nancy, Normandy, Poitiers, Poitou, Provence, Rouen, Strasbourg, Tours *and* Vienne).
Francis of Assisi, St., 227, 297
Franciscans, 50-51, 136, 251
Francisci, Erasmus, 223, n. 2
François-Henri, duc de Luxembourg, devil-compact of, 187
Frank, Grace (editor), 184, n. 3
Frankfort, 191, 195
Frazer, *Sir* James George, 37, 39, n. 8, 85, 128, n. 10, 171, n. 6
Frederick II, the Great, king of Prussia, 231
Frederick III, emperor of Germany, 195, 205
Freemasons (*see* Masons)
free-will, Catholic dogma of, 192
Freidus, A. S., 99, n. 8
French beliefs, 67; classical drama in Germany, 192-3; classicists, 275; expressions, meaning of, 32, 46, 228; fantastic fiction, 231; fashions, 93; legends, 185; literature, Devil in, viii, 7-10, 15-8, 23, 26, 28, 36-9, 41-3, 45-54, 58, 62-3, 66-9, 72, 74, 76-7, 79, 83-91, 93, 96, 98-112, 114-9, 122-3, 125-9, 134-6, 139, 142-4, 146-50, 154-61, 163, n. 28, 164-6, 174-5, 177, 179, 184, 186, 196-217, 219-20, 222-5, 227-9, 230-35, 239, 242, 245-53, 255-69, 272-3,

275-8, 280-81, 283, 285-308, 309, 312-6; medieval epics, 17, n. 1, 146-7; mystery-plays, 66, 84, 124, 208, n. 42; Revolution, 108, 206, 212, 276, 281, 286, as creation of Devil, 263-4, 296; Romanticism, Devil in, 276-8, 285-98, 299-308; Romantics, 15, 108, 198, 206, 212, 217-8, 277-8, 284-98, 299-308, 315; Romantics, humanitarianism of, 285, interest in Devil of, 205-6, 285-308, messianism of, 294, pessimism of, 289, 301-4, "redemptorism" of, 285, sympathy for Satan of, 284-98; sympathy for suffering of, 285, 289, 292-4; swear-words, 31
Frenchmen, ix, 31, 67
Freyja (*see* Frigga)
Freytag, Gustav, 154, 162, 177
Friar Rush, 84, 87
friars (*see* monks)
Fribourg, cathedral of, 144
Frida, Emil Bohuslav (*see* Vrchlicky)
Friday named after Frigga, 153
Friesland, 86
Frigaholda (*see* Frigga)
Frigga, Norse goddess, 41, 127, 153
Frija (*see* Frigga)
Friswell, James Hain, 191, n. 13, 313
frog, Devil as a, 310
Fuchsmund, Ferdinand (editor), 74, n. 3
Fulton, Robert, identification with Devil of, 251
Fundamentalists, 133, 249
Furcas, a demon, 18, 28
Furies (*see* Erinyes)
Fust, Hans, considered a magician, 250; identification with Johannes Faust of, 194, 204

Gabory, M., 316
Gabriel, archangel, 89, 123, 132
Galilei, Galileo, considered a magician, 250; devil-compact of, 187
Gandersheim, 182
Ganesa, Hindu god, 45, 311
Ganges, 16
Gaonim, 311
gargoyles on medieval churches, 67-8; meaning of, 133-4
Garnett, Richard, 104, 148, n. 2, 238
Gascon, shrewdness of, 177, n. 13
Gaspard de la Nuit, Devil's pseudonym, 315
Gassner der Jüngere, Peter (*see* Cranz)

122-3, 147, 149-50, 230, 244, 283
heretics, 158, n. 13a; spawn of Satan
in Catholic eyes, 147
hermeceutists, 207 (see also alchem-
ists)
Hermes, Greek god, 35; now a de-
mon, 28, 83 (see also Mercury)
Hermon, Mt., 19
Herod Antipas, 152
Herod the Great, 152
Herodias, identification with Berch-
ta and Freya of, 153; leader in
wild air-flight, 152-3; witch-queen,
152-3
Hertha, a variant of Perchta, 153
Hervey, William A. (translator),
154, n. 10, 177, n. 17
Hesiod, Greek writer, 22
hetæra, 94
Hetzel, Pierre-Jules (see Stahl)
Heva, name for Lilith, 28, 101
Heywood, Thomas, 8, 184
"hex murders," 163
Hickey, Emily, 262, n. 17a
Hildegard, visit to hell of, 71
Hill, Rowland, 255
Hindus, 129, 284, 302, n. 10, 308;
gods of, 2, 28, 38, 45-6, 64, 82-3,
146, 179, 311; mythology of, 2, 38,
43, 45-6, 64, 70, 82, 146, 179, 284,
302 (see also India)
Hinnom, Valley of, 57-8, 97 (see also
Gehenna and Tophet)
Hoberdidance (Hobbididance or Hop-
dance), a demon, 28, 84
hobgoblins (see goblins)
Hock, St., 314
Hocker, Jodocum, 310
Hoey, Mrs. (translator), 42, n. 14
Hoffmann, Ernst Theodor [Wilhelm]
Amadeus, 66, 110-11, 228, 262, 315
Hoffmann, Friedrich, inventor of car-
bonic acid, 251
Höhler, W., 74, n. 3
Hohlfeld, Alexander R., 196, n. 19
Holda (Hulda), name for Freya in
Lower Germany, 153
Holkot, Robert, 187
Holla (Holle), name for Freya in
Lower Germany, 41, 153
Holland, E. G., 169, n. 3
Holland, 9, 32, 204; abolition of
witch-persecution in, 162 (see also
Amsterdam, Friesland and Harlem)
Höllenkrücke (Hellekrugk), Devil's
mother, 28, 50, n. 23, 127
Holy Grail, 230; Ghost, 129; Land,
66; Mass, 85, 126, 166; water,

means of driving away the Devil,
135
Homer, Greek poet, 70, 193, n. 16,
272
Hop-dance (see Hoberdidance)
Hornblas, a demon, 28, 123
horse, Devil as a, 310; Devil with
foot of a, 45; man transformed into, 313
Horst, J. W., 310
Horus, Egyptian god, 2, now a demon, 28, 82
Hotspur (pseud. of Henry Percy), 66
household-spirits (see hearth-spirits)
Howey, M. Oldfield, 44, n. 15a, 311
Hrim-Grimmir, Edaic evil spirit, 40
Hroswitha, Abbess, 125, n. 6, 182
Hugo, Victor-Marie, 39, 48, 50, 53-5,
62-3, 66, 76, n. 3, 84, 98, 108-9,
114, 125-6, 144, 148, n. 1, 161, n. 16,
174-5 and n. 11, 210, n. 44, 212,
229, 251, 255, 260, 263-4, 272, 276-7,
287, 293-6, 305
Huguenots, devil-worshippers in eyes
of Catholics, 147
humanists, 189
humanity, liberation from political
oppression of, 195-6
Humanum genus, the papal encyclic,
167
Huneker, James Gibbons, 112, 118, n.
6, 127, 252
Hungarian literature, Devil in, 248,
301
Huns, diabolical descent of, 231
Huss, Johann, followers of, 149, 283
Husson, Jules (see Champfleury)
Hutgin, (Hugin), Odin's raven, now
a demon, 28, 82
Huxley, Thomas Henry, 270, 302
Huysmans, Joris-Karl, 41, 74, n. 3,
106, 109, 123, 139, 163, n. 20, 164-7,
219, n. 51, 223, 248, 314, 316
Hymer John B., 219 n. 51
Hypatia, neo-Platonic philosopher,
death of, 249

Iblis (see Eblis)
Ibsen, Henrik, 96, 269
Iceland, 63, n. 13; volcanoes of, 58,
66 (see also Drontheim and Hecla)
Icelandic literature, Devil in, 182
iconography of Eastern Church, 48,
121; of Western Church, 37-8, 314
Iggdrasil, an Eddaic ash-tree, 1, n. 1
Igymeth, Devil's concubine, 28, 98
Illuminism, 165, n. 24
Illuminists, 164